Trees and Development

ISBN: 1-881956-20-2

The ISA seal is a registered trademark.

Editorial Coordinator: Peggy Currid
Composition by: Amy Reiss
Cover Designer: Doug Burnett
Printed By:
United Graphics
Mattoon, IL

International Society of Arboriculture
www.isa-arbor.com
isa@isa-arbor.com
10 9 8 7 6

500/RF/1-08

Trees and Development

A Technical Guide to Preservation of Trees During Land Development

Nelda Matheny and James R. Clark

Published by
International Society of Arboriculture
P.O. Box 3129
Champaign, IL 61821-3129 USA

Dedication

This book is dedicated to Maureen, Phoebe, Brendan, and Ryan.

Table of Contents

Acknowledgements

Preparing this book has involved the support and assistance of a number of generous, helpful people within and outside of arboriculture. We frankly admit that the book would not have been possible without the guidance and contributions of others.

First and foremost, we acknowledge the continuing support and patience of the International Society of Arboriculture and its staff. Jim Skiera acted as our primary contact and was unfailingly supportive and helpful. A special thanks to Peggy Currid, Nancy Komlanc, and Amy Reiss for their efforts in editing, designing, and producing the book.

We also appreciate and give our sincere thanks to colleagues who contributed ideas and experience, particularly those on our review team: Ted Collins (Ted Collins and Associates, Victor, NY), Colin Bashford (CBA Ltd., South Hampton, England), Roy Finch (Roy Finch Tree Care Specialist, Malvern, England), Gary Mullane (Mullane Associates, Hilton Head Island, SC), Ken Ottman (City of Milwaukee, Milwaukee, WI), Steve Kunde (Kunde Co., St. Paul, MN), Virginia Kent Fortson (ASLA, Mandeville, LA), Larry Comegys (Pulte Homes, Tampa, FL), Bill Granger (Kwantlen College, Langley, British Columbia), Dan Neely (International Society of Arboriculture, Scott City, MO), Kim Coder (University of Georgia, Athens, GA), Robert Miller (University of Wisconsin, Stevens Point, WI), and Elizabeth Rivers (Seattle, WA). Both Tom Quaglia (The Riding Group, San Jose, CA) and Debra Bassert (National Association of Home Builders, Washington, DC) provided enthusiasm, ideas, and resource material from the developer-builder standpoint.

In addition, we acknowledge and thank the arborists who shared their ideas and experiences: Tom Smiley (Bartlett Tree Research Laboratory, Charlotte, NC), George Schrader (American Tree, Panama City, FL), Norm Easy (Sarasota County, FL), Jay Stipes (Virginia Tech University, Blacksburg, VA), Dick Harris (Davis, CA), Larry Costello (University of California Cooperative Extension, Half Moon Bay, CA), Carol Krawczyk (Chatham County, GA), and Joe McNeil (Pleasant Hill, CA). Jim Barborinas (Urban Forestry Services, Mt. Vernon, WA) was particularly helpful and generous on the topic of resource evaluation. Photographs and details were provided by Dick Harris (Davis, CA), Jim Barborinas (Urban Forestry Services, Mt. Vernon, WA), Mary Ann Beale (City of Charlotte, NC), Spence Rosenfeld (Arborguard Tree Specialists, Avondale Estates, GA), Environmental Care Inc. (Calabasas, CA), Mark Boyce (Homes by C.P. Morgan, Carmel, IN), Howell Beach (Robert E. Marvin & Associates, Walterboro, SC),

Larry Costello (University of California Cooperative Extension, Half Moon Bay, CA), and Gary Watson (The Morton Arboretum, Lisle, IL).

The case studies were created with the cooperation and generous contributions of a number of consultants and development professionals across the United States, including John Royster (ASLA, The Big Muddy Workshop, Omaha, NE), Donna Attewell and Kevin Hillary (Whole Tree Works, Portland, OR), and Spence Rosenfeld (Arborguard Tree Specialists, Avondale Estates, GA). Their willingness to share information for specific projects broadened the coverage of the book tremendously.

Appendix B (Relative Tolerance of Selected Species to Development Impacts) was the result of contributions from Molly Beck (Northwest Arborvitae, Woodinville, WA), Helen Bell (ANEW LEAF, Merlin, OR), Steve Clark (Steve Clark Inc., Brentwood, TN), Kim Coder (University of Georgia, Athens, GA), Scott Cullen (Greenwich, CT), Steve Day (Day & Associates, Littleton, CO), Julian Dunster (Dunster & Associates, Ltd., Bowen Island, British Columbia), Debbie Ellis (horticultural consultant, Saratoga, CA), Jack Siebenthaler (Clearwater, FL), and T. Davis Sydnor (The Ohio State University, Columbus, OH).

We also appreciate the cooperation and support of our clients and other development professionals with whom we are fortunate enough to work. We would like to specifically mention the support and contributions of Tom Quaglia (The Riding Group, San Jose, CA), Chris Cady, David Bradley, Carl Moxley, and Ron Freeman (UDC Homes, Inc., Walnut Creek, CA), Steve Zales (The O'Brien Group, San Mateo, CA), Bob Duchi and David Francke (dk Associates, Walnut Creek, CA), Rick Connett (Guzzardo & Associates, San Francisco, CA), and Mike Fulford (City of Pleasanton, Pleasanton, CA). Vicki Crews and Jane Whitcomb prepared many of the line drawings and illustrations. Bob Matheny and Sandra Hansen Matheny provided superb editing and advice about our writing styles and how best to provide continuity throughout the book. Finally, this book could not have been written without the knowledge and support of the staff of HortScience, Inc.: Ed Brennan, Nancy Tatarka, Judy Thrapp, and Jane Whitcomb. We wholeheartedly express our appreciation for their assistance, patience, and continuing commitment to our company.

Nelda Matheny
Jim Clark
Pleasanton, California
April 1997

Introduction

This is a book about preserving trees during the process of developing land and constructing buildings and infrastructure. Our goal is to provide a sound informational and technical base that will improve the ability of public agencies, development professionals, arborists, consultants, engineers, planners, landscape architects, and builders to preserve trees.

Successful tree preservation occurs when the goals of the project are achieved with minimal impact to trees designated for preservation. Success is measured over the long term, when trees continue to thrive for many years after development is completed. For that to happen, people making decisions about tree preservation must be knowledgeable in several areas. First, they must understand how trees grow, as individuals and in groups. Second, they must understand the processes of design and development, as well as the methods of construction. Third, decision-makers must understand how trees respond to changes in the environment imposed by development of the land. Finally, everyone involved on a project must acknowledge that tree preservation requires a commitment by members of the community and the project team.

Trees and Development provides information in each of those areas. First, the important aspects of tree growth are reviewed. Then, the development process, construction practice, and graphic conventions are described. The steps involved in tree preservation—from evaluating the resource through planning, design, impact evaluation, construction, and postconstruction management—are explained. The preparation of reports and other documents is described.

Appendices and case studies provide more detailed information. Appendix A discusses tools and materials used in preparing reports and plans. Appendix B provides species-specific information on tree responses to development impacts. Appendix C answers the most frequently asked questions about tree preservation. The case studies illustrate how the concepts and techniques were applied to specific projects.

Throughout the text, *development* is referred to in two ways. *Development* is first used to describe the process of planning and construction that occurs as structures are placed on land. In this context, development represents the series of changes by which the character of a site is altered. The second use of the word describes the changes that occur in tree growth over time and through the influence of the surrounding physical environment.

At first glance, referring to *development* in two different contexts may be confusing. It is our opinion, however, that doing so accurately represents both situations. For both land and trees, development reflects a process of change. Neither use of the land nor growth of trees is static. Instead, both are dynamic. Changes in growth are inevitable as a tree is established, matures, and declines with age. Similarly, the process of land development embodies change, as the land is modified through construction and as new uses are created.

The ideas and techniques presented in this book have been developed through our experience in preparing tree preservation programs for the development community, as well as in training programs. We use the term *consultant* to describe the person preparing a tree preservation plan or providing other technical services. Professionals offering these services may be consulting arborists, forestry consultants, foresters, urban foresters or, in some cases, landscape architects. We distinguish between consulting services and tree care services (pruning, planting, removal, etc.) that would be performed by an arborist.

WHY TREES ARE PRESERVED DURING DEVELOPMENT

Land development is a complex process. It entails making decisions and considering interactions that have significant implications on the character and image of a property or a community. Within a community, the prospect of development—commercial, residential, industrial, or institutional—may evoke strong reaction, both positive and negative.

The development process is even more challenging when trees are involved. With increasing frequency, trees on development sites become symbols of the commitment of a developer to the environment and the community, of the planning goals of the community, and of the desires of the users (Petit et al. 1995).

Although the focus of this book is on *how* to preserve trees during development, we recognize that *why* trees are preserved has an important influence on this process. The motivations for retaining trees are varied and encompass economic, environmental, and social considerations.

- **Trees are preserved because the community demands it.** Preparation and implementation of tree preservation programs may be regulated either directly through laws, such as tree preservation ordinances, or indirectly through a policy of linking tree preservation to project approval. Such requirements usually reflect an interest in retaining local heritage, beauty, and natural resources. These regulations operate at city, county, regional, or state levels.

- **Tree preservation may be part of a larger, resource conservation program.** Many local and regional governmental agencies have adopted programs of resource conservation that influence and regulate land development activity. For example, at the county level of government, the Tuolumne County (California) General Plan sets conservation of wildlife habitat areas as a goal. Development applications are evaluated for cumulative impacts using the county's *Wildlife Inventory and Planning Handbook*. Locations and requirements for habitat conservation within the county are clearly defined in the handbook and may be evaluated by the development team during the planning stages of a project. At the state level, the Maryland Forest Conservation Act mandates retention of existing forest cover on a statewide basis. The Act defines guidelines for tree preservation and replanting on development sites greater than 40,000 square feet.

- **Trees are preserved because they provide important environmental and social functions.** With greater emphasis on environmental issues, the role that trees play in energy conservation, pollution abatement, and storm water control is highly valued. For example, McPherson et al. (1994) estimate that the urban forest within and surrounding Chicago, Illinois, annually removed 6,145 tons of air pollutants, sequestered 155,000 tons of carbon, and reduced heating and cooling energy use by five to ten percent. In addition, trees provide benefits to the psychological and physical health of residents (Petit et al. 1995, Coder 1996).

- **Trees may be preserved because citizens demand it.** Many people want to live and work in communities enhanced with mature trees and forests. One expression of this desire is seen in the willingness of people to pay higher prices for lots with trees. Surveys of realtors, appraisers, builders, and residents have documented this observation. Petit et al. (1995) cite a survey of real estate agents in which more than 80 percent felt that a home with trees would be as much as 20 percent more salable that one without trees. On a project in the San Jose, California, area, the developer walked past a large oak and noted, "The lot with the tree will sell for $10,000 more, and the adjacent lot (which was shaded by the tree) $6,000 more." On this project, the tree had a value of $16,000, as measured by the willingness of buyers to pay more for a lot with a tree.

- **Trees are preserved because it is in the developer's best interest to do so.** Because many people desire sites with mature trees, it is in the developer's best interest to provide them. For example, home builders such as C.P. Morgan in Indiana and D. Yost in Oklahoma have found that wooded lots sell for 20 percent more than unwooded lots (Petit et al. 1995). Trees also enhance curb appeal and overall value of individual projects. Developers who strive to preserve trees may find the path to project approval and completion less difficult and time consuming than would be otherwise. Tree removal has an obvious and significant impact— one that will often arouse the opposition of neighbors, community leaders, and public agencies. In our experience, trees become one of the key issues in the project review and approval process. If existing land aesthetics (such as forested or treed lots) can be retained through tree preservation during the project, then approval may be more readily achieved.

- **Trees are preserved as a result of the developer's personal and professional commitment.** Some development professionals increasingly recognize a responsibility to plant and preserve trees (Andreasen and Tyson 1993). They also recognize the relationship between tree preservation programs and their image in the community (Petit et al. 1995). Moreover, many developers have expressed a strong personal commitment to tree preservation (when evaluated in relation to their competitors). Developers clearly pay attention to the activities of their competition and are ready to adopt new approaches (such as tree preservation) that enhance the success of their businesses.

In short, tree preservation during development provides varied and broad-based benefits to both the community and developer. Whatever the reasons for preserving trees, it is clear that successful retention during development does not occur simply because an agency or an individual demands it. Successful tree preservation requires the commitment and involvement of everyone connected with a project, from developer to builder to contractor to public agency. It requires that the implications for trees and their survival be considered at each step in the development process, from the initial concept for land use through design, grading and construction, and maintenance.

Both development professionals and communities, however, have expressed reservations about tree preservation (Table 1). Fortunately, for each of the commonly raised concerns, there is clear response that tree preservation makes a positive contribution to both the project and community.

Trees and Development combines a knowledge of tree growth with the practices and techniques commonly used during the development process. In so doing, we hope to have decisions about tree preservation be based upon sound technical information as well as an understanding of the effects of constructions practices on tree growth.

REFERENCES

Andreasen, A., and C. Tyson. 1993. *Improving Tree Management Practices of Home Builders: A Social Marketing Approach*. Washington, DC: Forest Policy Center. 44 pp.

Coder, K.D. 1996. *Cultural and Psychological Aspects of Trees and Forests*. Athens, GA: University of Georgia.

McPherson, E.G., D. Nowak, and R. Rowntree (editors). 1994. *Chicago's Urban Forest Ecosystem: Results of the Chicago Urban Forest Climate Project*. Radnor, PA: USDA Forest Service. General Technical Report NE-186. Northeast Forest Experiment Station. 201 pp.

Petit, J., D. Bassert, and C. Kollin. 1995. *Building Greener Neighborhoods—Trees as Part of the Plan*. Washington, DC: National Association of Home Builders Press. 117 pp.

TABLE 1. Responses to frequently raised arguments against tree preservation.

Argument	Response
Tree preservation costs too much.	Many developers experienced with tree preservation have found that the cost of tree preservation during construction is generally a trade-off, with savings in some areas and increased costs in others. However, any increase in cost associated with tree preservation is typically recovered in higher prices and faster sales of the developed land.
Tree preservation is an over-regulation of land use.	Courts have historically upheld challenges to carefully and clearly written aesthetic and environmental standards, including tree preservation ordinances. However, communities should be careful to tailor ordinances to their needs and allow flexibility in meeting the objectives of ordinances.
Tree preservation makes our community too expensive for new development.	We know of no factual basis to this concern. From a practical standpoint, projects with mature trees sell more quickly, do so at a higher price, and are more attractive to buyers. Rigid or inflexible tree preservation ordinances may result in an increase in the cost of new housing.
Tree preservation is simply a tactic to prevent development.	If a community holds tree preservation as an important goal and clearly defines its expectations to developers, then tree preservation simply becomes another aspect of project planning. Once a project (and its tree preservation plan) is approved, both development team and public agency staff have the moral responsibility to act in an honest, cooperative manner.
We don't know how to preserve trees.	Tree preservation primarily requires commitment by the developer and the application of specialized knowledge, just as engineering, architecture, and landscape architecture do. It is for this reason that an arboricultural consultant should be a part of the development team.
We can't control the actions of our subcontractors.	If following a tree preservation program is made a part of a subcontractor's contract (with appropriate penalties for noncompliance), then adherence will follow. For best results, developers should educate their builders and subcontractors about the tree preservation program and its requirements prior to the start of work.

CHAPTER

1

The Guiding Principles of Tree Preservation During Development

Tree preservation requires an understanding of tree biology, as well as of construction techniques and their impact on tree health and structure. Successful tree preservation efforts must adhere to several important principles.

- **Preservation requires the commitment of all parties.** Tree preservation is not the responsibility of the arboricultural or forestry consultant alone. Each participant on a development project—from the owner, engineer, architect, and landscape architect to the grading, demolition, construction, and landscape contractors—must be committed to tree preservation (Figure 1.1). Obtaining this commitment may involve a number of tactics, including specific penalties in the contracts of subcontractors for violation of tree preservation programs, educational programs for the project team, and the visible and vocal support of the

project manager and construction superintendent toward the program. The City of Chapel Hill, North Carolina, includes education of the contractor and subcontractors as part of its tree protection ordinance.

Successful tree preservation occurs when everyone involved in designing, constructing, and managing a development project is committed to that goal.

- **Tree preservation programs must respect patterns of tree growth and development.** All members of the project team, as well as staff from the public agency, must be familiar with the rudimentary aspects of tree growth and development if they are to understand the relationships between tree survival and construction practices. Myths and ignorance about trees and how they grow have no place in tree preservation programs. This is a particular concern given the finding that perceived knowledge of development professionals about trees does not always correspond to their actual knowledge (Andraesen and Tyson 1993). For example, the commonly held myth that roots grow as deep as the tree crown is tall, and spread as far as the crown is wide, still finds its way into construction documents and design drawings (Figure 1.2a). Such misinformation results in poor decisions about trees and construction. The reality is that, in most situations, roots are shallow in profile and spread far beyond the edge of the crown (Figure 1.2b). Arboricultural consultants must strive to provide the most accurate information available about trees.

Successful tree preservation occurs when decisions about trees are based upon accurate information gained from the scientific literature and accumulated experience.

Arboricultural Consultant

Geotechnical/Soil Engineer

Governing Agency

Developer/Builder/Owner

Architect

Land Planner

Landscape Architect

Civil Engineer

Environmental Consultants

Arborist

Landscape Contractor

Building & Grading Contractors

Maintenance Contractor

FIGURE 1.1 Tree preservation during development requires the commitment of everyone involved in the project's planning, design, construction, and management.

5

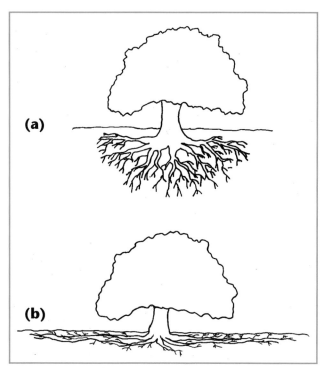

FIGURE 1.2 Tree preservation requires accurate information about patterns of tree growth and development. Inaccurate information depicts roots as extending only to the edge of the canopy and growing deeply into the soil (a). A truer image of how trees grow depicts roots as shallow in depth and extending well beyond the dripline of the canopy (b).

- **Tree preservation cannot wait until construction.** If efforts at tree preservation are delayed or ignored until construction begins, they are largely doomed to failure (Photo 1.1). By the time construction begins, the decisions, plans, and documents associated with a project have been finalized and a detailed set of plans has been approved by the governing agency. Once the project has progressed to this point, it is very difficult and expensive to make significant changes.

Successful tree preservation begins when the project is conceived and continues through the planning, design,

PHOTO 1.1 Attempts to begin tree preservation during the construction phase are doomed to failure. Successful tree preservation begins at the planning and design phases.

construction, and maintenance phases. In that way, decisions to preserve and remove specific trees can be discussed and determined at the same time as are decisions about site layout, grading requirements, and construction techniques.

- **All trees cannot and should not be preserved.** Stands, species, and individual trees vary in their suitability for preservation, both on the basis of their innate characters and their responses to potential construction impacts. Trees that are structurally unstable, in poor health, or unable to survive construction impacts are a liability to a project rather than an asset (Photo 1.2). A realistic tree preservation program acknowledges that conflicts between trees and development may sometimes result in the removal of some trees and recognizes the detrimental effect to the project and community when trees die after construction is completed.

Successful preservation is based upon the long-term survival, health, and structural stability of trees and focuses the efforts on those trees offering the best potential to be assets to the site for years to come.

PHOTO 1.2 Trees in poor health or with significant defects in structure are not suitable for preservation in areas where people or structures will be located.

- **Preservation focuses on preventing injury to trees.** Arboricultural techniques cannot repair construction damage to a tree or the degradation to its environment. Arborists have only a limited ability to "cure" specific injuries or generalized stress caused by construction activities. Once a tree has been damaged, few remedial are treatments available. The tree will either adapt to any construction damage and environmental degradation or it will die. We must acknowledge limitations in this area and respect the reality that "the tree is more important than the treatment."

Successful tree preservation occurs when construction impacts to trees are minimized or avoided altogether (Photo 1.3).

PHOTO 1.3 Successful tree preservation programs prevent injuries from construction activity by keeping equipment and structures away from the tree.

- **Construction impacts to trees are cumulative.** A tree accumulates wounds and injuries throughout its life. Trees do not have a healing or repair process; they can only compartmentalize and generate tissue. Moreover, tree death is often a long, slow process due to multiple and compounding factors. Small, apparently insignificant events add up over the length of the project and can result in a dying or stressed tree. The overall effect of the impacts and injuries that result from demolition, clearing, grading, and construction is cumulative (Photos 1.4a–d). This problem is aggravated by the reality that the participants in the development process change over time, as the work of each individual member is completed. Few people appreciate that an impact resulting from their activity is but one of a number that accumulate over time.

  Successful tree preservation occurs when all members of the project team interact with each other to minimize the impacts to trees, either through design decisions or construction practices.

- **Consultants must learn to communicate with design and engineering professionals.** Development professionals communicate ideas and information graphically. Plans express the use of a commonly shared language and allow everyone on a development project to communicate. If information regarding tree preservation is to be shared and understood by the project team, then it must also be also conveyed in that language. Arboricultural consultants must, therefore, be able to convey tree information graphically. Doing so involves creating maps, drawings, sections, and other details and incorporating them into the plan set.

  Successful tree preservation occurs when arborists present information about trees in a language that others on the development team can understand. That language must be visual and graphic.

PHOTO 1.4 Impacts to trees accumulate as the project proceeds from site clearing (a) through grading (b) and installation of improvements such as utilities (c) to final cleanup and installation of landscape plantings (d).

- **Tree preservation requires accurate site information.** Construction plans and activities depend on accurate site surveys and information. Decisions about grading requirements and the siting of buildings, roads, and utilities, etc. are all based upon field survey information. Because successful preservation involves minimizing construction impacts to trees, assessing those impacts also requires accurate information, including the correct location of trees (Figure 1.3).

  Successful tree preservation occurs when trees are accurately located on all relevant plans.

- **Forest fragments require active management.** Preservation of small remnant patches of a larger forest is a valuable and important part of a community's tree preservation effort and plays a significant

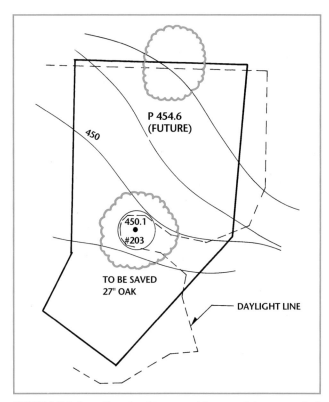

FIGURE 1.3 Information about trees must be accurately represented on all plans. This site plan designated tree #203 with a small circle, although the dripline actually was much larger (green). The tree at the top of the lot, which could have been retained, was not plotted on the plan.

role in the environmental and aesthetic qualities of a neighborhood. Forest fragments are small, residual pieces of what once was a forest (Photo 1.5) As such, they require ongoing management in the form of regeneration, safety, nutrition, and competition.

Successful preservation of remnant forests considers the composition, health, and structure of the fragment and provides for long-term management.

PHOTO 1.5 Small, remnant pieces of forest require active management and care.

- **Tree preservation requires space.** Trees occupy large volumes of space, above and below ground. Tree preservation and planting must include sufficient space to minimize both short- and long-term impacts from construction. In addition, trees grow. If they are to remain assets to a community, sufficient space is necessary to permit the increase in size that will occur over time.

  Successful tree preservation occurs when trees selected for retention are given adequate growing space.

These guiding principles have three themes. First, efforts at preservation must acknowledge and respond to the tree and its ecological support system. The tree itself defines the outer limit for preservation, quite apart from aspects of the project. We must acknowledge that not all trees are in excellent health or have good structural stability. Such trees may not be appropriate near buildings and high-use areas. Second, tree preservation cannot be the responsibility of the arboricultural consultant alone. Each member of the development team and each representative of involved governing agencies must understand that his or her activities and decisions influence the success of tree preservation efforts. Third, the ability of consultants to cure construction injury is very limited, so the focus of preservation efforts must be *prevention* of damage.

It is our experience, and that of other consultants in the field, that each development project must adhere to these guiding principles. To ignore them is to reduce the chances for success and increase the likelihood that trees will die.

SUMMARY

Tree preservation can and should be an integral part of the development process. Retaining trees on development projects offers benefits to the environment, to the community, to the development team, and to the subsequent users of the projects. Buyers prefer projects with trees and are willing to pay more for the privilege of living with that resource. In addition, there are indirect benefits (in the form of positive community recognition) to developers and builders active in tree preservation.

Tree preservation, however, does not just happen. Preserving trees during construction requires the commitment of developer, builder, contractor, subcontractor, and community. It requires knowledge about the trees and an understanding of the relationship of construction practice to their growth.

As a basic rule, tree preservation succeeds when the guiding principles are followed. If participants in a development project understand the needs of trees and the effect their activities have upon tree growth, then a greater sensitivity to tree preservation will result.

REFERENCES

Andreasen, A., and C. Tyson. 1993. *Improving Tree Management Practices of Home Builders: A Social Marketing Approach.* Washington, DC: Forest Policy Center. 44 pp.

Primer on Tree Biology

Trees do not grow in a random manner; they grow in predictable ways. The patterns by which buds, leaves, trunks, branches, flowers, fruit, and roots develop are defined by a genetic blueprint. Every aspect of a tree's growth adheres to a genetic plan set down through millions of years of evolution. The outward expression of this plan, reflected in characteristics such as tree height and location of flowers, is influenced by the physical environment surrounding the tree. Sunlight, wind, water, minerals, and other factors play a role in the tree's development. Over time, the interaction between genetics and environment results in trees that are marvelously adapted to the sites on which they naturally occur.

If trees are to be preserved during the development of a site, three aspects of a tree's biology must be understood. First, the growth patterns of the tree and the specific requirements of each species (or genetic type) must be considered. Second, the growth of a tree in relation to other trees in the woodland or forest must be assessed. Finally, the tree's potential for future growth and survival must be evaluated, recognizing that the existing environmental conditions, those under which the tree has grown for many years, will change.

The objective of this chapter is to introduce tree growth and development to people involved in the development process. This chapter is intended to provide basic concepts about tree growth as well as some terminology for tree care activities.

HOW TREES GROW

All trees have the same basic structure: roots, trunk, branches, buds, leaves, flowers, and fruit (Figure 2.1). While all trees have these features in common, their forms (the shape created by the trunk and branches) vary widely. Some trees have a single trunk; others have multiple stems. Some have upright, narrow forms, while others are rounded and spreading. Some trees (evergreens) hold their leaves for several years; others (deciduous) shed them each fall. Whatever the specific form, the pattern of growth of the roots, trunk, branches, buds, and leaves is the result of the interaction of the tree's genetic blueprint with the surrounding environment.

For a given environment, trees grow in a manner that optimizes their ability to function, that is, to compete with adjacent trees for light and resources,

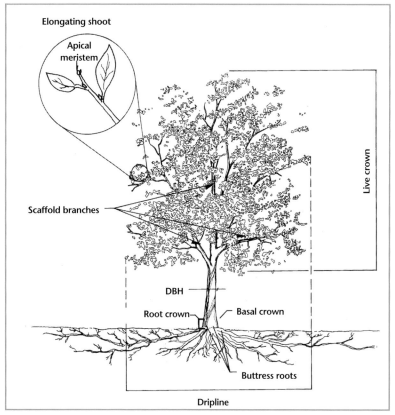

FIGURE 2.1 Components of a tree (DBH = diameter of the trunk measured 4½ feet above ground).

11

TREE STRUCTURE: FREQUENTLY USED TERMS

ABSORBING ROOTS
Common term describing the fine, nonwoody, short-lived roots that absorb water and mineral nutrients and that are often infected with beneficial organisms

BASAL AREA
The cross-sectional area of the trunk based upon measurement at 54 inches (4½ feet) above grade

BASAL (OR TRUNK) FLARE
The increased diameter where the roots and trunk meet (also known as the root flare or buttress)

BROAD-LEAVED
Trees whose foliage is flat and broad

BUTTRESS ROOTS
Large, woody roots emerging from the base of the trunk; contribute to basal flare

CENTRAL LEADER
The main stem, trunk, or bole

CONIFER
Trees that bear cones, usually having needled or scale-like foliage

CROWN (OR CANOPY)
The leaves and branches of a tree

DBH
Diameter at breast height; the diameter of the trunk measured 54 inches (4½ feet) above grade

DECIDUOUS
Trees that lose their leaves each year

DECURRENT
Trees that lack a central leader; the crown is composed of a number of equal-sized branches

DRIPLINE
The edge of the canopy

EVERGREEN
Trees that maintain foliage throughout the year

EXCURRENT
Trees having a strong central leader, normally pyramidal in form

FEEDER ROOTS
Common term to describe fine, nonwoody, short-lived roots that absorb water and mineral nutrients (see Absorbing Roots)

MULTI-TRUNKED
Tree with more than one trunk arising at or near the ground

ROOT CROWN
The point at which the trunk and buttress roots meet

SCAFFOLD BRANCHES
The major structural support branches that attach to the trunk

STAND
Community of trees sufficiently uniform in species, size, arrangement, and age to be distinguishable as a group

TAPER
The change in diameter associated with height or length; related to strength

ZONE OF RAPID TAPER
The area of root growth where the diameter of the root rapidly diminishes, usually measured 5 to 10 feet from the base of the trunk

---

to successfully reproduce, to tolerate disturbance, and to tolerate extremes in climate. As a result, there exists within a tree an intimate balance among its component parts and processes. The size and volume of the root area are large enough to adequately supply the crown with water. The transport capacity of the stem is large enough to deliver water to the leaves. The trunk and root systems are strong enough to support the mass and structure of the crown. The amount of foliage and storage capacity are large enough to meet the energy needs of the tree.

The component parts of a tree depend upon each other for growth materials and support. At a given time, the parts of the tree exist in balance with one another. Any alteration to either the environment or to any part of the tree necessitates an adjustment in this internal balance. This process of adjustment is acclimation (also acclimatization). For example, when young trees are transplanted, most of the root system is removed. Once planted, the trees acclimate to new growing conditions by regenerating lost roots. A similar process occurs when construction occurs around trees. They must also acclimate to a new physical environment. The ability to make this adjustment is constrained by the species of tree, its age, structure, and vigor. Not all trees can acclimate to the degree required for their survival.

THE TRUNK AND CROWN

The trunk and branches support the foliage and act as a transport highway for water, carbohydrates, and minerals between roots and leaves. In a mature tree, the bulk of its mass is located in the woody parts.

COMMONLY ENCOUNTERED STRUCTURAL DEFECTS IN TREES

CANKERS
Surface injuries caused by fungi or bacteria

CAVITY
An open wound characterized by the presence of decay

CODOMINANT TRUNKS
Stems or branches of equal diameter, often weakly attached

CONKS
Fruiting bodies of decay fungi

DECAY
Degradation of wood by fungi and bacteria

DECLINE
Loss of vigor of the entire tree; may be associated with root loss, rendering the tree prone to failure

DIEBACK
Death of twigs and branches in the upper crown

END WEIGHT
Accumulation of mass at the end of a branch

EPICORMIC SHOOTS
Shoots that arise from latent or adventitious buds

FAILURE
Loss of branch or trunk due to structural defects

GIRDLING ROOTS
Roots that encircle the base of the trunk and/or the buttress roots, and which may prevent their growth

LEAN
Departure of the trunk from the vertical

LOW CANOPY
Foliage and branches that are close to the ground; therefore, construction within the dripline will require extensive pruning for clearance

WOUNDS
Injuries on the surface of a trunk or branch

Leaves produce carbohydrates that sustain growth and defend against pests and decay. A healthy, vigorous tree requires a full, dense canopy of leaves to capture solar energy. Any injury or treatment that reduces the amount of foliage will reduce the tree's capacity to produce food and maintain good health. Because the amount of foliage depends on other parts of a tree, any loss in roots, transport capacity, or support will lessen the mass of leaves that can be supported.

Mature trees attain their characteristic large stature through the elongation of shoots as well as expansion of the trunk, roots, and branches. Growth (the creation of new cells and tissues) actually occurs in discrete locations, called meristems. Trees have two types of meristems. The first is associated with elongation of shoots and roots; the second with diameter growth. In shoots, the meristems are contained within protective structures known as buds. In roots, the meristem is found at the ends of small white tips. The activity of these tissues produces the increase in height and spread of the canopy and root system.

The second type of meristem is called the cambium (Figure 2.2). It is responsible for growth in diameter of the trunk, branches, and woody roots. The cambium is a very thin tissue (one or more cells thick), just beneath the bark throughout the tree. If lost through injury or disease, the cambium cannot regenerate in place.

The cambium produces both wood (xylem) and inner bark (phloem). These tissues conduct water,

mineral elements, carbohydrates, and other substances. In most temperate climates, the characteristic rings found in the stem represent the increment in wood produced in one growing season. Thus, a tree with 100 annual rings is at least 101 years old (the first rings develop in the young seedling).

While a tree's trunk may be quite large, only a very small amount of xylem and phloem is functional.

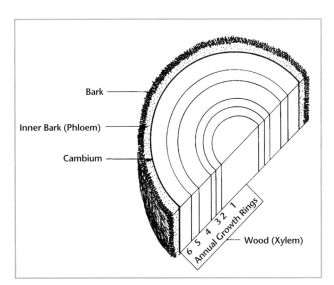

FIGURE 2.2 The cambium is the thin tissue just beneath the bark and is responsible for growth in diameter of the trunk, branches, and woody roots. To the outside, it produces the phloem, which transports carbohydrates. To the inside, the cambium produces xylem, which transports water and mineral elements. Wood is the collective mass of all annual growth rings.

The active elements are found just beneath the outer bark and in the outermost annual rings.

Contrast the development of a tree's trunk with that of a pipe (Figure 2.3). In a pipe, structural support is provided by a thin shell of material. The bulk of the structure is open, allowing transport of materials. In a tree trunk, the situation is exactly the opposite. Only a thin outer shell of tissue is alive—actively producing new cells and providing transport and storage. The vast bulk of the trunk provides only structural support.

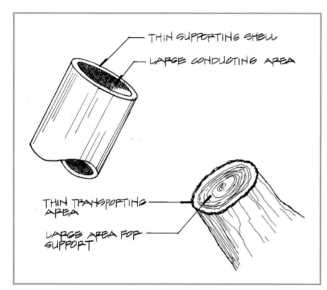

FIGURE 2.3 The structure and function of a tree stem and pipe differ in significant ways. In a pipe, support is provided by a thin shell, with the center open for transport. In a tree trunk, only a thin outer shell is active in transport, with the bulk of the trunk providing support.

Without this narrow shell of functional tissue composed of the cambium, phloem, and active xylem, no water would be moved, no minerals transported, no carbohydrates conducted. When this thin band is broken by injury or disease, the tree can die.

An understanding of meristems and their purpose in the tree leads to an important fact: any injury to meristematic tissues has wide-ranging consequences. While compensatory replacement of shoot and root tips often occurs, this cannot happen with the cambium. Mechanical injury that tears or breaks the bark will kill the cambium (Photo 2.1). The integrity of the cambium is so critical that injuries of 30 to 50 percent of the circumference of the trunk can cause death.

TREE STRUCTURE AND STABILITY

As the tree grows larger, it must continually overcome the force of gravity in order to remain upright. The mass of branches, stems, and leaves is enormous. The tree must also remain upright in strong winds and during snow and ice storms.

The adaptations made by a tree to meet the challenge posed by these forces are numerous, ranging from an increase in wood strength to the shedding of leaves each year. The crowns of most conifers form a cone. This form is called excurrent—the branches radiate from a strong central stem (Photo 2.2). With this pattern of growth, the stress created by wind and snow is distributed proportionally along the stem, thereby increasing stability.

PHOTO 2.1 Mechanical injuries remove the bark and kill the cambium below it, creating the entry point for decay.

This is not the case with most broad-leaved trees, which have an open, spreading form. In these species, the pattern of crown development is decurrent (Photo 2.3). Instead of branches radiating from a single

PHOTO 2.2 Most conifers and many deciduous trees have an excurrent form, in which branches radiate out from a central stem or trunk.

PHOTO 2.3 Most deciduous trees, especially as they mature, have a decurrent form, composed of a number of large branches.

trunk, the crowns of these trees are formed by a number of equally sized branches. Most decurrent trees lose their leaves each autumn. Their bare branches accumulate less snow and ice. Wind passes easily through them. The stress from weight and wind during winter, therefore, is less than that experienced by trees with an excurrent form.

Most trees grow so that the stresses created by wind, precipitation, and gravity are equally distributed along the stem. No point on the trunk becomes a focal point for stress because all points are under a similar load. The result of this growth pattern is taper—the change in diameter of the trunk (and branches) with length. The diameter is greatest at the base, which supports the greatest load and anchors the tree.

Taper develops as the tree sways in the wind and increases in mass. In response to these forces, the trunk grows larger in diameter. A tree growing in an open, windy environment will develop greater taper than one growing in a dense forest stand. It will also be smaller in height and greater in spread.

Branches are subject to the forces of gravity, snow, ice, and wind as well. They also develop taper along their length in response to these conditions. As shoots elongate, diameter is increased near the point of attachment to the trunk. This process is enhanced when the foliage on the branch is evenly distributed along its length. A situation in which the foliage is concentrated at the tip of the branch is known as end weight (Photo 2.4). Excessive end weight, whether it occurs naturally or through improper pruning, is a significant structural defect.

Branches are connected to the rest of the tree by either another branch or at the trunk. The strongest attachments are those in which one member is smaller in size than the one to which it is attached (Photo 2.5); for example, a scaffold limb attached to the main trunk, or a small lateral branch attached to

PHOTO 2.5 The strongest attachments between branch and stem develop when the branch is smaller in size than the trunk to which it is attached.

PHOTO 2.6 Codominant attachments occur where the component branches are equal in size. Because strong wood connecting the branches does not develop, these attachments are often weak and the site of failure.

PHOTO 2.4 Branches with a disproportionate amount of foliage at the ends are said to have "end weight." Limbs with this form are susceptible to failure (note that the branch has been moving downward and is separated from the rest of the canopy).

a larger scaffold branch. The weakest attachments are those in which the two members (either branches or trunks) are codominant (equal in size) (Photo 2.6). When this occurs, the members fail to develop strong connecting wood between them. This situation is made worse when the codominant members are pushed against one another.

TREE DEFENSE AND WOUND RESPONSE

Injuries to trees do not "heal" like wounds in animals do. Trees cannot replace injured parts with new tissues. Instead, trees grow new tissues over the injured areas. They develop chemical and physical barriers to resist the spread of decay and disease organisms from the injury. This process of defense—of surrounding an injury with barriers—is called compartmentalization.

Decay is the gradual deterioration of wood by fungi and bacteria (Photo 2.7). In the forest, these and other organisms digest fallen trees and branches as well as roots, recycling their components. Decay is

PHOTO 2.7 Decay is the gradual degradation of wood by fungal organisms. Over time, decay may severely reduce the structural stability of the tree.

also present in many standing, living trees. Wounds and other openings permit decay organisms to enter the tree and infect the wood. If the formation and maintenance of defense barriers and compartments is inadequate, decay can spread rapidly, rendering the tree structurally unstable. In valley oak (*Quercus lobata*), approximately 75 percent of all failures (breakage of branches and trunks) are associated with decay.

Wound response patterns in trees are central elements to be considered in planning both their retention during development and subsequent care. Any injury to the tree is a permanent one, requiring an active, energy-using response. Arboricultural treatments are, therefore, often aimed at enhancing compartmentalization. Pruning and other aspects of arboriculture are intended to maximize compartmentalization and minimize the extent of decay. Moreover, a tree's response is related to its health: a vigorous tree is best able to compartmentalize decay, thereby resisting its spread.

Finally, the ability to form and maintain defensive barriers varies by species. Cottonwood (*Populus* spp.) and willows (*Salix* spp.) have very poor compartmentalization response, and decay spreads rapidly through these trees. By contrast, other species, including many oaks (*Quercus* spp.), resist the spread of decay (with the exception of *Quercus lobata*, which is susceptible to decay).

THE ROOT SYSTEM

Roots anchor the tree and supply the crown with water and mineral elements absorbed from the soil. Their continued function is an important factor in a tree's survival during construction. In many ways, tree preservation is root system preservation. The best tree retention effort is doomed to failure if root protection is not emphasized during the project. Consultants recognize that grading, construction, utility installation, and other development impacts will in some

MYTHS, FANTASIES, AND HALF-TRUTHS ABOUT TREE ROOTS

Myth: Tree roots can grow as deeply as the crown is tall.
Reality: Most tree roots grow within 3 feet of the soil surface. Most fine roots are within the top 18 inches of the soil surface.

Myth: A tree's root zone extends only as far as the edge of the canopy.
Reality: Tree roots extend far beyond the crown and occupy from two to ten times the area beneath the canopy (Figure 2.4).

Myth: In forest settings, roots of adjacent trees are separate from one another.
Reality: Roots of trees in forest stands overlap and comingle, forming a dense mat (Figure 2.5).

Myth: Tree root systems form a circle around the canopy.
Reality: Root growth is highly opportunistic, creating very asymmetric forms.

Myth: Roots seek out water and mineral elements.
Reality: Tree roots proliferate in areas favorable for their growth, where water, nutrients, and oxygen are abundant.

Myth: The entire root system absorbs water and mineral elements.
Reality: Only the small, fine, short-lived roots function in this manner.

Myth: Trees have large taproots that anchor them into the ground.
Reality: Few mature trees possess a significant taproot.

Myth: Tree roots grow independently of other soil organisms.
Reality: Roots of forest trees coexist with many types of fungi and bacteria, forming mycorrhizal associations.

Myth: Root growth occurs only in the spring and fall.
Reality: Tree roots grow any time the soil temperatures is above the range of 32 to 40°F. In irrigated landscapes, the peak period of root growth is midsummer.

way reduce the ability of roots to grow and function. For both development and tree preservation to occur on a site, the root system must be protected.

The root system of a typical tree can be described as shallow, spread wide, and horizontally oriented (Figures 2.4 and 2.5). Although we think of some trees as being shallow rooted or having a taproot system, these images are not always borne out in nature. For example, while seedlings and young trees often

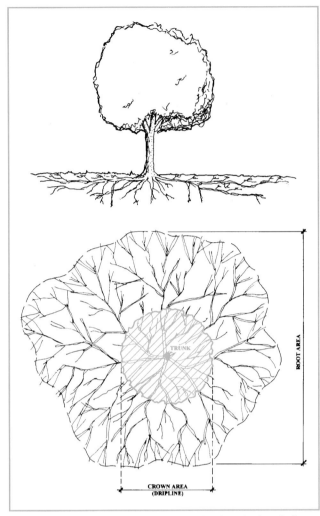

FIGURE 2.4 The root system of a tree can be described as shallow and widespread, extending far beyond the edge of the canopy.

FIGURE 2.5 In forest settings, root systems of individual trees overlap and intertwine, forming a dense mat of roots.

have a taproot (that is, a large, vertically oriented root), mature trees lack such a structure.

Soil and the water table largely determine the structure and depth of a tree root system. Because root growth is largely opportunistic, the chemistry, texture, structure, and depth of the soil will greatly influence the location and extent of root growth. In well-developed forest settings, the soil is a mix of mineral particles, organic matter, water, air, and living organisms. Soil particles and organic matter adhere to form aggregates of varying sizes. These crumbs, clumps, and clods create a matrix of pores, large and small. After a soaking rain, the large (or macro) pores drain, leaving air space. The small (or micro) pores retain water. Roots thrive within this matrix.

Tree roots do not exist alone. Instead, the fine root tips are infected by a wide variety of beneficial fungi. These root–fungi associations, known as mycorrhizae or mycorrhizal associations, are normal and common. Both partners benefit. The fungi aid the tree in the absorption of water and mineral nutrients

and may offer some resistance to pathogens. The tree provides the fungi with a supply of carbohydrates.

Unfortunately, construction often results in changes to the soil structure. To create a stable base for buildings, engineers specify that the soil be compacted, which squeezes out the air and water and destroys its inherent structure. Although compaction provides an excellent base for buildings and roads, it leaves little space for tree roots. Moreover, stripping of the organic layer (also known as the duff) removes many fine roots and their fungal associates.

Everyone involved in the development process must recognize the basic conflict between manipulating soil structure for buildings and preserving that structure for tree roots. Tree preservation is synonymous with root preservation, for the tree will die if its roots are killed. The interface between building area and tree protection zone is a critical one in the preservation process.

TREE GROWTH IN FORESTS AND WOODLANDS

Land development frequently converts existing forests and tree-covered land to other uses. As forests and woodlands are cleared for development, individual and small groups of trees (known as remnant stands, greenbelts, and buffer strips) are preserved. Decisions about retaining forest trees on cleared sites must be based on consideration of the potential response of the particular species and individual trees involved as the physical environment around them is altered.

"In a narrow technical sense," a forest is "a vegetation community dominated by trees . . . growing close enough together that the tree tops touch or overlap . . . " (Dunster and Dunster 1996). Also in a technical sense, forests are distinguished from woodlands by the degree to which the tree canopy shades the ground: heavy, almost complete cover in forest versus a more open, parklike arrangement in woodlands. Where canopy cover is less than 30 percent, the vegetation community is considered a woodland; above 30 percent, a forest (Dunster and Dunster 1996).

The basic unit of forest structure is the stand. In forestry terms, a stand is "an aggregation of trees occupying a specific area and sufficiently uniform in composition, age, arrangement, and condition so that it is distinguishable from the forest in adjoining areas" (Dunster and Dunster 1996). The key element in this definition is uniformity in tree development. A forest or woodland may be composed of many stands, representing different species, densities, and age mixes.

The composition and structure of a forest or woodland stand is an important concern to consultants working on development projects. First, individual species differ widely in their environmental requirements and their ability to acclimate to new site conditions. For example, the hardwood, bottomland forests of the southeast United States are frequently dominated by sweetgum (*Liquidambar styraciflua*), black gum (*Nyssa sylvatica*), and red maple (*Acer rubrum*). These species are adapted to wet sites with high water tables. If the site is drained and the water table lowered during development, these species decline. Their failure to acclimate to a site where the water table has been lowered is predictable based upon their requirements. Second, the species present in a stand, their size, and relative densities will change over time (see the following sections). Evaluating the character of a stand and the differential responses of its component species is, therefore, an important aspect of the resource evaluation.

Growth of Forest Trees Following Clearing

Trees that develop and mature in forest stands experience a environment different from isolated trees growing in the open. A tree growing in an open field receives the full impact of the sun and wind and has little competition for light and space when mature. In contrast, a tree in a dense forest receives direct solar radiation only from above and actively competes with its neighbors for space and resources.

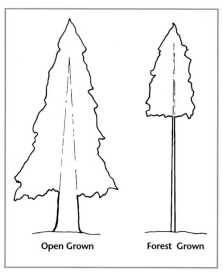

FIGURE 2.6 The relationship among parts of the tree is dependent upon the growing environment. For example, conifers grown in the open, without competition from others, retain more foliage and branches and develop greater trunk taper than trees grown in forest stands.

Open Grown   Forest Grown

In each setting, the tree develops a form and structure in response to its environment (Figure 2.6).

When the environment around the tree is changed because of site preparation, preserved trees that had been growing in forest conditions must now survive in the open. They must alter their patterns of shoot, root, and trunk growth to respond to the new environment. If forest trees are unable to acclimate to the increased exposure that results from opening stands, they may fail mechanically shortly after opening or slowly decline, with failure potential slowly increasing over time. Trees that fail may cause personal injury, property damage, power outages, fires, and other catastrophes.

The reasons for the failure of newly exposed trees fail are connected to their history. Trees in forests have grown in response to the environment of a stand and have high crowns and little taper. When surrounding trees are removed, exposure to the elements increases. As trees are exposed along newly created forest edges, they accumulate more snow and experience greater wind speeds (Seischab et al. 1993). Such trees, having little trunk taper, may lack the wood strength to hold themselves upright and are more likely to fail.

Because growth patterns of trees in forests differ from those in the open, one of the key activities for the consultant is to assess the ability of a tree or a stand to acclimate to an altered site. One should not assume that a tree growing well in a forest environment will remain healthy and vigorous following clearing. Given an opportunity to evaluate existing conditions and structure of a forest, one can identify those stands and trees with the greatest likelihood to survive development and thrive in the future. In addition, those trees that may not tolerate change can be identified and development can be directed away from these sensitive areas.

Forest Composition and Change over Time

The composition of forests and woodlands does not remain static but changes over time, and does so in a predictable way. This process of change is called succession, "a series of dynamic changes in ecosystem structure, function, and species composition over time as a result of which one group of organisms succeeds another through stages leading to a potential natural community or climax stage" (Dunster and Dunster 1996).

Succession occurs because the environment within a forest changes as trees age and enlarge. The forest floor becomes shaded and cooler. The tree species that initially colonized the site are not able to regenerate in these altered conditions and eventually decline. As they do so, new species become established. Understanding the patterns of succession within a forest allows the consultant to assess and predict the character of a forest into the future.

For example, the process of succession on abandoned farm fields has been well studied across the United States and illustrates the importance of understanding succession in tree preservation efforts. In the Piedmont area of North Carolina, 20 to 30 years after a field is abandoned, the forest is composed of an overstory of maturing pines with hardwoods filling in the understory (Barbour et al. 1987) (Table 2.1). In this situation, the pines have a potential lifespan of approximately 30 more years. As they age, the overstory pines fail, thereby creating gaps in the canopy. At 60 to 70 years of age, the forest consists of a discontinuous canopy of mature pines with limited longevity. At this point, the best opportunities for tree retention lie in the young hardwoods that are growing beneath the pines. At 150 years after abandonment, the forest would be dominated by mature oak and hickory trees. In this stage, evaluation of individual mature trees would be critical because the oldest trees may be structurally unstable. Below this canopy would be many young oak and hickory trees.

This pattern of succession can be explained by understanding the basic requirements of the species involved. Pines require bare ground for seed to germinate and grow. They also require full sun to develop; they cannot grow in the shade of other trees. For these reasons, pines proliferate shortly after a field is abandoned (cleared, cultivated, or burned). Over time, the pines shed leaves, branches, and other structures. As this litter accumulates on the forest floor, it forms a layer of organic matter in which pine seeds can no longer germinate. However, the seeds of other species (notably oak and hickory) are able to germinate in the litter layer. The seedlings and saplings that result grow slowly in the understory, below the pines. As the tall pines decline and die, they fall to the ground, creating gaps in the canopy. The oaks and hickories that had been growing slowly in the understory are released, that is, they respond to the new environmental conditions (high amounts of sunlight) and grow rapidly to fill in the gaps. As the mature pine trees die, the species composition of the stand is changed; the pines are replaced by the oaks and hickories that have developed in their shade.

The aspect of succession—change in the species composition of the overstory—is a common one throughout North America. In many forest types, species that initially dominated the stand following disturbance are replaced by others, known as late successional species. The ability of a tree species to grow and develop in the understory is known as "tolerance" or "shade tolerance." Oaks and hickories have high tolerance, while the tolerance of pines is low.

The implications of this pattern for tree preservation are significant. In forest stands in which the early succession/low tolerance species are mature, the best opportunities for long-term preservation will be with the understory, late successional species. For example, in the U.S. Midwest, the overstory of many forests is composed of aspen (*Populus tremuloides*) and birch (*Betula pendula*). These are early successional species that would be succeeded by late successional types such as red oak (*Quercus rubra*) and red maple (*Acer rubrum*). If a development project were to clear all of the understory and remove the oak and maple, only mature and overmature aspen and birches would be retained. These species are likely to fail during storms and offer little long-term potential for preservation. In this situation, retaining the understory preserves the natural pattern of forest succession and allows a canopy of oak and maple to develop (Miller 1997).

TABLE 2.1 Successional patterns in the North Carolina Piedmont (adapted from Barbour et al. 1987).

Years after abandonment	Tree species
10	First young pines appear: •loblolly (*Pinus taeda*) •shortleaf (*P. echinata*)
60	Pine overstory (trees) with hardwood understory (seedlings and saplings)
100–150	Hardwood overstory develops: •white oak (*Quercus alba*) •post oak (*Q. stellata*) •hickory (*Carya* spp.) •dogwood (*Cornus florida*) •large old-growth pines (*Pinus* spp.)

The patterns of species composition and succession paths vary widely across North America. For this reason, foresters have described numerous cover types to distinguish among them. Eyre (1980) described cover type as "a descriptive classification of forestland based on present occupancy of an area by tree species." One hundred forty-five cover types have been described for the United States and Canada (Eyre 1980). Similar descriptions are available on a regional basis. For example, 57 cover types have been described for California's hardwood rangelands (Allen 1989). These two references illustrate the diversity of species, form, structure, ecosystems,and landscapes.

Forest Structure

Forest stands possess a wide range of structure—the vertical and horizontal arrangement of trees within the group. Factors determining the structure of a stand include species composition, climate, and time. Stands that arise from catastrophic events such as fire or storms will initially have trees that are uniform in size and age. As the stand develops, its structure becomes more complex. Competition between individuals, differential reproduction by component species, invasion by new species, and variable availability of resources combine to cause differential growth.

In assessing stand development, consultants evaluate the relative size and position of individual trees in stands (Figure 2.7). Four classes are commonly used.

- **Dominant.** Trees with crowns above the upper layer of the canopy and generally receiving light from above and sides. Also known as emergent.

- **Codominant.** Trees that define the general upper edge of the canopy, receiving light primarily from above.

- **Intermediate.** Trees that have been largely overtopped but may receive some light from above.

- **Suppressed.** Trees that have been overtopped, occupy an understory position in the canopy, and grow slowly.

Other terms commonly associated with crown class are edge (existing on the fringe of the stand) and interior (growing in the center of the stand). Edge trees frequently possess asymmetric crowns (heavier on the open side) and trunks that bow out of the stand.

TREE DEVELOPMENT OVER TIME

As forest stands change over time, so do the individual trees that comprise them. Tree growth is dynamic over time, reaching limits defined by the interaction of their genes and the environment. For example, all tree species reach an upper limit of height. They may grow rapidly for a number of years, then slow in

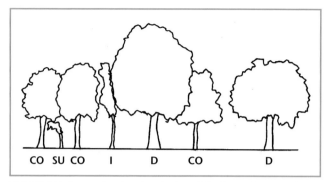

FIGURE 2.7 Crown class is a description of the form of a tree relative to others in the stand, usually described as dominant (D), codominant (CO), intermediate (I), and suppressed (S) (adapted from the Hazard Tree Assessment Program, Recreation and Park Department, City of San Francisco, California).

elongation as mature height is reached. At this point, the tree acts to maintain the existing structure rather than grow larger.

Age-Related Changes

As trees age, a number of changes occur in their development. Many of these changes are associated with the large size that develops over many years. In some mature trees, the distance between the tips of absorbing roots and the top of the tree may be over 500 feet. To efficiently move water, mineral elements, and carbohydrates, the tree must have a highly developed, well-coordinated system of transportation, exchange, and control. Similarly, as the tree increases in size, the mass of branches and leaves that must be held upright against gravity and storms is disproportionately greater. In short, as a tree enlarges, it must expend ever-increasing amounts of energy simply to maintain its structure.

The most significant change associated with old age in trees is a decrease in the relative amount of tissue active in photosynthesis. Because the amount of foliage relative to roots, trunk, and branches declines with age, so do the net carbohydrate resources produced on an annual basis. (It is this production that forms the basic building block of tree growth and defense.) The possible reasons for this decrease are 1) increased maintenance respiration, 2) limited nutrient availability, and 3) reduced gas exchange and photosynthetic potential (Gower et al. 1996). Whatever the fundamental reason for the observed decline in growth, it is clear that old trees are less able to respond to changes brought about by site development. The ability to acclimate to new site conditions and to tolerate environmental stress of all types simply declines with age.

It appears that old age in trees is associated with an increase in susceptibility to disease, decay, and other causes of death (Manion 1981). For example, we observe root rots such as *Phytophthora* to be a significant cause of death in mature oaks (*Quercus* spp.) in California and madrone (*Arbutus menziesii*) in Washington. These root disease organisms are ubiquitous in the soil, but they do not proliferate in dry soil. When trees receive heavy irrigation during the summer, root rots become more prevalent and severe. The susceptibility of trees to these fungi appears to be age dependent. Young seedlings of oak and madrone are frequently observed growing in heavily irrigated landscape beds without symptoms, yet mature trees rapidly succumb to the disease under similar conditions. We do not know if the death of mature trees is the result of a decrease in host resistance or to some change in soil environment due to irrigation. We observe only that the ability of these species to survive infection by root rot appears to decline with age.

A similar situation exists with many pine species, including loblolly (*Pinus taeda*) and Monterey pine (*Pinus radiata*), and susceptibility to bark beetles (Photo 2.8). Attack by bark beetles is a frequent cause of death, and old trees are more susceptible than young trees (Barr et al. 1978). Because this observation appears to be true regardless of the intensity of care and maintenance, we must conclude that host resistance changes with age.

PHOTO 2.8 As some pine trees grow older, they become more susceptible to attack by insects. In this case, bark beetles have infested Monterey pine trees.

How Trees Die

Tree do not live forever. Species, however, vary widely in their potential longevity, with average lifespan ranging from tens to thousands of years (Table 2.2). The extremes in potential lifespan are rather misleading and do not appear to represent the typical tree. Most individual trees survive for only a fraction of

TABLE 2.2 Typical lifespans of selected North American trees in forest settings (Loehle 1988).

Common name	Scientific name	Typical age of mortality	Maximum longevity
Bigleaf maple	*Acer macrophyllum*	150	300
Red maple	*Acer rubrum*	80	150
Sugar maple	*Acer saccharum*	300	400
Paper birch	*Betula papyrifera*	100	140
American beech	*Fagus grandifolia*	300	400
White ash	*Fraxinus americana*	260	300
Sweetgum	*Liquidambar styraciflua*	200	300
Tuliptree	*Liriodendron tulipifera*	200	250
Southern magnolia	*Magnolia grandiflora*	80	120
Colorado spruce	*Picea pungens*	150	350
Lodgepole pine	*Pinus contorta*	120	300
White pine	*Pinus strobus*	200	450
Loblolly pine	*Pinus taeda*	100	300
Balsam poplar	*Populus balsamifera*	100	150
Eastern cottonwood	*Populus deltoides*	60	100
Quaking aspen	*Populus tremuloides*	70	200
Coast live oak	*Quercus agrifolia*	150	——
White oak	*Quercus alba*	300	600
Valley oak	*Quercus lobata*	200	300
Red oak	*Quercus rubra*	200	400
Live oak	*Quercus virginiana*	200	300
Douglas-fir	*Pseudotsuga menziesii*	750	1,200
Black locust	*Robinia pseudoacacia*	60	100
Eastern hemlock	*Tsuga canadensis*	450	800
American elm	*Ulmus americana*	175	300

the potential lifespan of the species. In evaluating trees for preservation during development, consultants must focus less on the maximum potential longevity of a species and more on the landscape lifespan. In its native habitat, white alder (*Alnus rhombifolia*) trees live for 25 to 30 years. In the cultivated landscape, however, these trees die after only 10 to 15 years, even with the best possible care. Monterey pine (*Pinus radiata*) trees live to be 120 years in their native forest along California's central coast. When planted in the San Francisco Bay area, they may live for only 50 to 80 years and in the Central Valley of California, only 25 years.

Tree death is frequently a slow and complex process. While diseases such as Dutch elm and oak wilt may kill a tree quickly, a gradual death involving a number of factors is more common (Clark and Matheny 1991). Most trees die from one of three causes: structural failure, environmental degradation, or pest infestation. A single factor may not be severe enough to cause death, but the cumulative effect of two or more stresses can be.

For consultants, the question of how tree health, environmental stress, pest organisms, and other factors move from weakening the tree to killing it is a critical one. The pattern of death for many trees can be described as a "mortality spiral" (Clark and Matheny 1991) (Figure 2.8). For example, the most common causes of death of both coast live oak (*Quercus agrifolia*)

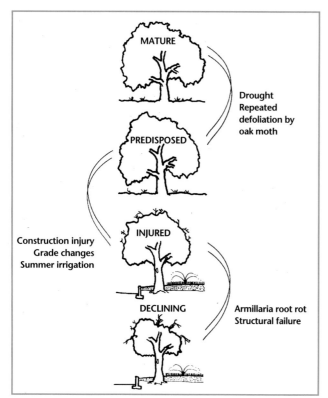

FIGURE 2.8 A mortality spiral for coast live oak (*Quercus agrifolia*). Drought, construction impact, and over-irrigation are important stresses that increase the susceptibility of the tree to decay and root disease.

growing in the San Francisco Bay area, and water oak (*Quercus aquatica*) in the Southern United States are structural failure and root rot (*Armillaria mellea*). The degree of each problem is aggravated by frequent summer irrigation, drought, changes in grade, mechanical injury to roots, and defoliation by oak moth. These predisposing factors reduce tree health and the ability to combat the spread of fungi. Over a period of years, decay and *Armillaria* affect more and more of the tree's wood, until either death or structural failure occurs.

A similar situation exists for Monterey pine (*Pinus radiata*). A frequent cause of death is the five-spined engraver beetle (*Ips* spp.). Healthy Monterey pines usually resist attack by producing large amounts of pitch that kills the beetles. Trees weakened by a variety of predisposing factors are less able to either manufacture pitch or produce it in amounts sufficient to kill the beetles. Predisposing conditions are those that decrease health and vigor and may include drought stress and infestations of the red turpentine beetle (*Dendroctonus valens*) (Koehler et al. 1978). In addition, wounding the tree (by pruning, for example) during the growing season attracts adult bark beetles. Once the tree is infested with the engraver beetles, chemical control is rarely effective. The most effective control programs are those that prevent the predisposing factors.

In both of these examples, there is no control for the cause of death (structural failure, *Armillaria* fungus, *Ips* beetle). To prevent death from these causes, the tree must be maintained in good health without predisposing stresses. Once decay is extensive or the *Ips* infestation is heavy, there is no treatment or cure.

Predisposing factors are keys to understanding and preventing the decline and death of trees. Soil compaction, changes in grade, mechanical injury, changes in the environment around the tree, and changes in drainage may not kill the tree by themselves. But they may so weaken a tree that death by some other cause occurs; the further a tree is along the mortality spiral, the less likely it is to escape from it and survive. Prevention of stress and maintenance of health are the key elements in tree longevity.

SUMMARY

Trees grow in predictable patterns. Their shapes, sizes, and features are all determined by the interaction of a genetic blueprint with the surrounding environment. Over time, the parts of a tree—the leaves, roots, branches, and stem—exist in intimate balance with each other. This balance allows these parts to share resources, bear weight, compete with neighbors, and defend against pests in a integrated manner. When this balance is disturbed, either by injuring the tree or changing the environment around it, the tree responds so as to re-establish it. The ability to respond to change is a function of the species, health, age, and structure. When the extent of change is too great, the tree becomes weakened and subject to attack by pests.

The pattern of decline and death is not a random one, but is often species dependent. As a tree ages, its capacity to overcome injury, adapt to changes in its site environment, and to resist pests declines. It is for this reason that retention of old trees during development requires special attention, minimal disturbance, and a program of long-term care.

REFERENCES

Allen, B., R. Evett, B. Holzmann, and A. Martin. 1989. *Rangeland Cover Type Descriptions for California Hardwood Rangelands*. Sacramento: California Department of Forestry and Fire Protection. Forest and Rangeland Resources Assessment Program. 318 pp.

Barbour, M., J. Burk, and W. Pitts. 1987. *Terrestrial Plant Ecology*. 2nd edition. Menlo Park, CA: Benjamin/Cummings Co. 634 pp.

Barr, B., D. Hanson, and C. Koehler. 1981. *Red Turpentine Beetle: A Pest of Pines*. University of California Cooperative Extension. Leaflet 20155. 4 pp.

Clark, J., and N. Matheny. 1991. Management of mature trees. *Journal of Arboriculture*. 17:173–183.

Dunster, J., and K. Dunster. 1996. *Dictionary of Natural Resource Management*. Vancouver: University of British Columbia Press. 363 pp.

Eyre, F. (editor). 1980. *Forest Cover Types of the United States and Canada*. Washington, DC: Society of American Foresters. 148 pp.

Gower, S., R. McMurtrie, and D. Murty. 1996. Aboveground net primary production decline with stand age: Potential causes. *Trees*. 11:378–382.

Koehler, C., D. Wood, and A. Scarlett. 1978. *Bark Beetles in California Forest Trees*. University of California Cooperative Extension. Leaflet 21034. 8 pp.

Loehle, C. 1988. Tree life history strategies: The role of defenses. *Canadian Journal of Forest Research*. 18:209–222.

Manion, P. 1981. *Tree Disease Concepts*. Englewood Cliffs, NJ: Prentice-Hall. 399 pp.

Miller, Robert. 1997. University of Wisconsin, Stevens Point. Personal communication. January.

Seischab, F., J. Bernard, and M. Eberle. 1993. Glaze storm damage to western New York forest communities. *Bulletin of the Torrey Botanical Club*. 120:64–72.

Primer on the Development Process

Development is the process of preparing land and building structures to accommodate a variety of uses. At a fundamental level, development is about land: acquiring it, working with it, transforming it, improving it. Whether it be the conversion of forest and agricultural land, the reclamation of refuse land, or the redevelopment of urban land, without land there can be no development. With development comes change, particularly to natural resources. Our focus is on development associated with trees. To that end, we do not consider conversion of agricultural lands or restoration of derelict land except when trees are present.

The development process occurs in four stages:

1. **Planning:** Assessing potential land uses, selecting the most feasible and appropriate use, determining the general project layout.
2. **Design:** Creating plans and other documents to describe the development.
3. **Construction:** Building the project.
4. **Maintenance:** Managing the project following construction.

This chapter focuses on two aspects of development. First, we introduce the process of development, considering the perspectives of both the developer and community. In so doing, we refer to the development team as the group of professionals who conceive, plan, and implement a project (Table 3.1). Second, we consider how tree preservation is affected at each stage in that process. In this discussion, we focus on the relationships among the development team, the public agency, and the consultant. We also emphasize the need for timely information about trees at each stage.

DEVELOPMENT FROM THE DEVELOPER'S PERSPECTIVE

Development is initiated by the intent to build on a piece of property. Basic questions then follow: Will this be a residential or commercial project? If residential, is it single or multiple family? Projected price range? Size of lots? Will the project be taken from start to sale of the homes or will lots be sold following site development and approval by the community? What permits are required and which municipal rules are in effect? What is the economic viability of any project proposal? What is the timeline for completion?

There are three types of development professionals:

- **Developers** acquire land and financing, plan the project, conduct site analyses, and prepare plans and documents required by the governing agency. They typically install off-site improvements such as grading, roads, and utilities that are deeded to the public for future maintenance.

- **Builders** acquire building sites within the overall project following construction of the off-site improvements by the developer and approval by the public agency. For residential projects, the sites are generally improved lots. Builders construct the buildings and other structures and manage their sale or lease.

- **Builder/developers** undertake the entire process from planning and approval through construction.

Developers of residential property may also sell improved lots (that is, lots on which public improvements such as roads, graded pads, and utilities have already been installed) directly to homeowners, who then contract with a builder for construction.

Development companies often specialize in one type of project or market segment and typically acquire land appropriate for this focus. Examples of corporate specialization include entry-level homes (for first-time buyers), high-end residential, custom homes, and multifamily residential. Some predevelopment master-planning companies, however, may not own land at all. Rather, they form partnerships with cities, private investors, institutions, and development firms to assemble financing for a project and obtain necessary permits and approvals. The resulting projects may combine residential, commercial, and public use.

TABLE 3.1 Common participants in the development process.

Developer	Acquires land and oversees preparation of plans through approval by public agency. Installs public improvements such as roads, drainage, graded lots, and utilities. Clears, grades, and otherwise prepares building sites.
Builder	Acquires improved lots and oversees construction of structures.
Arboricultural consultant	Provides information on tree resources, prepares tree preservation plan, and monitors construction activity.
Civil engineer	Designs grading, drainage, and utility plans.
Utility engineer	Designs utilities and develops plans.
Geotechnical and soils engineer	Assesses existing geology and soils, prepares specifications for soil work.
Biologist	Conducts inventory of biological resources. Prepares environmental impact report and statements.
Land planner	Develops conceptual land-use plans and assesses their feasibility.
Architect	Develops program goals for structures and designs models and plans.
Landscape architect	Develops landscape theme and designs landscape plans for project.
General contractor	Constructs the project and oversees activities of subcontractors.
Demolition contractor	Clears the site of existing structures and vegetation.
Grading contractor	Changes elevation of the site to conform to the grading plan.
Landscape contractor	Installs plants, builds structures, etc. to conform to the landscape plans.
Maintenance contractor	Maintains landscape plantings following completion of construction.
City/county planner	Acts as public agency's liaison to development team. Reviews plans and site development on public agency's behalf.

Other development companies, particularly in urban areas, are founded as nonprofit corporations. Their development activity is focused on specific communities or neighborhoods. The range of development specialization can be characterized as follows:

RESIDENTIAL
  single- or multifamily
  detached, semidetached, or attached units
  high or low density (units per acre)
  price range (entry, low, mid, high)

INDUSTRIAL

COMMERCIAL
  retail
  office
  recreational (e.g., golf courses)

INSTITUTIONAL
  public
  private

The size and location of a parcel of land also determine how it will be used and the potential for tree preservation (Table 3.2). A large property (hundreds to thousands of acres) usually will require master planning (more detailed advance planning and market feasibility analysis) to determine the potential use(s) for the property and the significant planning issues. The density of construction on the project can place a significant limit on tree preservation. Projects involving redevelopment of sites and projects that develop open land within an already developed area (known as infill projects) have specific development concerns, particularly related to demolition of existing improvements.

DEVELOPMENT FROM A COMMUNITY PERSPECTIVE

Development must operate within a broader community framework. The days of "This is my land and I'll do what I want with it" are largely past. Cities, counties, states, and the federal government all have some authority to impose constraints and restrictions on activities that change the land, although the level of regulation varies widely from location to location.

There are at least three levels of community involvement in development projects. The first level occurs

TABLE 3.2 Types of development: Constraints, opportunities, and strategies for tree preservation.

Type of project	Constraints	Opportunities	Tree preservation strategies
Redevelopment	Tree growth limited and shaped by existing structures (above and below ground).	Existing trees blend with surroundings. Plants may have historic value.	Focus preservation on high-quality trees with good tolerance for impacts.
	Demolition may require extensive work close to trees.		Be realistic about ability to demolish structures and retain trees.
	Development density may be high.	Existing utilities may be adequate, reducing new impacts.	Determine if existing utilities can be used in new development.
	Trees on abandoned or derelict sites may have declined significantly from lack of care.		
Infill	Service and utility locations and depths determined by existing lines.		Focus preservation on high-quality trees with good tolerance for impacts.
	Development will occur in close proximity to trees on adjacent properties.		Consider impacts and potential mitigations to trees on adjacent properties.
	Existing tree species may be dominated by invasive exotics.		Be realistic about potential for escape of existing species.
	Trees may have declined significantly from lack of care.		
	Development density normally high.		
High-density residential/ commercial	Limited space for tree preservation.		Focus preservation on high-quality trees with good tolerance for impacts.
	Few, if any, opportunities for preserving groups and stands of trees.		
Low-density residential	Large lots.	Large lots provide options for locating building envelopes and preserving trees.	Designate open-space areas for stands of trees. Cluster homes away from trees.
	Installation of site improvements may involve extensive disturbance.	Flexibility on locating streets and associated improvements.	Locate site improvements away from trees.

TABLE 3.2 *(continued)*

Large-scale master plan (PUD)	Disturbance of existing forests and stands.	Localized habitat conservation may be possible. Natural regeneration of native stands can be enhanced.	Evaluate existing resource. Provide management information.
	Requirements for mass grading.	Flexibility in assigning land use to given areas.	Restrict grading to areas away from trees.
	Installation of site improvements may involve extensive disturbance.	Flexibility in locating streets and associated improvements.	Locate site improvements away from trees.

through city- and regionwide general and specific plans and ordinances. General and specific plans create the blueprint for the future growth by providing an overall structure of the community. They identify goals for development by providing guidelines on parcel size, building density, and development standards. General and specific plans may even place limits on growth by restricting the number of available building permits. General or comprehensive plans also define the type of land use (housing, open space, institutional, recreation, industry, etc.) across a community.

Coughlin et al. (1984) note that programs regulating land use fall into two categories: 1) controls such as zoning ordinances and limits on acquisition, and 2) incentives, including differential assessments and flexibility in building densities. Under ideal conditions, the various programs of land regulation define, for both the community and developer, the areas available for development and the rules regarding the process. Tuolomne County, California, provides developers with a habitat conservation plan that details areas of critical wildlife habitat. With this information, development professionals can more easily focus their activities in areas outside the critical habitats.

The second level of involvement in a project is that of review and approval. A project may receive an initial review and comment by agency staff, followed by submission to the appropriate decision-making body, usually an elected or appointed board (e.g., planning commission, city council or county board of supervisors). The process of review and consent, described by the terms "application" and "approval," tests the project for compatibility with the community and its master plan, goal, and standards. Agency approval allows the project to proceed. Without it, the project must be either reformulated or abandoned.

The approval process varies as a function of the scope and nature of the project and the complexity of local government requirements. Unfortunately, the approval

process is not standardized across the United States and varies widely from community to community. For example, the city of Pleasanton, California, distinguishes between residential development projects and residential improvement projects. Pleasanton further separates the former into PUD (planned unit development) projects and nonPUD projects. PUDs are large-scale efforts (such as large subdivisions) that require extensive review and permitting.

The third level of community involvement in development takes place through public hearings. During project review, many communities hold public meetings during which comments from the general public are taken. Developers are acutely aware of the significance of the public hearing phase of project review. It is increasingly common for the project team to solicit views and comments from neighbors and adjacent property owners during the conceptual planning phase in order to resolve problems before the public hearings.

As the project moves through the latter two stages of community review, a series of specific standards and requirements applicable to the project may be created. In most cases, approval of the project is subject to these "conditions of approval." The conditions of approval usually are written by city or county staff, then modified and approved by the governing agency (often with public comment). The conditions specify requirements for all aspects of a project, including streets, lighting, erosion control, architecture, and tree preservation. Many communities incorporate recommendations from tree reports and preservation plans in the conditions of approval, including requirements for individual trees.

Tree Preservation Ordinances and Policies

As the public decides on the nature of their community, they create opportunities and constraints for people to manage their land. Because we believe that tree preservation reflects communitywide values about trees, without public support, tree preservation policies are unlikely to be successful. If the community demands tree preservation, developers will act to preserve trees.

Communities usually employ ordinances to establish tree preservation standards and guidelines. A variety of resource materials provides background on tree ordinances, including aspects of tree preservation during development (Hoefer et al. 1990, Bernhardt and Swiecki 1991, Duerksen and Richman 1993, Dunster 1994).

When development professionals find regulations regarding tree preservation burdensome and unrealistic, they may want to be involved in their revision (or creation). The level of understanding and cooperation between community and development professionals is thereby enhanced. For example, the city of Eden Prairie, Minnesota, wanted to end its case-by-case review of development proposals and create a comprehensive approach to evaluation. In developing its tree preservation policy, Eden Prairie requested the participation (and eventual endorsement) of the local Developer's Forum (Fox 1990). In so doing, Eden Prairie worked to bring the needs of the development profession together with the desire of the community for tree preservation.

Some communities resist creation of tree preservation policies, generally for two reasons. First, there is a fear that any restrictions on development will cause developers to move elsewhere, with economic hardship the result. Second, many communities hold a philosophy that landowners should be free to manage their land however they see fit, without interference. Tree preservation ordinances, however, are aimed at preserving trees, not prohibiting development. From our perspective, communities enact tree preservation ordinances to preserve valuable natural resources and a sense of place, not to prohibit development. In so doing, they make trees an important planning concern and focus attention on their preservation.

Communities can enhance the value and success of their tree preservation regulations by writing ordinances that explain requirements clearly, are easy to apply, and are well formulated. A good tree preservation ordinance does several things.

- **It identifies the major goals of the policy.** Is the ordinance aimed at preserving a locally important species or group of species, a native species, a certain size of tree, a percentage of existing canopy cover, or some other aspect of the forest resource? Or is the ordinance aimed at preserving the benefits that are provided by a specific group of trees? The ordinance might focus on specific environmental objectives, such as erosion control.

- **It identifies the approaches for meeting those goals.** If the goal is preservation of canopy cover, the ordinance should identify the acceptable

methods of doing so—preservation, new planting, or a combination of both.

- **It requires a tree report and preservation plan as part of the project submittal package.** The best way to ensure that tree preservation becomes incorporated into project planning is to make it part of the initial application process. The ordinance should define the topics to be addressed in the report.

- **It identifies the department, staff, or agent responsible for reviewing tree reports and/or preservation plans and related submittals.** From both the developer and community perspectives, it is much more effective to know the individual or office responsible for tree preservation. Ideally, the person responsible would have appropriate arboricultural and forestry expertise.

- **It requires a fencing plan identifying the tree protection zone as part of the final tract map/ application.** Because the tree protection zone is one of the key elements of a preservation program, it must be identified early enough in the design phase that it becomes an element in construction planning (Photo 3.1). For example, the location of haul roads and storage, waste, and wash-out areas must be sited outside the tree protection zone.

- **It requires bonding for trees identified for preservation.** A bonding requirement for trees to be preserved helps ensure that the specifications outlined in the tree preservation plan are implemented. In this way, posting a bond for the value of the tree becomes a tool for compliance— not a penalty.

- **It requires monitoring during construction.** There are two important implications for monitoring. First, the maintenance of the tree protection zone is one of the most important measures of success

PHOTO 3.1 A requirement for a fencing plan, defining the tree protection zone, should be a part of the ordinance.

of a tree preservation program. Second, every project requires field changes and uncovers unforeseen problems. Routine monitoring enables decisions in both areas to be made with the tree's health and survival in mind.

- **It requires replanting/reforestation as part of the tree preservation plan.** Most development projects, even those with good preservation plans, will include some tree removal. It is only appropriate to plant new trees, to replace any removed, as well as to augment the existing forest.

- **It provides for consequences should the regulations be broken.** Damage to trees during construction cannot be corrected. Enforcements (such as fines for violating the conditions of approval) and the ability of the local government authority to stop work can be effective in preventing accidents and oversights that might otherwise result in damage to trees. In our experience, the need for strong enforcement is particularly useful when dealing with subcontractors and independent home builders.

- **It acts in a reasonable fashion.** Tree preservation reflects the joint commitment of the development team and the community. We suggest that tree preservation ordinances accommodate the development process and provide for flexibility in specific cases.

An ordinance or policy that includes these provisions creates a framework for successful tree preservation. We caution against simply adopting ordinances from other communities. Ordinances must respect the types of forests and trees in a particular community. An ordinance that works in the deciduous hardwood forests of the midwestern United States will probably not be appropriate in the desert southwest. In addition, ordinances must reflect the values within a community. Because many of the aspects of an ordinance are community specific, we suggest that a community consider the aspects of other ordinances that appeal to them, but incorporate them into a policy framework specific to their location.

DEVELOPMENT FROM THE ARBORICULTURAL CONSULTANT'S PERSPECTIVE

The arboricultural or forestry consultant's role during development is to provide the best information possible about trees and to convey that information in an appropriate format. These tasks may include:

- understanding the goals of the project and how trees are involved
- knowing the community's restrictions and requirements regarding trees and ensuring compliance

- assessing the composition and condition of the tree resource
- compiling all site information significant to trees
- appraising the value of the trees, when required
- evaluating the impacts that development will have on the trees and how the trees are likely to respond
- suggesting alternative designs to minimize impacts
- recommending trees for retention or removal
- assisting in securing necessary permits and approvals relative to trees
- determining how work should proceed to protect trees from damage
- preparing necessary drawings, reports, and specifications
- communicating with all people involved in the project
- educating people involved in the project
- responding to tree-related issues throughout the development process
- maintaining records of actions and decisions regarding trees
- monitoring construction activity and tree response to site change and determining appropriate actions

Because tree preservation cannot begin during construction, the earlier in the process the consultant is involved, the greater the chances of successful tree preservation. In the best situation, the consultant works with the developer and development team during the initial stages of project concept and planning. As tree information is included in the planning process, decisions about site planning will reflect tree issues. It is for this reason that we favor having the consultant as a member of the development team, rather than an as employee of the governing agency. In the United Kingdom, retention of an arboricultural consultant by the development team is a requirement (Bashford 1997).

The consultant may also act as an agent of the community or agency, most often to review and enforce the conditions of approval and other regulations. In some communities, the consultant performs the tree evaluation and identifies which trees must be preserved. During the conceptual and planning phases, the consultant may be asked to assess the scope of the project and address tree-related issues. Upon submittal of project plans or documents, the consultant may be involved in the review process and may appraise the trees for bonding purposes. During construction, the consultant might monitor implementation of the tree preservation plan and adherence to the conditions of approval. In some communities, the consultant has enforcement authority and may issue "stop-work" orders when violations to municipal code or the conditions of approval occur.

The consultant must remain objective—whether working for the developer, the community, or some other party. Once a project is approved by the community, the consultant should assist in "getting the job built" in a timely manner and according to the conditions imposed. Maintaining a spirit of cooperation and teamwork is much more effective than one of confrontation.

Two other roles are often undertaken by a consultant during the tree preservation and development process. He or she may act as an advocate for tree preservation to both the community and the development team. A consultant might assist in obtaining waivers for such items as the amount of grading permitted or the width of the right-of-way. In other situations, a consultant might serve in an enforcement role, ensuring compliance with the regulations or conditions.

TREE PRESERVATION AND THE DEVELOPMENT PROCESS

Tree preservation is involved at each stage of development. Rather than focus strictly on a development process, we submit a process of parallel importance: the tree preservation process (Table 3.3). In this view, we acknowledge that developers must satisfy the requirements of a public agency as well as their own needs. We also recognize that every step in a development process has implications for tree preservation.

This process represents an ideal version of tree preservation. First, it assumes that clear policies and requirements exist for tree preservation in the community and that they are enforced. Second, a tree report and preservation plan are considered integral parts of the project application. This requires the developer to take an active role in tree preservation activity by including a consultant on the development team and communicating tree protection goals to all other members of the development team. Finally, this process assumes a mutual trust between agency staff and the development team, so that the project may be discussed in an atmosphere of cooperation.

The tree preservation process describes the development and review activities that occur at each stage of project planning and construction. It also considers tree preservation activities at each stage.

1. Preapplication (Project Planning)

During the planning phases of the project, the developer may not yet own the subject property. Rather, he or she may place an option on the property for purchase or form a partnership with the owner. Alternatively, the financial backer of the project (private investor, financial institution, or other source) may have a deadline for obtaining approvals. Time really is money and becomes a critical factor in the conceptual and planning stages of a project and in determining whether the project is feasible.

The primary goals at this stage are to create a project that is economically viable and will win approval from the agency. Meeting these goals requires evaluation of a variety of factors affecting the site's development potential: soils, geotechnical factors, hydrology, trees, wetlands, wildlife, cultural and historical elements, engineering, traffic, visual analysis, and local regulations) (Figure 3.1). The outcome of these analyses is a clear understanding of the major opportunities and limitations presented by the site.

With regard to tree preservation, the consultant plays an important role in preparing a tree survey or stand delineation that describes the nature of the resource and the opportunities for optimizing preservation (see Chapter 5). The consultant also can identify significant trees of particular interest to the community (i.e., heritage, historical, legacy). Moll (1981) presents an excellent overview and example of this process.

The consultant should provide general information and guidelines about tree preservation by evaluating the suitability for preservation of trees or groups of trees (see Chapter 5). In addition, the consultant can assess the potential for tree preservation based upon the proposed development plan (see Chapter 6).

Many communities and public agencies provide descriptions of rules and procedures for project submittals, including guidelines for tree preservation. The city of Benicia, California, publishes a developer's handbook that describes how the city handles plan review, subdivisions, annexations, and the permit process. It also describes situations in which other agencies (such as the San Francisco Bay Conservation and Development Commission or the U.S. Army Corps of Engineers) will be involved. This type of community assistance is invaluable, for it defines policy for project application and review.

As information from each of these disciplines becomes available, a land plan is developed and refined. The plan is discussed with the local community, governing agencies, and other interested parties. As planning becomes more specific, the developer may also produce mitigation plans in response to the proposed impacts.

2. Application

The application phase is the point at which the developer submits a project plan for review and approval by the appropriate public agencies (city,

TABLE 3.3 Tree preservation process (HortScience, Inc. Adapted from a figure prepared by James Dean, Lee Newman & Associates, Westlake Village, California 1981).

Action taken by	Prior to application for approval	Time of application	Project review	Project approval	Construction period	Maintenance phase	Postconstruction maintenance
Applicant	Seeks information regarding tree preservation policies. Develops preliminary site plans.	Provides required information; may include tree report, EIR, or stand delineation.	Responds to requests for changes to plans.	Prepares final tract map (PUD only). Submits for final approval. Prepares construction drawings.	Obtains permits and begins site work, implementing conditions as approved.	Completes construction; requests final inspection and clearance	Requests and receives bond exoneration.
Agency (may include city, county, state, and federal agencies, as appropriate)	Provides tree preservation policy, including ordinances and requirements for submittals. Identifies other involved agencies.	Reviews submittals; requests appropriate changes.	City may require review and approval by a design review committee, planning commission, and city council. Each may request changes to plans.	Reviews final submission. Sets bond for mitigation of impacts to trees. Prepares conditions of approval.	Monitors progress of project.	Agency inspects; notes deficiencies. Issues clearance upon adequate inspection.	Bond exonerated.
Consulting arborist	Performs tree survey or stand delineation. Provides background on tree preservation issues. Identifies trees suitable for preservation. Provides design guidelines for tree preservation.	Prepares tree preservation plan. Reviews site plans. Identifies tree protection zone.	Responds to questions regarding tree preservation issues.	Prepares fencing plan. Prepares final tree preservation plan, including recommendations and specifications for tree protection.	Provides preconstruction treatments to trees. Monitors activity around trees.	Evaluates trees following construction. Provides needed remedial treatments.	Prepares and implements tree management plan.

Additional steps/actions	Prior to application for approval	Time of application	Project review	Project approval	Construction period	Maintenance phase	Postconstruction maintenance
Agency enforcements and incentives to the developer	Land exchanges and purchase options.	Fast-track for project approval.	Flexibility on design and density rules.	Acceptance of tree preservation plan. Assessment of bond for trees to be preserved.	Stop-work notices.	Postpone occupancy permit, pending completion of required mitigation treatments.	Delay final acceptance and/or release of bond.
Requirements for successful tree preservation	Clearly stated tree preservation policies. Understanding of tree-related issues.	Cooperation between applicant and community or agency. Accurate site and tree information.	Clearly defined conditions of approval.	Commitment among project members.	Sensitivity to field conditions. Commitment of construction superintendent. Respect for tree preservation zone.	Accurate base information for use as a comparison.	Commitment of new owners to long-term tree care.

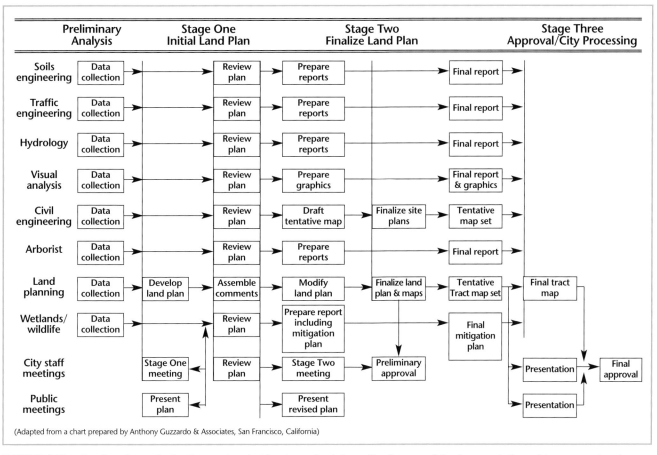

	Preliminary Analysis		Stage One Initial Land Plan	Stage Two Finalize Land Plan		Stage Three Approval/City Processing	
Soils engineering	Data collection		Review plan	Prepare reports		Final report	
Traffic engineering	Data collection		Review plan	Prepare reports		Final report	
Hydrology	Data collection		Review plan	Prepare reports		Final report	
Visual analysis	Data collection		Review plan	Prepare graphics		Final report & graphics	
Civil engineering	Data collection		Review plan	Draft tentative map	Finalize site plans	Tentative map set	
Arborist	Data collection		Review plan	Prepare reports		Final report	
Land planning	Data collection	Develop land plan	Assemble comments	Modify land plan	Finalize land plan & maps	Tentative Tract map set	Final tract map
Wetlands/ wildlife	Data collection		Review plan	Prepare report including mitigation plan		Final mitigation plan	
City staff meetings		Stage One meeting	Review plan	Stage Two meeting	Preliminary approval	Presentation	Final approval
Public meetings		Present plan		Present revised plan		Presentation	

(Adapted from a chart prepared by Anthony Guzzardo & Associates, San Francisco, California)

FIGURE 3.1 The planning phase of a development project involves using information from a variety of sources to formulate a comprehensive plan, including opportunities for review and comment by the public agencies involved.

county, state, federal). The application contains a detailed description, including site evaluation, tests, and supporting documents. An environmental impact report (EIR) or statement (EIS) may be required.

Including tree information in the planning phase is an important part of tree preservation. This element can be strengthened by including a tree preservation plan in the application package. The preservation plan should clearly detail the nature of the resource, impacts of the proposed project, recommendations for tree preservation, and a plan for implementing the recommendations (see Chapters 5 and 6).

3. Project Review

Following application, the community reviews the project and supporting documents. During the review period, staff may request additional information and/or design changes from the applicant. In such cases, the consultant may be asked to evaluate the proposed changes' impact on tree preservation.

Following review of the project application, staff recommends approval or denial to the approving body, including determinations of significance

or nonsignificance of project environmental impact reports. Recommendations for approval usually include a list of specific conditions that the developer must follow. Very often, the guidelines defined in a tree report or preservation plan are included in these conditions of approval.

4. Preparation of Plans

After initial or preliminary project approval, the site plans are refined into working drawings. A final tract map may be required by the community and must be prepared and approved. The agency or community might also require that bonds be posted, including those for tree preservation. A final tree preservation plan might be required, as well as a homeowner's tree maintenance manual (see Chapter 10). The last stage of this fourth phase is securing necessary permits (construction, grading, etc.) that allow construction to begin. At this point, the developer might sell all or part of the project to a builder. In such situations, the conditions of approval continue to apply to the new owner.

5. Construction Phase

Ideally, construction should begin with a pre-construction meeting of the developer, contractors, and consultant, during which the major points of the tree preservation plan are reviewed. Issues of tree protection fencing and signage, demolition techniques, circulation, erosion control, and materials storage should be discussed (see Chapters 6 and 9).

6. **Postconstruction Maintenance**

Most development projects include a maintenance period, during which the developer is responsible for correcting errors and omissions and maintaining landscapes and preserved trees. For the consultant, this may involve recommending remedial treatments and providing a postconstruction evaluation (see Chapter 10).

As the project nears completion and the development becomes occupied, responsibility for maintenance of the property passes to the new owner(s), the governing agency (for streets and parks, for example), or an owners' association (for open space and common-use areas). From the developer's standpoint, the end of the acceptance period is the end of the project. Control of the project (and the trees) now rests with the owners. The agency and developer end their relationship on the project once bonds are released.

This phase benefits from rigorous, accurate information about trees obtained in the preapplication phase. A tree survey, for example, would include predevelopment condition and structure. Any postconstruction evaluation would then allow a comparison of tree health before and after construction.

SUMMARY

Land development takes many forms and involves numerous participants. Yet no matter the type or size of project, the process of development follows the path of planning, design, construction, and maintenance. Because the decisions about the project are made at the planning and design phases, it is critical that tree preservation be included during these discussions. Only when trees are recognized as an important

part of the project will they be included in the early stages of planning. Such recognition can arise from either the development team or from the community. In the latter case, tree ordinances are one way to require that trees be included in project planning and not left until construction and maintenance. In our view, unless tree preservation is made an integral part of project planning, efforts to retain them are largely doomed.

REFERENCES

Bashford, C. Bashford Associates, Ltd. N. Baddesley, Hampshire, England. Personal communication. February 1997.

Benicia, California, City of. 1990. City of Benicia: *Developer's Handbook.* 68 pp.

Bernhardt, E., and T. Swiecki. 1991. *Guidelines for Developing and Evaluating Tree Ordinances.* Sacramento: California Department of Forestry and Fire Protection. 76 pp.

Coughlin, R., D. Mendes, and A. Strong. 1984. *Private Trees and the Public Interest: Program for Protecting and Planting Trees in Municipal Areas.* Philadelphia: University of Pennsylvania, Department of City and Regional Planning. Research Report Series No. 10. 113 pp.

Duerksen, C., and S. Richman. 1993. *Tree Conservation Ordinances: Land-Use Regulations Go Green.* Chicago: American Planning Association. 106 pp.

Dunster, J. 1994. New legislative ways of protecting trees in municipalities: An overview of the British Columbia approach. *Journal of Arboriculture* 20:109–113.

Fox, S. 1990. Trees versus development: A delicate balance. Presentation to the Minnesota Society of Arboriculture. 6 pp.

Hoefer, P., E. Himelick, and D. DeVoto. 1990. *Municipal Tree Manual.* Savoy, IL: International Society of Arboriculture. 42 pp.

Moll, G. 1981. *Land Development in Wooded Areas.* Annapolis, MD: USDA Forest Service and the Maryland Forest Service. 21 pp.

Tools of the Trade: Development Plans and Construction Practice

Successful tree preservation depends on an understanding of how land development occurs. The simple fact is that structures—buildings, roads, patios, and utility trenches—must be built in such a way that they are stable and safe. Specific engineering standards regarding soil compaction, footing and foundation design, and depth and separation of utilities must be attained. In many situations, the building standards and local codes allow limited flexibility for modification. The consultant usually must work within these requirements to ensure preservation of trees.

Being involved on the development team requires that the consultant learn a language that relies heavily on engineering and surveying terms. In addition, communication occurs primarily through maps and other graphics. The first section of this chapter describes how to read and interpret grading and construction plans. In the second section, typical construction practices for grading, preparing building pads and foundations, constructing roads, and installing utilities are described. The purpose of this chapter is to provide a base of knowledge about construction to aid the consultant regarding anticipated impacts that may affect trees (see Chapter 7).

READING AND INTERPRETING PLANS

The consultant must become proficient in reading and interpreting plans: plans guide the clearing, grading, and construction processes. Every line on the drawing can have implications for trees.

A set of drawings may include a variety of information: plans, legends, details, sections, profiles, specifications, and notes that describe all the work to be performed for specific parts of the development. How information is communicated on plans is a matter of convention. Different line thicknesses, patterns, and letters are used to convey specific information. Symbols should be clearly explained somewhere in the plan set (Figure 4.1).

PROPOSED	DESCRIPTION	EXISTING
	PROPERTY BOUNDARY	
	LOT LINE AND RIGHT-OF-WAY LINE	
	CENTER LINE	
	CONTOUR LINE	420
420	SLOPE	
SD	STORM DRAIN	SD
SS	SANITARY SEWER	SS
W	WATER LINE	W
G	GAS LINE	G
JT	JOINT TRENCH	JT
	FENCE	
	CUT/FILL LINE	
	LIMIT OF GRADING/DAYLIGHT LINE	
	RETAINING WALL	
	CONCRETE DITCH	
	TELEPHONE POLE	
	MANHOLE	
	STORM WATER INLET	
	FIRE HYDRANT	
TC	TOP OF CURB ELEVATION	
TW	TOP OF WALL ELEVATION	
BW	BOTTOM OF WALL ELEVATION	
R/W	RIGHT OF WAY	
AC	ASPHALTIC CONCRETE	
AB	AGGREGATE BASE	
FC	FACE OF CURB	
PE	PAD ELEVATION	
5%	STREET GRADE	
#13	TREE IDENTIFICATION NUMBER	

FIGURE 4.1 Typical symbols used on grading and site improvement plans.

Drawing Perspective

Most plans are drawn from an aerial perspective (plan view) (Figure 4.2a). Sections translate the plan view to a horizontal plane along a section line (Figure 4.2b). Road improvement plans usually include profiles (Figure 4.2c). Profiles show the changes in grade along the center line of the road from a vertical perspective and usually include depth of excavation for sewers, storm drains, and other utilities. Architectural drawings usually include elevations showing what the face of the building will look like; elevations are helpful for determining vertical clearance and pruning requirements under trees (Figure 4.2d).

Drawing Scale

Plans are drawn to a specified scale. The scale of the drawing represents the relationship between the distance on the plan and actual distance on the ground. Most grading, site construction, and landscape architectural drawings use an engineering scale

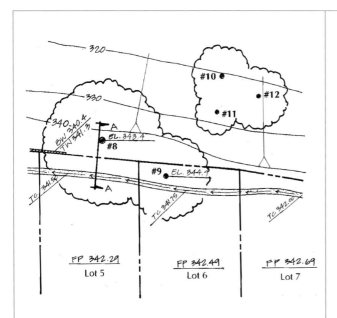

(a) Most plans are drawn from an aerial perspective, called the *plan view*.

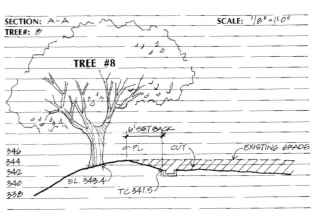

(b) *Sections* are drawings that translate the plan view along a section line into a horizontal view. They are helpful for visualizing impacts to trees.

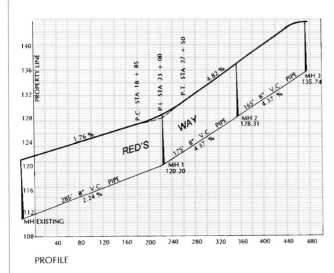

PROFILE

(c) Street construction and underground utilities are indicated on *profile* drawings. These show changes in grade along the center line of the road from a vertical perspective, and usually include depth of excavation for sewers, storm drains, and water lines.

(d) *Elevations* show one face of a structure from a vertical perspective. These are helpful for determining vertical clearance and pruning requirements for adjacent trees.

FIGURE 4.2 Grading and construction plans include drawings from a variety of perspectives.

measured in tenths of a foot (e.g., 20 scale means 1 inch = 20 feet). Architectural and building construction drawings, however, use scales graduated in fractions of an inch (e.g., ⅛ scale means 1 inch = 8 feet).

Large scales are useful for laying out land-use areas and defining groups of trees to be retained. Preliminary plans for large projects may be drawn at 100 to 200 scale (1 inch = 100 feet, or 1 inch = 200 feet). Overall site changes (e.g., drainage) and general impacts to trees, particularly major removals, can be estimated using these scales. As the project progresses into the design phase, more detail is developed and plans are usually drawn at 20 or 40 scale. It is at this point that the specific impacts to individual trees usually begin to be identified.

Topographic Maps

The base for most site plans is the topographic or contour map. Topographic maps (usually called "topos") indicate the existing grades on the site using lines

(e) *Perspective* drawings represent three-dimensional space and depth on two dimensions. They are primarily illustrative and not adequate for evaluating impacts to trees.

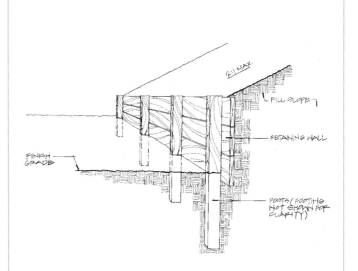

(f) A *cut-away perspective* provides the perspective of three dimensions, with a section drawn in for the foreground. While this drawing helps visualize the site changes, it cannot be used alone for construction because distances cannot be scaled.

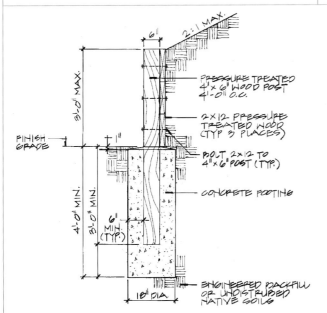

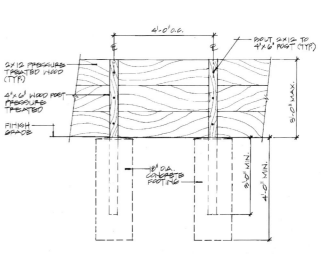

(g) *Details* provide specific construction information, including dimensions and materials, and are drawn to scale. They may be shown both in section (left) and elevation view (right).

FIGURE 4.2 *(continued)*

READING TOPOGRAPHIC MAPS

Topographic maps show land forms with contour lines representing points of equal elevation. The contour lines are drawn at equal intervals, usually from 1 to 10 feet. A number, placed in or above every fifth line, indicates the elevation along the contour. (Adapted from Untermann 1973, Munson 1974, and Ching 1985.)

On fairly flat land, the contour lines are far apart; on steep land, close together (Section A).

PLAN

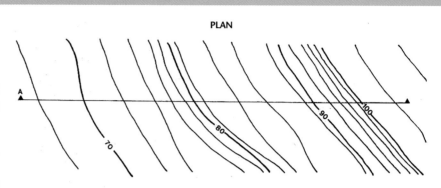

SECTION A

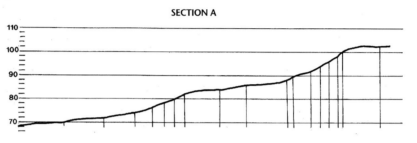

PLAN

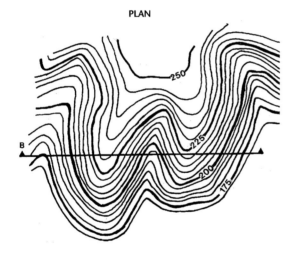

PLAN

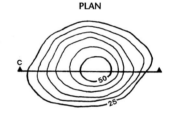

SECTION C

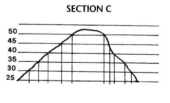

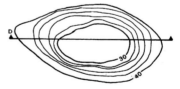

SECTION D

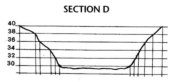

SECTION B

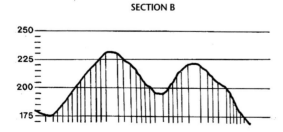

A swale or ridge is indicated with U-shaped contours. If the elevation increases, it is a ridge; if it decreases, a swale or valley (Section B).

Closed, concentric circles indicate a hill or a depression, depending on whether the elevation is increasing (Section C) or decreasing (Section D).

drawn along points of the same elevation. Contour lines are continuous and never cross each other. They may be drawn in intervals of 1 to 10 or more feet, depending on the scale of the drawing, size of the site, and nature of the topography. Every fifth contour line is drawn darker, or with a heavier line weight, and is labeled with the elevation. The contour interval, or distance between contours, is the relationship of the vertical rise in elevation to the horizontal distance. The closer together the lines, the steeper the grade; the farther apart, the flatter the grade. Smooth lines indicate uniform slopes; zigzag lines, rugged slopes. With practice, the relief of the site can be readily visualized from the topographic map. Topographic maps may also include other site features such as the canopy edge of existing vegetation, and ponds, fences, buildings, and roads.

Most topographic maps are drawn from aerial photographs. Stereo-aerial viewers are used to determine a line of equal elevation on the photograph, corresponding to a contour line. Contours cannot be distinguished under dense canopy. Accuracy is increased when a field survey to establish spot elevations is performed.

Consultants use topographic maps when preparing a tree stand delineation or tree survey (see Chapter 5). To move around the site and locate trees on the map, the consultant should be proficient in reading topo maps.

Development Plans

Many types of plans may be prepared for a project (Table 4.1). A simple project such as a home addition may require only a set of construction drawings. Larger developments, however, often require many plans, each containing specific sets of information that, together, communicate the design intent and how construction work will be performed on the site by a variety of contractors.

Plans may be packaged into units for submittal for agency approval. These plans may be identified as tentative tract maps, improvement plans, or vesting tentative maps.

TABLE 4.1. Types of plans and maps commonly used in development projects.

Type of plan	Information provided
Construction plans and documents	Contain drawings, details, and specifications for construction of buildings and other site features. Requirements for tree protection should also be included.
Demolition plans	Structures, vegetation, and other features to be removed and protected. May include temporary erosion control.
Drainage and erosion control plans	Use the rough grading plans as a base; show locations and specifications for subdrains, storm drains, outfalls, detention and retention ponds, and swales. Slope protection, sedimentation control, siltation fences, tree protection, and other erosion control devices and techniques are also shown.
Geotechnical report	Maps and descriptions of soil units, soil profile characteristics, and limitations to land use. Includes specifications for soil compaction for subgrades, pavement sections, engineered fills, and slope stabilization.
Grading plans	Use a screened topographic map as the base to show future contours, pad and street locations, trees to be preserved, and elevations. May also show storm drains, curbs and sidewalks, stream improvements, drainage swales, and slope repair.
Improvement plans	Similar to site plans and grading plans; includes street plans and profiles.
Land plan	Show general-use areas and roads, typically using a topographic map as a base.
Landscape and irrigation plans	Contain plans, details, and specifications for finish grading, landscape patios and other features, irrigation design and installation, and tree protection.
Site plans	These include existing site features, including topography, buildings, trees, roads, and utilities, usually screened to a lighter value. In full value, future grades, lots, roads, curbs and sidewalks, building footprints, fences, utilities, trees to be preserved, and other features are shown.
Tentative tract map	Plan of residential project design for submittal to governing agency.
Utility plans	Locations and specifications for electric, gas, telephone, and cable television lines, and splice and junction boxes. Existing trees should be shown.

READING SITE AND GRADING PLANS

Reading site and grading plans is a matter of learning commonly used symbols and terms and of visualizing the two-dimensional drawing in three dimensions. This portion of a grading plan provides a variety of information needed to evaluate impacts to trees.

1 **Existing contours** are usually dashed or screened so that they are fainter than proposed contours. This line is at elevation 418'.

2 **Finish contours** are drawn over the existing contours. The finish contour must meet existing contour of the same elevation at some point within the property boundary on the plan.

3 The **limit of grading** (also called the **daylight line**) is the point at which future grade meets existing grade. It is shown on this plan with a thin dashed line.

4 The existing tree is shown by a vegetation canopy drawn from the aerial photograph. The exact trunk location, true dripline, and tree tag number should be determined by the consultant in the field and added to the plan.

5 The **spot elevation** is shown at the top-of-curb (TC 425.94). The engineer station point at the location is also given (8+57.13). In this case, the spot elevation is located at the property line between lots.

6 The **cut/fill line** shows the point at which cut and fill meet. Existing grades below the line are raised; those above are lowered. Lot #4 is a transition lot because it contains both cut and fill.

7 The **match line** indicates which sheet of drawings continues the plan.

8 The alignment of North Phoebe Street is shown by five parallel lines. What each of these lines means is determined by referring to Section B-B, located somewhere in the plan set (see inset).

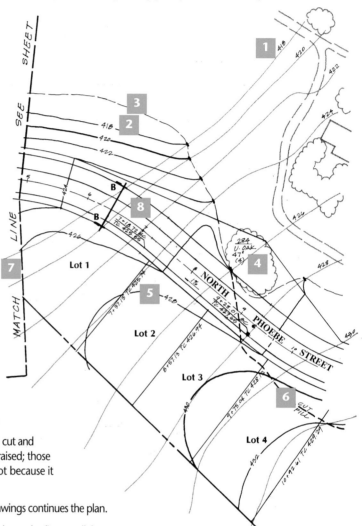

9 **Section B-B** indicates that the portion of the construction that will encroach within the dripline of the tree is the landscape strip and utility easement. Because the sidewalk is indicated to be meandering within the easement, it could be placed as far as possible from the tree. The arborist should investigate where within the easement the utilities will be placed and to what depth. The amount of excavation required for subbase preparation under the street also must be determined.

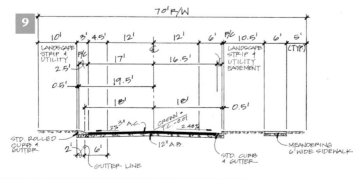

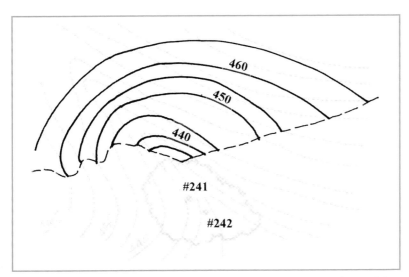

FIGURE 4.3 Most often, the topographic map is used for the base of grading and site plans. The topo map is screened so that the printing is lighter. Full-value, dark lines indicating new grades are laid over the topo.

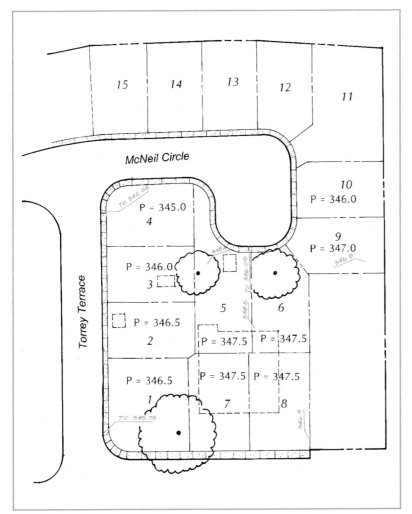

FIGURE 4.4 For sites that are relatively flat, spot elevations may be provided on the plans to indicate elevation of specific points between contour lines (examples are shown in green). Because base elevation of trees is not provided, it must be estimated from the spot elevations. On this plan, future grades are shown for pads (e.g., P = 345.0) and top-of-curb (e.g., TC = 342.05). Dashed lines indicate existing structures that will be removed. The combination long- and short-dashed lines represent property lines between lots.

On grading plans, both proposed and existing grades are indicated with contour lines (Figure 4.3). Existing contours, shown as dashed lines, may be screened so they are lighter. Proposed contours are solid lines.

Site plans also may include spot elevations that show the surveyed elevation of an existing point (Figure 4.4). Typically, spot elevations are provided for proposed grades at top-of-curb (TC) or other fixed features. The elevations for pads on which structures will be built generally are noted near the center of the pad. The limits of the pad usually are drawn with a solid, thin line.

Utility plans should be examined carefully for locations of existing and future lines, as well as junction and splice boxes (Figure 4.5). Like contour lines, existing utilities are indicated by dashed lines; proposed utilities are indicated by solid lines. The depth of the trench to install the utilities can be determined from the details and notes. Splice and junction box locations are shown, but may not be drawn to scale. Box dimensions may be noted near the box or in a detail in the plan set.

Interpreting street construction requires examining both plans and profiles (Figure 4.6). The plan view shows the edge of pavement or curb, the center line of the road, any right-of-way easement, and storm, water and/or sewer lines in the street. The profile drawing shows changes in grade along the center line of the road from a vertical perspective (Figure 4.2c). The depth of existing and proposed sewer, storm, and water lines are shown, as well as junction boxes and manholes.

Construction Details

Plan sets often include details showing how the installation or construction is to occur. Details may be drawn in plan view, section, or elevation of one or more faces (north, south, east, or west). Measurements shown on construction and grading details are used to estimate the width and depth of excavation next to trees (Figure 4.2g).

Locating Trees on Plans

Trees must be located on all plans if they are to be adequately considered and protected. Their location is as important for design and development as any other feature on the site. The amount of tree location information required depends on the

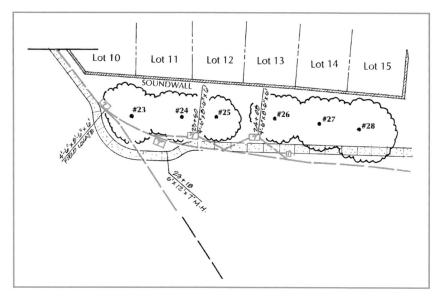

FIGURE 4.5 Joint trench composite plan showing location of distribution trench for electric, gas, telephone, and TV cable adjacent to a row of trees. Splice box locations and trench sizes are very important in evaluating impacts. This information should be included in the specifications, notes, and details in the plan set. In this case, each gas and electrical splice box (7) is 4½ x 8½ x 6 feet, with the excavation at least one foot larger in all directions. The telephone splice box (T) is 6 x 12 x 7 feet deep. The electrical splice box (1) is 13 x 24 x 24 inches. The joint trench is dug 10 feet wide and 4 feet deep with a backhoe. The joint trench was originally placed between the sidewalk and the trees. It was moved into the street to reduce impacts to trees. Because of severity of impact, tree #23 was removed. (Actual area of excavation is shown in green.)

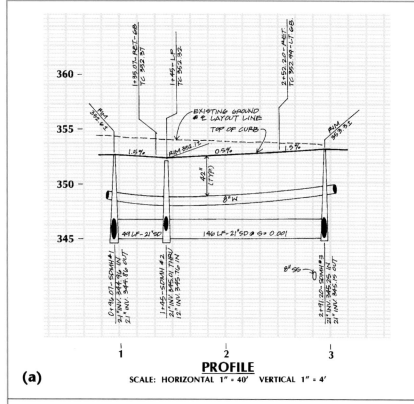

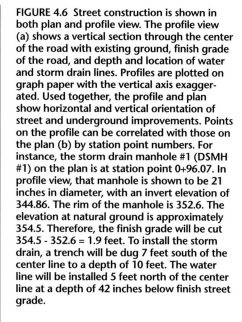

FIGURE 4.6 Street construction is shown in both plan and profile view. The profile view (a) shows a vertical section through the center of the road with existing ground, finish grade of the road, and depth and location of water and storm drain lines. Profiles are plotted on graph paper with the vertical axis exaggerated. Used together, the profile and plan show horizontal and vertical orientation of street and underground improvements. Points on the profile can be correlated with those on the plan (b) by station point numbers. For instance, the storm drain manhole #1 (DSMH #1) on the plan is at station point 0+96.07. In profile view, that manhole is shown to be 21 inches in diameter, with an invert elevation of 344.86. The rim of the manhole is 352.6. The elevation at natural ground is approximately 354.5. Therefore, the finish grade will be cut 354.5 - 352.6 = 1.9 feet. To install the storm drain, a trench will be dug 7 feet south of the center line to a depth of 10 feet. The water line will be installed 5 feet north of the center line at a depth of 42 inches below finish street grade.

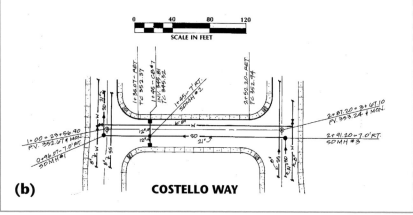

trees' position relative to development. For trees on the property but outside the development area where construction and site changes will occur, it may be adequate to indicate the general canopy conformation on the plans.

For trees that are near grading or construction, however, it is absolutely essential to have accurate information about the location of each tree. After conducting the initial tree survey and reviewing the proposed project plans, the consultant should prepare a list of which trees should be accurately located by the project engineer or surveyor (see Chapter 6). Horizontal and vertical locations of tree trunks should be established. The center line of the tree trunk should be plotted on all applicable plans, and the elevation at the base on the trunk indicated.

Locating trunks by measuring from the canopy edge shown on the plan is not accurate. Base maps that show existing site topography, vegetation, and other features are usually prepared from aerial photographs. Two problems for tree retention arise from this procedure. First, it may be difficult to distinguish the actual edge of the tree canopy from the shadow cast by the tree on the photographs, so the dripline may be incorrectly drawn. If working with maps at 100 scale, the error can easily be as much as 10 to 20 feet. Second, photometry does not distinguish changes

in topography under tree canopies in leaf. The photo interpreter must interpolate topographic lines under the canopy. This can result in significant errors. These two problems are avoided by having the site engineering surveyor accurately locate tree trunks both horizontally and vertically and verify grades under the trees.

Verifying Plans in the Field

Grading and construction information in the field is conveyed on survey stakes. Typically the survey crew sets up reference points and/or hubs that identify a point on the ground. Elevations are determined from the top of the hub (2 x 2-inch stake driven into ground). Distances are measured from hubs or reference stakes. Near the hub is an information stake describing in surveyor's code the distances to specific points and changes in elevation (Photo 4.1). When the point cannot be staked without interfering with construction, stakes are installed at some distance offset from the actual point. Measurements are given in tenths of a foot.

Where grading will be close to trees and when knowing the precise amount of impact is critical, it is important to stake the proposed construction and grading in the field. It is quite common for plans to be a few to several feet off from surveyed locations in

---

SURVEY STAKES

Survey stakes identify distance to specific points and associated changes in grade. The stake faces toward the point being described. Information on the stake sometimes includes elevation and station point. Typical codes are:

RS	Reference stake—the point from which measurements are made
C	Cut
F	Fill
BC	Back of curb
TC	Top of curb
HP	Hinge point
EP	Edge of pavement
₵	Center line
3+50	Station point—this station is 350 feet from station 0+00, where the survey began
PG	Projected center-line grade
⑩	Offset—this stake is 10 feet from the point being described
EL	Elevation of hub

Examples:

Hub is offset 10 feet from face of curb. The grade at the top of curb is 1.5 feet lower than at the hub. To locate the curb, measure 10 feet from the hub and 1.5 feet lower. To determine actual cut, add the depth of the pavement section to the cut.

Elevation at the hub is 122.4 feet above sea level. The stake is located at station point 2+10, which is 210 feet from where the survey started. Station points may be shown on grading plans, street profiles, and other site improvement plans.

(After Capachi 1978)

the field (Photo 4.2). Plans often go through several generations of drawings throughout the development process. At each phase, as maps are photo-enlarged and originals stretch in reproduction, errors are compounded. Staking allows a check, in the field, of locations before the start of actual grading or construction.

CONSTRUCTION PRACTICE

The most important aspects of construction for the consultant to understand are those that occur below ground. Requirements for these activities are largely determined by soil (or geotechnical), civil, and structural engineers. The consultant should become familiar with common terminology and work procedures involved in these processes (Tables 4.2 and 4.3).

Construction typically follows a sequence of events:

1. demolition and clearing
2. rough grading
3. installation of water, storm drains, sewers, and other improvements in roads
4. establishment of finish pad and road grades
5. construction of roads and buildings and installation of utilities to structures
6. fine grading and installation of landscapes

Demolition and Site Clearing

Demolition and clearing involves the removal of unwanted structures, pavement, and vegetation. In some cases, site clearing may include removing hazardous wastes or abandoned underground features such as septic systems, or capping unused wells. Public health and safety requirements largely dictate much of this work.

Site clearing can be accomplished with a variety of types of equipment, the most common being a crawler tractor or rubber-tired tractor with various attachments (Table 4.4). There are three equipment size/weight classes: light, medium, and heavy. Generally, the largest equipment that is practical for the job will be selected by the contractor performing the work.

The demolition or clearing contractor requires space in which to maneuver machinery, store equipment, and stockpile material. Tree protection zones must be clearly identified and fenced before demolition to avoid damage (see "Identifying a Tree Protection Zone" in Chapter 6). Vegetation is sometimes disposed of by burning or burying on site, which can damage other nearby vegetation. Vegetation can be chipped and stored for later use by the landscape contractor.

Grading

Grading is remodeling the land form (Untermann 1973). The amount of grading that will occur on a site depends on many factors, including natural topography, need for flood protection, requirements for surface or subsurface drainage, suitability of native soil for building, potential for landslides, need to match grades of adjacent properties, type of development (e.g., estate lots or commercial development), methods of construction of structures (e.g., slab or pier foundation), and land-use regulations limiting development on slopes greater than a given percentage.

Where extensive site modification and/or high-density development will occur, the site usually is mass graded. The development area is defined by a "limit of grading" or "daylight line," and all the area within is altered. In most cases, all existing vegetation within the daylight line is removed.

In low-density developments, selective grading may occur in designated construction areas and roadways. In this case, pad envelopes are defined to include enough space for the structures and required

PHOTO 4.1 Grading and construction information is conveyed in the field on survey stakes. This stake indicates that it is offset 10 feet from the face-of-curb and that there will be a fill of 2.10 feet at the top-of-curb.

PHOTO 4.2 Distances and grades depicted on plans sometimes do not match those in the field. Plans indicated the street behind and to the right of these trees would be 2 feet lower and 7 feet farther away from the tree than depicted in the photograph. Before a site is graded, the grade changes are surveyed and staked. If the arborist had reviewed the staking beforehand, this problem might have been corrected.

setbacks. The extent of grading in the envelopes depends primarily on soil conditions and foundation design of structures. Because smaller areas are disturbed with selective grading, this technique allows greater potential for retaining existing vegetation around building pads than mass grading does.

Creating a Stable Building Base

Soil is a mixture of mineral particles, organic matter, air, and water. About half of the soil is pore space containing varying amounts of water and air. Soil engineers call pore spaces "voids." Voids reduce a soil's stability as structural material because of the potential for the soil to subside as voids collapse. Organic

TABLE 4.2. Common terms used in soil engineering.

Term	Description
AASHO Classification	American Association of State Highway Officials Classification, based on performance of highways on soils classified by particle size distribution and on Atterberg consistence limits. Soils are grouped based on their load-bearing characteristics (A-1 through A-7 for mineral soils; A-8 for organic soils).
Atterberg limits	System for classifying soils based on their mechanical properties at different moisture contents. Used extensively in soils engineering to evaluate the suitability of soils for different uses. Each limit is defined by the water content that produces a specified consistency from solid to plastic to liquid.[4]
Consistency	Ability of soil to resist deformation by compressing, shearing, or pulling forces.[2] Varies in part by water content. Indicated by such terms as soft, firm, or hard.[1]
Compaction	Artificially increasing the density of a soil. When water is added to a soil, cohesion is reduced and the resistance to compaction is reduced.
Density	Weight of the soil relative to its volume. Density is usually expressed as pounds of dry soil per cubic foot (dry density) or pounds of wet soil per cubic foot (wet density).[3]
Optimum moisture	The particular moisture content that results in maximum dry density.[3]
Percent compaction	The ratio of the fill material as compacted in the field to the maximum dry density of the same material, expressed as a percentage of the dry density (see sidebar on page 49).
Plasticity	The ability of a moist clay to be molded into a flexible rod and deformed without cracking. Coarse particles cannot be formed into a flexible rod at any moisture content and thus are nonplastic.[3]
Plasticity index	The range in water contents through which the soil is in a plastic state (difference between the liquid and plastic limits). Clay soils have high plasticity indexes. Nonplastic soils are better for engineering purposes.[4]
Shrinkage limit	The water content at which the saturated soil reaches its minimum volume as it dries out. The soil acts more like a solid than a plastic material. Shrinkage results in settlement.[3]
Shrink-swell	Change in volume when a clay soil wets and dries. The volume change depends on the type and amount of clay in the soil. Soils with a high shrink-swell capacity are unstable for construction purposes and can lead to cracked pavements, foundations, and walls.[4]
Soil	Any unconsolidated, porous material composed of discrete solid particles with gases or liquids in the voids between particles.[1]
Strength	The soil's ability to support a load. Strength is determined by frictional resistance and cohesion. As moisture content increases, soil strength decreases.[4]
Unified Soil Classification	Identifies soils according to textural and plasticity values, and identifies soil performance as construction material.[3]

[1]Sowers and Sowers 1951
[2]Hausenbuiller 1985
[3]Pomerening 1972
[4]Singer and Munns 1987

TABLE 4.3. Common grading and construction specifications and terms.

Term	Description
Base material	A layer of porous, compacted material (e.g., sand, gravel, aggregate rock) on which pavement is placed (Figure 4.10).
Bedding	Trenches for pipes are excavated 6 inches below the pipe, and a 6-inch layer of bedding material such as gravel is placed in the bottom of the trench. The bedding material is compacted to 95 percent. The sides of the trench extend at least 6 inches beyond the outside surface of the pipe.
Clearing and grubbing demolition	Removal of all structures, vegetation, footings, septic tanks, abandoned utilities, and other material as required by the geotechnical engineer.
Excavation	Removal of soil to required grades. Often accomplished with large, heavy equipment. Excavations are made to the required depths to permit preparation of the subgrade.
Expansive soil	Soils with potential for expansion (swell when wet; shrink when dry) can exert significant uplift pressures on shallow foundations and pavements. Foundations and slab-on-grade floors may need to be supported on sections of engineered fill or select fill, requiring additional excavation into the native grade.
Fill	Soil or rock material placed to raise the natural grade of the site or to backfill excavations (including trenches).
Fill, buttress	When fill is placed on a slope it is usually stabilized or buttressed by cutting steps or horizontal benches into the slope (Figure 4.8). This prevents the compacted fill from creeping down the slope.
Fill, engineered or compacted	Fill subjected to geotechnical engineering tests for proper compaction. Required percentage of compaction is created through the depth of the fill by spreading the fill material in uniform lifts not exceeding 6 to 12 inches in uncompacted thickness. Each layer (lift) is brought to a water content at or near the laboratory optimum and compacted with heavy equipment; 90 to 97 percent compaction is usually required.
Fill, select	Fill that meets geotechnical requirements for use under footings and floor slabs. Expansive soils (e.g., many clay soils) and organic soils are unsuitable for select fill.
Footprint	Outline of the base of the structure as it will sit on the ground.
Import material	Soil brought onto site from an off-site borrow area. Ideally, grading is designed to balance cut and fill areas so that no import soil is needed. If cut/fill cannot be balanced, or if the site soil is not suitable for use in engineered fills, suitable soil that meets geotechnical specifications may be imported. Import soil characteristics may be very different than native soil; this factor should be considered when evaluating impacts and future maintenance needs.
Keyway	To stabilize the toe of a slope, a keyway is created by excavating into the natural grade 3 to 5 feet deep and 10 and 15 feet wide (Figure 4.8). The engineered fill is then placed. If trees are near the toe of the slope, the keyway can sometimes be moved upslope several feet from the toe.
Leveling	Removal of all ruts, hummocks, and other uneven surfaces by surface grading prior to placement of fill.
Lime-treated subsoil	When soils are unsuitable as subgrade material (e.g., high shrink-swell capacity), they may be stabilized by incorporating high concentrations of hydrated lime or quicklime to a specified depth. Lime-treated areas extend beyond the building or pavement area a distance equal to the depth of treatment and are a minimum of 5 feet. Lime-treated subsoils are toxic to roots.

TABLE 4.3. *(continued)*

Overbuild	Area of compacted pad beyond the footprint of the structure (usually 3 to 5 feet for buildings; 2 to 3 feet for roads).
Pad	Compacted subgrade and, in some cases, subbase, on which structure is built (Figure 4.7).
Pavement section	A typical pavement section for roads includes from 2 to 5 inches of asphalt pavement underlain with 3 to 20 inches of compacted aggregate base, placed on 6 to 12 inches of compacted subgrade (Figure 4.10). Unstable soils that must bear a heavy load may have pavement sections up to 4 feet thick. Concrete pavements usually require thinner sections than asphalt pavements.
Scarification	After debris is removed, the soil surface is loosened to a depth of 6 to 12 inches, moistened, and compacted to 90 to 95 percent. Soils to be covered by fills, pavement, and other structures are subject to this treatment.
Slopes	The engineer determines the maximum steepness of cut and fill slopes (e.g.. 2:1, 3:1) (Figure 4.9). Fills on or against existing slopes in excess of 6:1 are placed on horizontal benches cut into the slope. The toe of the slope may be keyed into native soils by cutting in the native grade 3 to 5 feet (Figure 4.8).
Spoil	Soil that is removed in an excavation.
Stripping	Removal of all surface vegetation, organic-laden topsoil, roots, and debris, usually to a depth of 6 to 18 inches. Often results in removal of soil through the major root zone.
Subbase	Layer of select fill to replace unsuitable site soil or to bring an area up to finish grade (Figure 4.10)
Subgrade	The soil below structures, pavements, and fills that is removed and compacted in lifts to create a stable base (Figure 4.10).
Transition lot	Lot which, when graded, contains both cut and fill. The fill portion must be over-excavated (cut) and replaced with compacted fill to a depth specified by the soil engineer (usually 3 to 5 feet) (Figure 4.7).
Trenches	Trenches may be dug for installation of utilities or construction of footings. Methods used for digging may include backhoe, trenching equipment, or by hand. The bottom of the trench must either be into naturally compacted material, or the bottom 6 inches of the trench must be compacted to 95 percent. The trench is backfilled in 8-inch lifts and compacted to engineering standards (Figure 4.14).

materials also reduce soil strength. As the organics decompose, voids are created. Soils containing roots, leaf litter, and other plant growth must be removed, and the voids eliminated to the greatest extent possible.

Often, the first task in grading is stripping the site of the organic-laden topsoil. This is the layer in which most of the absorbing roots are located. The soil that is removed is unsuitable for use in engineered fills but could be stockpiled outside the root area of protected trees and used in future landscape areas (although its structure will be degraded).

The second task is to reduce the voids by compacting the soil. The soil is worked with heavy equipment to break down its structure and create a compact mass. This requires removing the friable soil to a depth at which it is naturally compact, then adding the soil back in layers, or lifts, 6 to 8 inches deep. Each lift is brought to the optimum moisture content (as determined by the geotechnical engineer) by either wetting dry soil or aerating wet soil. At optimum moisture, soil cohesion and the resistance to compaction are reduced. The lift is then run over by heavy equipment designed to maximize the compaction effort.

The amount of work required to compact a soil and the degree and depth of compaction required vary with soil type and the structure to be supported. The degree of compaction that must be accomplished in the field is expressed by engineers as "percent compaction." This is the ratio, expressed as a percent, of the dry density of the soil compacted in the field to the maximum dry density of the same materials determined by standard, specified tests.

Construction soils are usually compacted 90 to 98 percent. This does not mean that 2 to 10 percent of

TABLE 4.4 Examples of equipment used for grading and clearing sites of vegetation (after Russell 1985).

Equipment	Task performed
Crawler tractor	Used for pushing or pulling heavy loads. Best for rough work over short distances.
Rubber-tired tractor	Performs similar tasks to crawler tractor, but has greater speed. Has less traction than crawler tractor, except on hard surfaces (e.g., concrete, asphalt). Has high ground-bearing pressure, so causes more compaction than crawler tractor.
	Tractor attachments:
Straight ("S") blade	Most widely used attachment. Handles heavy material.
V-tree cutter	Shaped in a sharp V-angle. Each side of blade is a sharp cutting edge for shearing trees, stumps, and brush at ground level.
K/G blade	Used for land clearing; can cut trees, pile vegetation, cut V-type drainage ditches.
Rake blade	Used for land clearing. Handles vegetation up to tree size and removes small stumps, rocks, and roots.
Clamp rake	Like rake, but with hydraulically operated clamps that can pick up and carry trees or large objects.
Root plow	Designed to kill brush and growth by undercutting at the crown. Large roots are forced to the surface.
Rolling choppers	Steel drum with cutting blades welded on; towed behind tractors. As they turn, rolling choppers fracture and shatter undesirable low growth, penetrating to about 6 to 10 inches deep. They destroy low growth with a minimum of damage to topsoil.
Hydraulic tree shear	Prunes whole trees at ground level. Fells softwood trees up to 30 inches in diameter and hardwoods up to 22 inches. Ability to work in tight spaces makes it good for thinning and selectively removing trees from residential development sites.
Brush chains	Used in large lengths (300 feet of 2½-inch anchor chain) that are dragged behind two crawler tractors; primarily for land clearing. Fairly large trees can be felled.
Scrapers	Used in earthmoving to self-load, haul, and dump. Towing unit may be crawler tractor or rubber-tired tractor.
Motor graders	Used for grading, shaping, maintaining roads, leveling, light soil stripping, light spreading of loose fill, scarifying, and backfilling ditches.

the pore space remains. It means that the soil has been compacted to within 2 to 10 percent of the maximum compaction possible as established in laboratory tests (see sidebar on page 49). The actual bulk density and porosity that occur at a given percent compaction depend on the texture of the particular soil.

In most cases, the soil that supports structures (the subgrade) must be at 95 to 98 percent compaction. The degree of compaction, as well as the depth to which the compaction must occur, depends on the soil characteristics and the load it must bear (Table 4.5). A soil that will support a road with heavy traffic must be compacted to a greater percentage and deeper than soil that will have a sidewalk placed over it. A silty or clay soil must be compacted more than a sandy soil.

In some cases, the geotechnical engineer may determine that the native soil is unsuitable for building because it cannot be made adequately stable. The "unfit" native soil is then removed to a specified depth and replaced with a "select fill" having the desired properties and compacted to engineered standards. This is called the subbase. Highly organic soils and expansive clay soils that swell when wet and shrink when dry may be considered unfit.

The compacted soil area is overbuilt (extended beyond the edge of the structure) to provide stability. The building envelope usually includes the overbuild requirements. Typically, building pads are overbuilt 3 to 5 feet and roads, 2 to 3 feet.

The geotechnical engineer determines compaction requirements. Specifications for location,

PERCENT COMPACTION

Percent compaction is the ratio of the dry density of the soil compacted in the field to the maximum dry density of the same material determined by standard, specified tests. In the laboratory, soil is mixed thoroughly with different amounts of water and compacted in a container. The water content and weight of solids per cubic foot (dry density) are determined. Then a graph is plotted of dry density and water content (see below). There is a particular water content, known as optimum moisture, that results in the maximum dry density. For any given soil and structure to be supported, the engineer will specify the percentage of compaction that must be achieved and at what moisture content the soil should be worked (after Sowers and Sowers 1951).

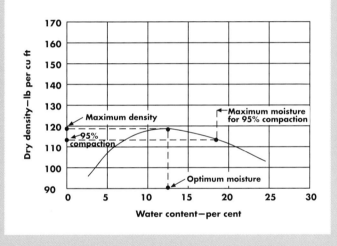

depth, and percent compaction required for different types of construction and use areas are defined in the geotechnical report for a given site.

Grade Changes

Grade changes include cuts (lowering natural grade) and fills (raising natural grade). Cuts are created by removing soil until the proper elevation is attained. If the cut will support a structure, the soil is scarified to a depth of 6 to 12 inches and compacted, as described previously, to prepare the subgrade. Creating a fill takes several steps. In most cases, fills must be compacted to standards determined by an engineer (engineered fills). To create a stable base for the fill, the natural grade is cut 1 or more feet to the depth at which it is naturally compact and scarified. Then a layer of fill soil is placed, mixed into the native soil, and compacted (often called "knitting in" the fill). Fill soil is added in shallow layers called "lifts," then wetted to help break down soil structure, and compacted to the specified percent compaction until the desired grade is reached. Thus, fills

are first cut, then compacted throughout their entire depth.

Pads that contain both cut and fill are called transition lots. To protect from differential settlement of the pad, the fill portion must be over-excavated (cut) and recompacted to provide a stable transition from the cut portion of the lot to the fill portion (Figure 4.7).

If natural grade is a slope, the toe of the fill (where the fill meets natural grade) usually will be "keyed in" to keep it from moving down slope. This requires cutting a keyway 2 to 3 feet deep (or deeper if necessary to reach stable base) and usually the width of the blade (8 to 15 feet) of the equipment being used (Figure 4.8). To further stabilize the fill on a slope, it may be necessary to create a buttress fill by cutting horizontal benches, or steps, out of the natural grade.

The need for keyways and buttressing for fill slopes is designated on the grading plan notes, details, and specifications. These modifications are most often required when fills are placed on unstable soils or slopes. Early in the planning process, before grading plans are prepared, it is helpful to talk with the geotechnical engineer about the possible need for over-excavation, keyways, and buttresses.

Slope Stabilization

If unstable slopes are encroached upon during grading, the entire unstable area must be removed and replaced with an engineered fill. Active and dormant landslides are identified and mapped by the geotechnical engineer.

Another situation in which slope grading may be required occurs when the project grading intercepts an existing steep slope that could become unstable as a result of the grading. The slope may have to be cut to a less steep gradient (e.g., 2:1) (Figure 4.9). This is called "laying back the slope."

Slopes requiring repair should be shown on the grading plan. In the case of landslides, however, the extent of the work necessary is often not known until the soil is removed and limits of the unstable area can be accurately determined. Such situations may require extensive soil work beyond the designed limit of grading.

Pavement

The amount of excavation required to install pavement is defined by the pavement section (Figure 4.10). The pavement section includes

TABLE 4.5 Examples of requirements for compaction of engineered fills with different soil types (Unified Soil System classes) and load classes (after Pomerening 1972).

Unified Soil System class	Required compaction		
	Class 1	Class 2	Class 3
Clean gravels (little or no fines)	97	94	90
Gravels with fines (appreciable amount of fines)	98	95	91
Clean sands (little or no fines)	97–98	95	91
Sands with fines (appreciable amount of fines)	98–99	95	92
Silts and clays (liquid limit less than 50)	100	96	92
Silts and clays (liquid limit greater than 50; medium plasticity)	——	97	93
Silts and clays (liquid limit greater than 50; high plasticity)	——	——	93

Class 1: Upper 8 feet of fills supporting one- or two-story buildings
Upper 3 feet of subgrade under pavements
Upper 1 foot of subgrade under floors

Class 2: Deeper parts of fills under buildings
Deeper parts (to 30 feet) of fills under pavements, floors

Class 3: All other fills requiring some degree of strength or incompressibility

- **Surface layer:** for example, asphalt, concrete, brick, pavers
- **Base:** porous, compacted material such as gravel, sand, or aggregate rock
- **Subbase:** select fill to replace unsuitable native soil or raise area to finish grade (may or may not be needed)
- **Subgrade:** graded, compacted native soil

The thickness of each of these layers depends on the paving material, amount of load to be carried, and the ability of the existing soil to carry that load (Table 4.6). For instance, asphalt pavement for a residential driveway requires a thinner pavement section than a major road. Concrete pavements usually require a thinner section than asphalt. Pavement on an expansive clay soil requires a thicker section than on a nonexpansive loam. Pavement section requirements are specified by the geotechnical engineer or landscape architect.

Road pavements usually require some edge treatment. On streets, this treatment is normally a curb and gutter. Excavation to construct the standard curb and gutter is generally 6 to 12 inches behind the curb and 12 to 18 inches deep (Figure 4.11). Rolled curbs require less excavation.

Foundations and Footings

A building's foundation transfers the building load to the ground. The footings are those parts of the foundation that rest directly on the soil (Ching 1985). The type of foundation and footing appropriate for a given building depends on the load, soil conditions, climate, and topography.

The amount of soil excavation and compaction required varies greatly with footing and foundation type. A basement wall foundation usually requires excavation 8 to 10 feet deep (Figure 4.12a). A perimeter wall foundation, also called a "frost footing," has a continuous footing, the depth of which varies with the load to be borne, but is probably 2 to 4 feet deep, or below the frost line (Figure 4.12b). The edge of the excavation for the footing is 6 to 12 inches beyond the outer extension of the horizontal portion at the base, which may be 2 to 3 feet beyond the foundation wall. The soil under the footing must be excavated and compacted, usually to a depth of 6 to 18 inches.

Ground slab foundations are entirely in contact with the soil and derive their strength from the subbase (Figure 4.12c). The slab can be reinforced to reduce the need for soil compaction. The edge of the slab may be thickened to provide support and stability, depending on soil and climate variation.

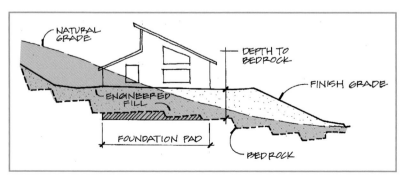

FIGURE 4.7 A transition lot contains both cut and fill. The fill portion must be overexcavated (cut) and recompacted to provide a stable transition from the cut portion of the lot to the fill portion. (Cut portion is shaded.)

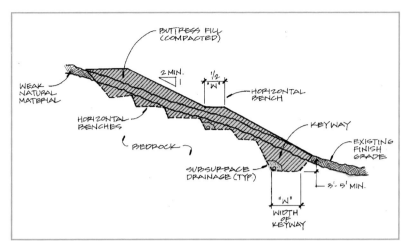

FIGURE 4.8 A buttress fill often is required when a fill is placed on a natural slope. To prevent the fill from slipping down the slope, it is stabilized by two methods: First, horizontal benches, or steps, are cut into the native grade to bedrock or stable soil. Second, a keyway is constructed along the toe of the slope to anchor it. A trench is cut approximately 3 to 5 feet deep and 10 to 15 feet wide. Subdrains are installed, and the area is brought to finish grade with compacted fill. Therefore, extensive cuts are required to construct a buttress fill. If trees are located at the toe of the slope, it may be possible to move the keyway several feet up the slope to reduce root interference.

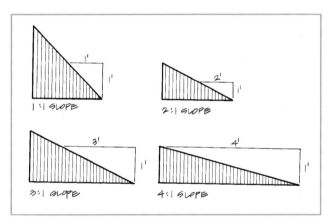

FIGURE 4.9 Slopes are designated by the ratio of the horizontal distance over the vertical (the run over the rise). For example, a 2:1 slope extends 2 feet horizontally for every 1 foot of rise in elevation.

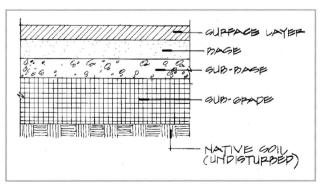

FIGURE 4.10 A typical pavement section includes the surface layer (brick, concrete, asphalt), base (sand, gravel, aggregate rock), subbase (select fill; not always needed), and subgrade (graded, compacted native soil) (after Peurifoy and Ledbetter 1985). The thickness of each layer (asphalt, aggregate base, and compacted subbase) depends on the soil characteristics and load that the pavement will bear.

Pier and grade beam foundations are supported by piers spanned by a grade beam (Figure 4.12d). Grade beams are normally 12 to 18 inches below grade, requiring that a trench be dug. The foundation can be specially engineered to place the grade beam above grade.

Pier foundations are supported by vertical piers (Figure 4.12e). The diameter, depth, and spacing of the piers depend on the soil characteristics and the weight to be borne. If the pier is end supported, the excavation must be as wide or wider than the base of the footing.

Retaining Walls

Retaining walls are used to retain a fill placed on native grade or to retain natural grade where a cut is made. Retaining walls may be used to minimize damage to tree roots by maintaining natural grade some distance from the tree. Like any other load-bearing structure, retaining walls need footings for support. The footings can be either continuous or discontinuous. Continuous footings require excavating a trench, usually about 18 to 24 inches deep, along the length of the wall. The face of the excavation is usually about 2 to 3 feet beyond the face of the wall. The distance of the excavation from the face or back of the wall depends on the design of the footing (Figure 4.13a).

Discontinuous footings include pier and beam or post and caisson design. Vertical members are placed in holes drilled into natural grade (Figure 4.13b). Horizontal members retain the soil. The spacing, depth, and diameter of the posts depend on the load the wall must bear.

Retaining walls can be made of bricks, concrete blocks, stone, or concrete poured in place. Wood can also be used, although its use is sometimes discouraged by engineers because it decomposes more quickly than brick or concrete.

Retaining walls taller than 4 or 5 feet must be specially engineered (if so regulated) and are expensive to build, even though the expense may be justified. They also appear quite massive. For these reasons, builders usually prefer to keep retaining wall heights below 5 feet whenever possible.

Crib block walls are constructed of interlocking structural members (usually reinforced concrete) set into the slope. They usually require a construction area approximately 10 feet behind the wall face. Installation methods vary with specific design; check manufacturer's recommendations.

Utilities and Services

Utilities and services include water, storm water system, sanitary sewer, telephone, electric, gas, cable

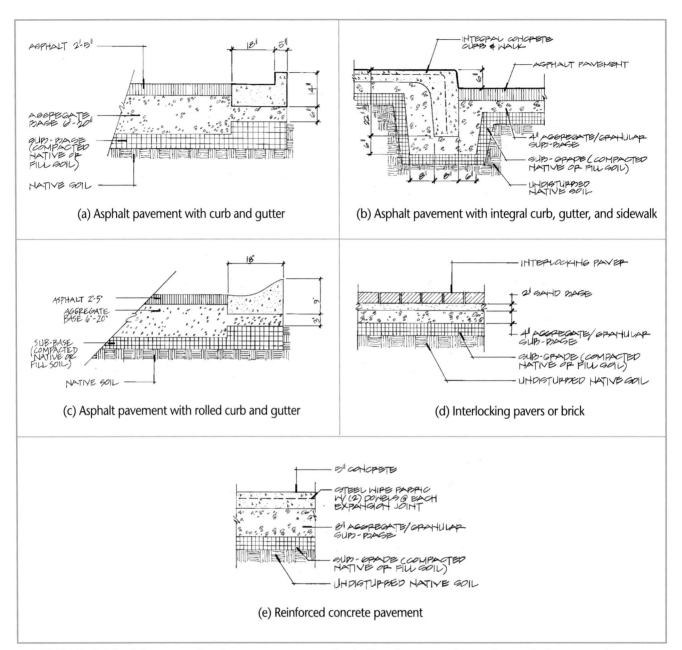

FIGURE 4.11 Typical details for construction of common pavements and curbs. Note the amount of excavation required to prepare the pavement section and bedding for curbs (after Robinette 1976).

TABLE 4.6. Pavement section requirements for a shopping center parking lot constructed on silty clay soil of high plasticity (after Merrill 1985).

Proposed use	Asphalt concrete	Aggregate base	Select engineered fill	Compacted native subgrade	Total excavation
Auto parking	2"	8"	18"	6"	34"
Access aisles	3"	10"	18"	6"	37"
Major aisles and driveways	3½"	15"	18"	6"	42½"
Trash truck loading pad	5"	20"	18"	6"	49"

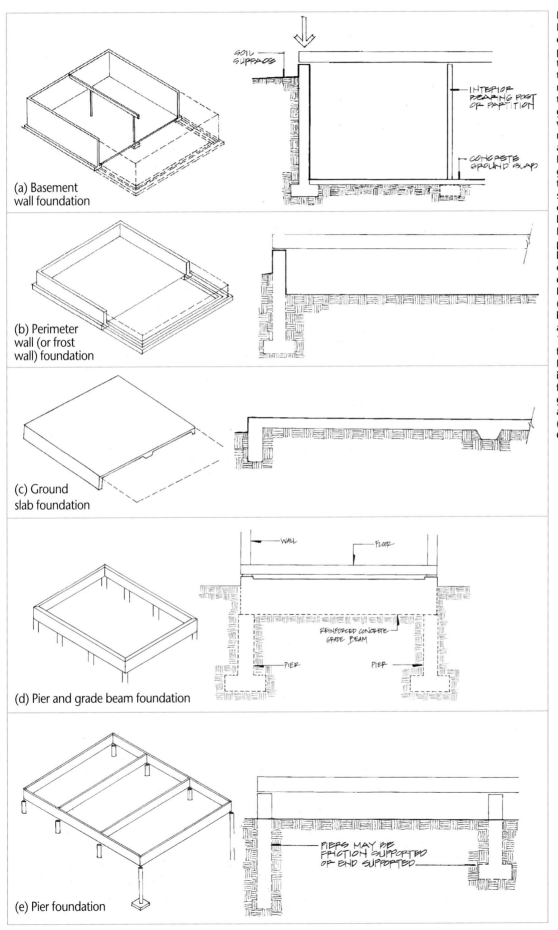

(a) Basement wall foundation

(b) Perimeter wall (or frost wall) foundation

(c) Ground slab foundation

(d) Pier and grade beam foundation

(e) Pier foundation

FIGURE 4.12
Foundation systems differ in how they provide support to the structure, and the excavation needed to construct the footing also varies greatly. A basement wall foundation (a) requires the greatest amount of excavation. Perimeter wall (b) and ground slab foundations (c) require a specified depth of compacted soil beneath them. Excavation to compact the soil should be added to the depth of the footing to determine impacts. Pier and grade beams (d) require drilling holes for piers as well as excavating a trench 12 to 18 inches deep for the grade beam. Minimum excavation is required with pier foundations with grade beam placed above grade (e). (Drawings a–c after Ching 1985.)

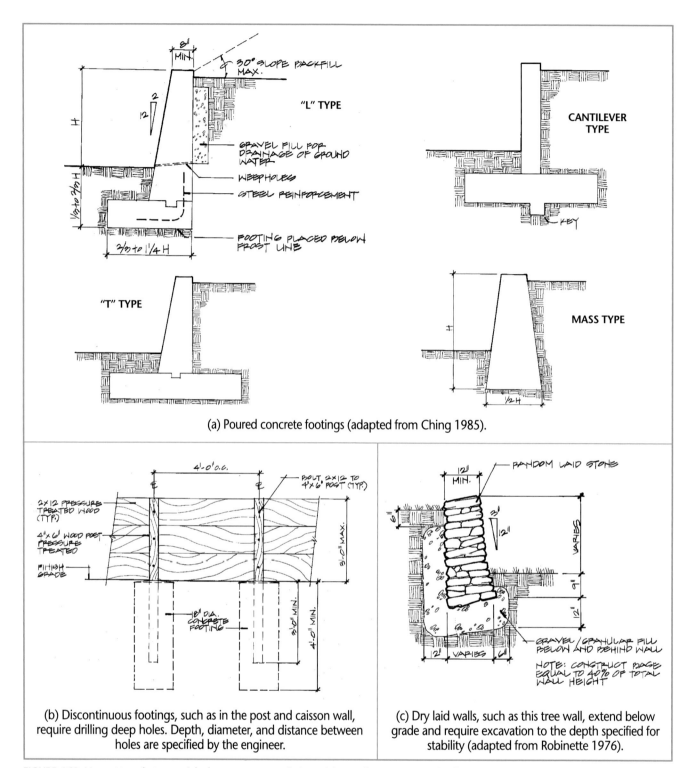

(a) Poured concrete footings (adapted from Ching 1985).

(b) Discontinuous footings, such as in the post and caisson wall, require drilling deep holes. Depth, diameter, and distance between holes are specified by the engineer.

(c) Dry laid walls, such as this tree wall, extend below grade and require excavation to the depth specified for stability (adapted from Robinette 1976).

FIGURE 4.13 No matter what materials they are composed of, retaining walls are supported at least in part by footings that require excavation into the soil. The amount of excavation required depends on the design of the footing.

television, and fiber optic cable for telecommunications. In most new developments, these are placed below ground. In some cases, however, electric, telephone, and cable television lines are above ground on poles.

Main lines for water, sewer, and storm drains are usually placed in the street. Water and sewer lines must be placed some minimum distance apart, usually

several feet, depending on local requirements. Depth of the pipes is set by the invert elevation (elevation at the bottom of the pipe) of the connection points and the frost depth. Pipe diameter is based on the overall system design; pipes are placed in a sand or gravel envelope, with a minimum 3 feet cover of compacted soil (Figure 4.14).

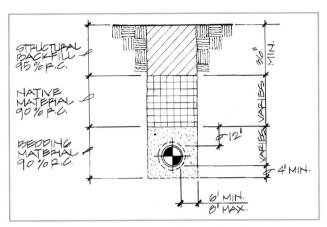

FIGURE 4.14 A typical detail for installation of a main water, sewer, or storm drain line includes the pipe laid on 6 to 8 inches of bedding material (sand or gravel) with 12 inches cover, and at least 36 inches of structural backfill (native soil, if suitable) compacted to 95 percent relative compaction. Native material compacted to 90 percent can be used below the structural fill if the pipe is deeper than 4 feet.

Storm drains have inlets at the surface. Inlets at street curbs require excavation from the face of the curb back from the street, 3 to 5 feet into the right-of-way, and a minimum of 3 feet deep. Catch basins placed in streets or landscape areas are typically 2 feet square and require at least an additional 13 to 24 inches of excavation. Depth varies, but usually is a minimum of 3 feet. Surface grades must be adjusted to create adequate slope to the inlets.

Storm water sewer and sanitary sewer systems include manholes for maintenance access. Manholes require extensive excavation to construct the 4-foot-wide vertical chamber to the depth of the pipe it is servicing. Where two or more collector pipes join, or where lateral pipes join at different elevations, a junction box is required. The excavation is about 3 to 4 feet wide and to the depth of the lowest pipe, usually at least 3 feet.

Electric, gas, cable television, and telephone lines often are placed in the right-of-way between the street and the project. Distribution lines are sometimes consolidated into a joint trench. Although fewer trenches are dug, the size of the joint trench is usually quite large, up to 10 feet wide by 4 feet deep, to accommodate all of the lines, each in its own conduit, with the minimum spacing required by local standards (Table 4.7).

For underground electric, telephone, television, and gas utilities, splice boxes are constructed to allow access. The size of these underground structures ranges from 2 to 8 feet wide and 2 to 5 feet deep, and therefore may require extensive excavation to construct.

Trenching

The normal procedure for installing underground utilities is to dig a trench of sufficient depth and width to accommodate the lines, pipes or conduit, bedding material, and backfill. The backfill usually is the native soil compacted to between 90 and 95 percent relative compaction. If the geotechnical engineer considers the native soil unsuitable for backfill, a select fill will be specified. The trenches are dug with trenching equipment or backhoes. For deep trenches, the top of the trench may be made much wider than the bottom to prevent caving in of the sides.

Tunneling

An alternative to open trenching is tunneling. Tunneling can be accomplished by hand for short distances, or with mechanical tunneling equipment. Tunneling, however, does not exclude the need for excavation. In some cases, work pits must be dug for launching and recovering the tunneling equipment. Furthermore, where two utility lines cross, or the equipment encounters other underground infrastructure, a "pot hole" must be excavated (Goodfellow 1995).

Table 4.7. Example of minimum cover and clearances for underground utilities.

	Minimum space from					
	Gas	Telephone	Cable TV	Electrical secondary	Electrical primary	Minimum cover
Gas	——	6"	6"	12"	12"	24"; 30" in street
Telephone	6"	——	0"	0"	12"	24"; 30" in street
Cable TV	6"	0"	——	0"	12"	18"
Electrical secondary	12"	0"	0"	——	6"	24"; 30" in street
Electrical primary	12"	12"	12"	6"	——	30"; 36" in street

Drainage Swales

Drainage swales carry surface water to some outlet, usually storm drains or existing waterways. They may be lined with either earth or concrete. The size of the swale, and therefore, the excavation required, depend on the volume of water to be carried. Refer to the drainage, grading, or site improvement plans for details and specifications.

Stream Improvements

Construction activities along streams, creeks, and other waterways include bank protection, culverts in road fills, drop structures, and storm drain outfalls. Excavation is required into the banks and channel bottom for stabilization. Outfalls require bank protection (e.g., concrete aprons, riprap) from erosion. Refer to the construction drawings and details to determine the extent of soil disturbance.

Retention and Detention Ponds

The amount of runoff allowed to leave a site usually is strictly controlled by local regulation. Generally, runoff volume and velocity cannot exceed that of the predevelopment condition. In some areas, no runoff is allowed. Ponds may be constructed to retain or detain runoff. These ponds may be incorporated into the project as a landscape design feature.

Detention ponds temporarily hold runoff during peak flows and then discharge it into waterways at a slower rate (Figure 4.15). Detention sites may be large, flat areas that can be occasionally flooded, such as parking lots, playing fields, and parks, or excavated ponds with enough capacity to accommodate storm flows (Landphair and Motloch 1985).

Retention ponds collect runoff and allow it to seep through the pond bottom to recharge the ground water (Figure 4.16). Proper siting of the pond, in appropriate soil areas that will allow recharge, is critical. If retention ponds are placed so that water does not percolate downward, surrounding water tables will be affected.

SUMMARY

Plans guide the clearing, grading, and construction processes. A set of drawings may include a variety of information: plans, legends, details, sections, profiles, and specifications. Ask for clarification if portions of the plans, terminology, or symbols are not understood, or if conditions on the site do not seem to conform to the plans.

Trees must be located on plans if they are to be considered in the design process. When site development will occur near trees, accurate location of the trunk is critical information. Tree driplines typically are drawn from aerial photographs and are not accurate enough for design purposes. Once trunks are accurately located by survey, the driplines can be measured and plotted.

Construction follows a sequence of events, and the consultant must understand what activities take place during each phase of construction in order to estimate what changes will occur around trees. With practice, the consultant can become proficient in reading plans, details, and survey information. Without those skills, the effectiveness of the consultant in evaluating impacts and communicating with the design and construction teams is seriously compromised.

REFERENCES

Capachi, N. 1978. *Excavation and Grading Handbook.* Revised. Carlsbad, CA: Craftsman Book Co. 380 pp.

Ching, F. 1985. *Architectural Graphics.* 2nd ed. New York: Van Nostrand Reinhold. 187 pp.

Goodfellow, J.W. 1995. Engineering and construction alternatives to line clearance tree work. *Journal of Arboriculture* 21(1):41–49.

Hausenbuiller, R.L. 1985. *Soil Science: Principles and Practices.* 3rd ed. Dubuque, IA: Wm. C. Brown.

Landphair, H.C., and J.L. Motloch. 1985. *Site Reconnaissance and Engineering.* New York: Elsevier. 248 pp.

Merrill, M.J. 1985. Geotechnical Exploration and Engineering Study. Merrill, Sweeley, Mullen, Sandeful, Inc. Nov. 14, 1985. Unpublished.

Munson, A.E. 1974. *Construction Design for Landscape Architects.* New York: McGraw-Hill, Inc. 212 pp.

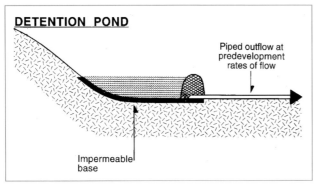

FIGURE 4.15 Detention ponds temporarily hold runoff during peak flows and then discharge it at a slower rate (after Landphair and Motloch 1985).

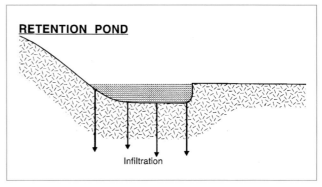

FIGURE 4.16 Retention ponds collect runoff and hold it for ground water recharge. These ponds must be located in areas with suitable soil to allow infiltration (after Landphair and Motloch 1985).

Peurifoy, R.L., and W.B. Ledbetter. 1985. *Construction Planning, Equipment and Methods*. 4th ed. New York: McGraw-Hill. 683 pp.

Pomerening, J.A. 1972. *Elementary Engineering Applications of Soil Science*. Pomona: Plant and Soil Science Department, California State Polytechnic University. 35 pp.

Robinette, G.O. 1976. *Landscape Architectural Site Construction Details*. Reston, VA: Environmental Design Press.

Russell, J.E. 1985. *Construction Equipment*. Reston, VA: Reston Publishing Co.

Singer, M.J., and D.N. Munns. 1987. *Soils: An Introduction*. New York: Macmillan. 492 pp.

Sowers, G.B., and G.F. Sowers. 1951. *Introductory Soil Mechanics and Foundations*. New York: Macmillan.

Untermann, R.K. 1973. *Grade Easy*. Washington, DC: American Society of Landscape Architects. 119 pp.

Evaluation of the Resource

The most important role the arboriculture or forestry consultant may play during the tree preservation process is providing accurate information about the tree resource. While it may be the surveyor's job to locate tree trunks and the engineer's task to design retaining walls, it is the consultant's job to know the composition and condition of the tree resource and anticipate how it will respond to development.

Consultants must strive to provide the best information about trees as well as their response to development. This role as information provider is critical because of the amount of myth and ignorance that surrounds trees. In a study of development professionals, one of the primary impediments to making tree preservation a goal was lack of knowledge about tree management practices (Andreasen and Tyson 1993). Even more startling was a related observation: many builders who lack knowledge about trees perceived themselves as knowledgeable!

This chapter describes the type of information the consultant should collect and evaluate about trees and forests on a development project. This information should be collected early in the planning process and be used to determine appropriate land uses and location of improvements.

THE RESOURCE EVALUATION

The resource evaluation provides the base information that will influence tree-related decisions throughout the planning, construction, and maintenance phases. The information must be accurate, complete, and readily accessible. It must be usable both in the field and at the planning table.

The resource evaluation is an inventory that describes the character of trees and their suitability for preservation at a level of detail appropriate for the project and the phase of planning. For example, assessing the construction impacts for one mature tree on a quarter acre requires specific and detailed information about the condition, location, and canopy conformation of the individual tree. By contrast, early planning for multiple-use sites hundreds of acres in size may require general information on the type and extent of tree cover. Then, as specific site use is defined, resource information must be more detailed and describe individual trees in and adjacent to use areas.

In many communities, a tree ordinance defines the requirements for the resource evaluation. Alternatively, communities may request certain information about trees as part of the planning process, but not coded by ordinance. Following are some examples.

- **From the City of Charlotte, North Carolina:**
  "Applications for grading, building, demolition, and change of use permits on all property except that which is excluded by Sec. 21–42 shall provide a tree survey which shall include all trees of 8-inch dbh and larger within the tree protection zone and all trees over 1-inch caliper and 6 feet in height on the City right-of-way. Stands of southern yellow pine and other species may be indicated by groups with the average tree dbh."

- **From the City of Pleasant Hill, California:**
  "The tree removal plan shall indicate the location, species, state of health, size, and approximate age of all trees on the development site." [Applies to subdivision of property.]

- **From the City of Vancouver, British Columbia:**
  "An applicant for a development permit is required to submit a site plan identifying all existing trees with trunks greater than 20 centimeters [approx. 8 inches] thick, measured 1 meter [approx. 3.1 feet] above the ground, that may be affected by the proposed development. . . . the species and condition of the tree should be noted by the applicant."

- **From San Mateo County, California:**
  "All applications for building permits, use permits, variances, and other applicable permit applications shall be accompanied by a scaled plot plan indicating the location, size, and species of heritage trees . . . which may be impacted by said permit

execution." [Heritage tree is defined earlier in the ordinance as a tree meeting either of two criteria: 1) trees or groves designated as such by the Board of Supervisors, or 2) a tree of 17 named species meeting a minimum trunk diameter (measured at 54 inches above grade).]

- **From British Standard 5837 (1991):**
"In most circumstances [the land survey] will include all trees over 75 mm [approx. 3 inches] stem diameter, measured 1.5 m [approx. 5 feet] above ground level. In some circumstances, smaller specimens should be noted. . . . The species and condition . . . should be assessed [for] health, vigor and condition, . . . structural defects, . . . life expectancy, size and form, . . . and suitability within the context of the proposed site development [and] location . . . relative to existing site features."

These regulations have several common themes. They designate what species of tree and trunk diameter are to be surveyed. They identify the specific information to be reported. They frequently require that survey information be displayed graphically.

However, for the most part, agency requirements address only a percentage of the trees on the site (those of minimum size or specific species). Often, the requirements may not include trees that could be assets to the project (e.g., trees smaller than the specified size limit). The consultant should advise the client of this opportunity and determine whether to include additional trees in the survey.

TYPES AND METHODS OF RESOURCE EVALUATION

Resource evaluation information covers a broad spectrum, from general to specific (Table 5.1). At one end of the spectrum, information about patterns of cover, species, and topography can be obtained using topographic plans and aerial photographs. It is possible to collect this information without visiting the site. At the other end of the spectrum would be a total tree survey, in which data are obtained for individual trees. Between these two extremes are a number of techniques for sampling a segment of the site.

A comprehensive tree preservation plan for a large, complex development would probably use all levels of resource evaluation, each at different stages in the process. A general description of existing vegetation, or stand delineation, would be used in initial

TABLE 5.1 Methods of resource evaluation.

Method	Level of resolution	Characteristics examined
Topographic plan	Very low	Amount and pattern of tree cover, including gaps Land use (roads, buildings, etc.) Adjacent properties Topography
Air photography	Low	Amount and pattern of tree cover, including gaps General species patterns (conifer vs. hardwood) Riparian corridors (if species are different) Land use (roads, buildings, etc.) Adjacent properties Stocking density
Ground survey—no sampling	Moderate	Cover types and associations Estimates of diameter range, height, density Stand structure and regeneration potential Root rot pockets Live crown ratio
Ground survey—point or transect sampling	High	Statistical sample Species Height and diameter Live crown ratio Condition Density Structural defects
Total tree survey	Absolute	All trees tagged and located

site planning. As a land plan is created, a detailed tree survey, involving all or part of the population, would be performed for trees within and adjacent to the development area. Management plans for any greenbelts and open space areas might be derived from sampled surveys. The following sections describe these approaches to resource evaluation.

Tree Stand Delineation

A tree stand delineation is "a general accounting of existing vegetation, both in quantity and quality" (Fazio 1994). This resource overview describes trees and other features such as vistas, wildlife habitat, and water features. For trees, a delineation would include species composition, stocking density, diameter distribution, age class, and condition at a stand level. Depending upon forest type and size of the site, the resource may be divided into stands with similar characteristics. In addition, individual trees, either outstanding or in poor condition, may be noted.

The goal of a stand delineation is to provide a general overview of the opportunities and constraints at a site. Stand delineations are particularly useful at the conceptual stage of project planning. A site could have a mix of cover types and species associations that may vary widely in their response to construction impacts. Alternatively, if there is a mix of overmature and young developing stands, these could be identified as such.

Tree stand delineations should be compatible with existing forestry methodology and terms. These are normally based upon such site resources as soils. Where possible, delineations should employ regional descriptions of vegetation. For example, in California, oak woodlands are normally described using the associations found in *Rangeland Cover Type Descriptions for California Hardwood Rangelands* (Allen et al. 1989). Consultants in the Pacific Northwest rely on *Natural Vegetation of Oregon and Washington* (Franklin and Dyrness

1984). Consultants in other regions may wish to refer to more general references such as *Silvics of North America* (USDA Forest Service 1990) and the Society of American Foresters' *Forest Cover Types* (Eyre 1980).

As with any resource evaluation, the results of a stand delineation should include both graphic and written summaries (see Appendix C). The map or plan is usually derived from the aerial photograph or topographic plan (Figure 5.1). We generally use the latter to display the following:

- **Patterns and extent of tree cover.** Assess both the spatial distribution (three-dimensional) of trees within the stand as well as the amount of land covered by canopy.

- **Cover types.** Identify the broad species associations present. For example, Eyre (1980) describes 145 forest cover types for the United States. Types are distinguished by regions (e.g., southern or north Pacific) and broad species categories (e.g., Southern yellow pines or blue oak - foothill pine).

- **Riparian corridors and potential wetlands.** Identify the location and extent of riparian (creek, stream, river) corridors. To the extent possible,

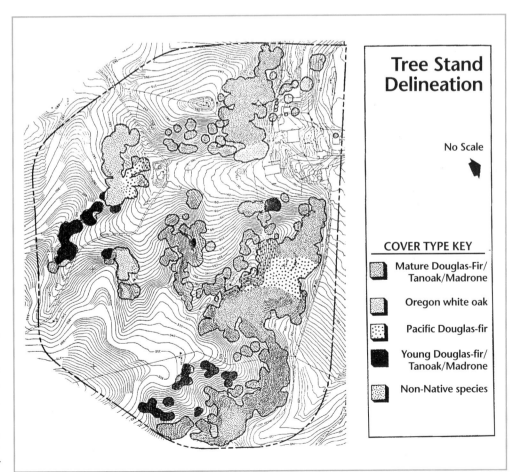

FIGURE 5.1 A tree stand delineation map depicts the patterns and extent of tree cover, as well as the species composition. It is usually prepared on a topographic map.

locate the edge of the tree canopy. If wetlands are located on the site, identify their general location. Provide this information to the project biologist or environmental consultant.

- **Stocking density.** Estimate the number of trees per acre or hectare.

- **Patterns of land use (including adjacent properties).** Describe the existing land use within and immediately adjacent to the subject site. Where existing forests are being developed, identify the history of cutting, reforestation, and other management efforts.

- **Other vegetation.** Identify the presence, location, and general extent of other vegetation (turf, grassland, shrubs, chaparral, invasive weeds, etc.).

Conducting a stand delineation may include the following steps:

1. obtaining and inspecting aerial photographs (may include using stereoscope) or topographic plans

2. performing a walking survey (we often use binoculars to observe distant trees)

3. recording information [we collect information directly onto the topographic map (normally at 100 or 200 scale) or aerial photograph]

4. summarizing the information both graphically and in text form

Total Tree Survey

In a total tree survey, detailed information is collected for all trees (Figure 5.2). Many cities require surveys of all trees of a particular species or above a given size (see previous section). This type of resource evaluation should identify the individual tree. Numerically coded tags attached to the tree are commonly employed. The tree number can be referenced on a plan as well as in the report. A tag also permits the tree to be located in the field.

In the absence of specific requirements by a governing agency, information collected in a tree survey might include the following (see also Muir 1984):

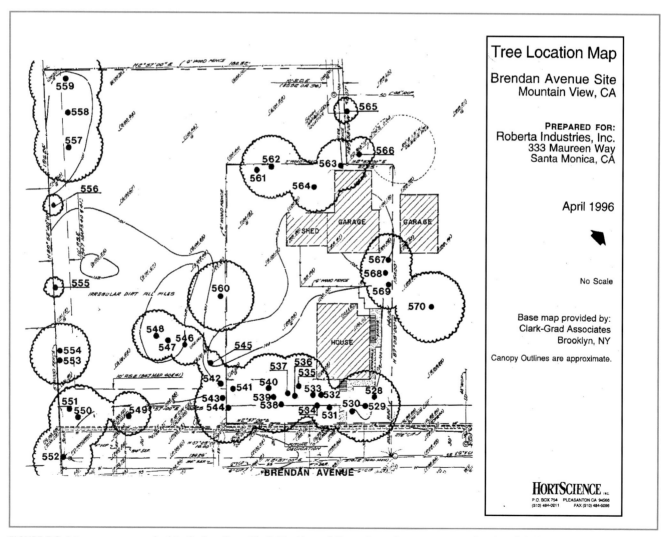

FIGURE 5.2 A tree survey map depicts the location of individual trees (often referencing tree tag numbers) and their canopy outlines. A topographic plan is generally used as a base map.

- **Species.** Identify the tree to the lowest taxonomic level possible. For example, honey locust should be described as either the species (*Gleditsia triacanthos*), the thornless form (*G. triacanthos* f. *inermis*), or one of the cultivars (*G. triacanthos* f. *inermis* 'Moraine').

- **Size.** Measure the diameter of the trunk to the nearest inch at 54 inches above grade (unless otherwise specified by the agency). Estimate the height.

- **Health or condition.** Assess the overall health and condition of the tree (Table 5.2). This is normally a measure of overall vigor and vitality appropriate for the age of the tree and would include shoot growth rate.

- **Structure.** Identify specific features of tree structure that are important to structural stability and failure potential (e.g., decay, conks, codominant trunks, history of failure). For use in developed areas, assess limitations (e.g., low or asymmetric crown form, bow in trunk) or other significant features (Photo 5.1). See Matheny and Clark (1994) for a list of factors important to structural stability.

- **Pests and disease.** Identify significant pest problems, particularly those that attack stressed or disturbed trees.

- **Crown class.** Assess the position of the crown relative to others in the grove or stand—normally described as dominant, codominant, intermediate, or suppressed (see Chapter 2). The assessment may also include relative position such as interior or edge.

- **Live crown ratio (LCR).** Estimate the ratio of the length of live crown to the height of the tree, usually expressed as a percentage (Photo 5.2). For example, if a tree is 100 feet tall and the live crown is 40 feet long, the LCR would be 40 percent (40 ÷ 100). LCR is most commonly applied to conifers. A LCR of 30 percent is often considered a threshold value for Pacific Northwest native conifers. Trees with this value or less do not respond well to site change (Muir 1984).

- **Height:diameter ratio.** An alternative to live crown ratio is the ratio of tree height to trunk

PHOTO 5.1 Although tree health and structure are related, the resource evaluation must consider the presence of structural defects and the potential for failure. The codominant trunks of this pine have split open. Although the tree appears healthy, it would receive a low rating for condition based upon its structure.

Table 5.2 Assessment of relative condition of trees in individual tree survey.

Condition rating	Factors considered[1]					
	Overall vigor	Canopy density	Amount of deadwood	History of failure	Pests	Extent of decay
1	Severe decline	< 20%	Large; major scaffold branches	More than one scaffold	Infested	Major—conks and cavities
2	Declining	20–60%	Twig and branch dieback	Scaffold branches	Infestation of significant pests	One to a few conks; small cavities
3	Low	60–90%	Small twigs	Small branches	Minor	Present at pruning wounds
4	Good	90–100%	Little or none	None	Minor	Present at pruning wounds
5	Excellent	100%	None	None	None, or insignificant	Absent

[1]Application may vary slightly with age and species of tree.

PHOTO 5.2 Live crown ratio is based on the length of crown divided by the height of the tree. In this example, the crown is approximately 20 feet long and the tree is 60 feet tall. The live crown ratio is 20:60, or 33 percent.

diameter. For example, a 100-foot-tall tree with a trunk diameter of 12 inches (1 foot) would have a height:diameter ratio of 100:1.

- **Crown integrity.** Estimate the amount of crown that is missing, dead, or dying. This measure is also known as ragged percent.

- **Crown spread.** Measure the width of the crown to the dripline, either on cardinal points or in the direction of developed areas.

- **Age.** Estimate or assess the relative age of the tree(s). Terms such as young, semi-mature, mature, or overmature are adequate descriptions. If known, the absolute age of the tree(s) can be given. We do not recommend taking a core sample to assess tree age unless there is a compelling reason to do so.

- **Pruning history.** Describe the history of pruning activity: crown cleaning, raising, restoration, etc. Note if the tree has been topped, involved in line clearing, or lost its central leader due to pruning.

The procedure for conducting a tree survey might include the following steps for *each* tree:

1. tagging the tree with a numerically coded metal tag
2. locating its position on a topographic map
3. identifying the species of tree
4. measuring the trunk diameter (and height if appropriate)
5. rating the condition on a scale (1 = poor; 5 = excellent)
6. identifying any specific defects in structure, presence of pests, etc.

7. assessing the tree's suitability for preservation (Chapter 6)
8. noting any other significant site or tree features

Physically collecting this information is greatly facilitated by using handheld computers or data-logging equipment. We normally collect information as a spreadsheet file that can be downloaded to a desktop device with little effort. Jim Barborinas (1995) uses a handheld computer with a custom-designed database management program. In both cases, summarizing the data for analysis and presentation is simplified.

When data will be transferred to a geographic information system, tree location can be determined using global positioning systems and/or aerial photographs.

Sampled and Partial Surveys

Intermediate between stand delineations and evaluation of all trees are surveys of a portion of the site. These may be either statistically valid samples of the entire site or complete surveys of specific sections.

In the case of statistically valid samples, trees within defined sampling points (either circular or linear transects) are evaluated as if they were part of a total survey (Photos 5.3a,b). This information is then expanded to describe the entire site. Results describe very specific parameters of the resource, including species mix, basal area, canopy cover, diameter class distribution, regeneration potential (canopy stratification), potential longevity, canopy gaps, soils, and understory associates.

Another approach to a partial survey calls for an evaluation of only those trees within or adjacent to proposed use areas (Figure 5.3). For example, following a tree stand delineation, a developer may choose to build only in a small portion of a large site. A more detailed tree survey would include only those trees close to areas proposed for development.

APPRAISING THE VALUE OF TREES IN DEVELOPMENT AREAS

Some agencies request that the value of each tree be established as part of the tree survey. Most commonly, they ask that each tree be appraised using the methodology contained in the *Guide for Plant Appraisal* (Council of Tree and Landscape Appraisers 1992). This method is based upon four factors: size, species, condition, and location. *Size* is trunk diameter, measured 54 inches above grade. *Species* considers the adaptability of the specific tree to the local environment. *Condition* considers tree health and structure. *Location* assesses the site, the tree's function and aesthetic contributions to that site, and its placement in the landscape. Consultants preparing such appraisals

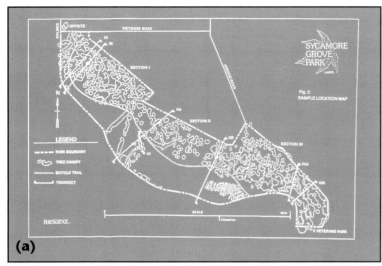

(a)

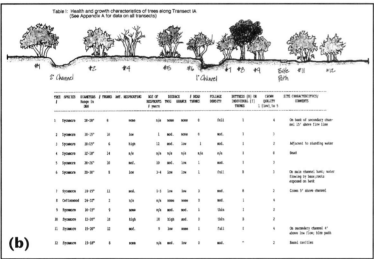

(b)

PHOTO 5.3 In some cases, the most appropriate evaluation involves sampling a portion of the site. In this case, linear transects were made across the site (a) and information summarized for each (b).

should refer to local or regional species rating guides (e.g., the *Species Classification and Group Assignment for Northern California*).

SUMMARIZING THE RESOURCE EVALUATION

The purpose of a resource evaluation is to provide the client (developer or agency) with accurate information about the woody vegetation at a site. The consultant must summarize and present the results in a way that facilitates decision-making during the planning design phases. During these stages of project development, resource evaluation information might be used only by the client. But as project submittals are prepared, the information will be compiled into a more formal report. To that end, information collected in a resource evaluation

should be summarized in a manner useful to the user(s). This is commonly occurs in two forms: text and graphic (see Chapter 11).

Compiling Information as Text and Tables

A summary of a resource evaluation depends on the nature of the evaluation. The tabulated results of a stand delineation may be sufficiently displayed as a simple list of species and cover types. For a tree survey, more detailed information about individual trees is required. This is most easily presented as a table sorted by tree number and including tree number, species, size, condition, suitability for preservation, and comments about structure, pests, etc. (Table 5.3). Because the tree tag number distinguishes among individual trees, we normally organize survey forms on this basis.

From the basic tree survey information, summary tables may be prepared that compile topics such as species and frequency, species and condition, and trees with low suitability for preservation. Results can also be organized around specific criteria. For example, communities with heritage or legacy tree provisions will want to know which trees meet their specific criteria. Development team members often want to know the locations of trees in the proposed development (e.g., within a specific lot).

Compiling Information onto Plans and Maps

Maps and plans are important project documents that communicate tree information in a special and powerful way. Like text

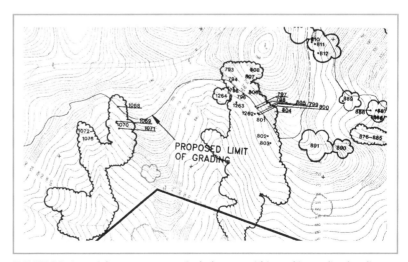

FIGURE 5.3 A partial tree survey may include trees within and immediately adjacent to the proposed limits of grading. Trees away from graded areas need not be individually tagged and evaluated.

TABLE 5.3   Example of tree survey summary table.

Tree no.	Species	Trunk diameter (in.)	Heritage tree	Condition[1]	Comments
774	Valley oak (*Quercus lobata*)	24	Yes	3	Codominant trunks w/included bark; trunk elliptical in shape
775	California black walnut (*Juglans hindsii*)	28	Yes	3	Trunk wounds; seam
776	Siberian elm (*Ulmus pumila*)	29	yes	2	Large burls/galls along trunk; some with decay
777	Valley oak	69	Yes	5	Large, massive tree
778	California black walnut	26	Yes	2	Basal cavity; branch dieback in crown
779	California black walnut	16	No	4	Full crown with good branch structure; minor twig dieback
780	California black walnut	8	No	4	Full crown
781	California black walnut	11, 8	Yes	3	Codominant trunks arise at base with decay
782	Cottonwood (*Popular fremontii*)	32	Yes	1	Basal trunk wound; crown dead; trunk sprouts only
783	Valley oak	72	Yes	2	Extensive trunk decay; large branches dead; failed
784	California black walnut	22	Yes	1	Extensive trunk decay
785	California black walnut	22	Yes	1	English walnut scion dead
786	English walnut (*Juglans regia*)	14, 12	Yes	1	Extensive crown dieback

Corresponds to tag number in field.

In the city of Pleasanton, heritage trees are those over 18" in diameter (or for which the combined diameter of the 2 largest trunks on multiple stem trees is greater than 18").

Relative health and structure on a 1 to 5 scale (see Table 5.2).

Information about structure, pests, previous failures, history of pruning, and other observations may be included as comments.

[1]On a scale of 1 to 5, where 1 = poor and 5 = excellent

information, the content and format of a graphic presentation must reflect the nature of the evaluation and the phase of planning. Maps and plans are very useful for identifying the location and spatial distribution of trees on the site. In a stand delineation, the overall patterns of vegetation and their type are the key elements of the evaluation. Similarly, in a tree survey, the location of individual trees is also best defined in plan view.

REFERENCES

Allen, B., R. Evett, B. Holzmann, and A. Martin. 1989. *Rangeland Cover Type Descriptions for California Hardwood Rangelands.* Sacramento: California Department of Forestry and Fire Protection.

Andreasen, A., and C. Tyson. 1993. *Improving Tree Management Practices of Home Builders: A Social Marketing Approach.* Washington, DC: Forest Policy Center. 44 pp.

Barborinas, J. 1995. Urban Forestry Services, Inc., Mt. Vernon, WA. Personal communication. May.

British Standards Institute. 1991. *Trees in Relation to Construction*. British Standard 5837.

Charlotte, North Carolina, City of. 1989. An ordinance rewriting Chapter 21, "Trees," of the code of the City of Charlotte (Ordinance Book 38, Page 228). 25 pp.

Council of Tree and Landscape Appraisers. 1992. *Guide for Plant Appraisal. 8th ed*. Savoy, IL: International Society of Arboriculture. 103 pp.

Eyre, F. (ed.). 1980. *Forest Cover Types of the United States and Canada*. Washington, DC: Society of American Foresters.

Fazio, J. (ed.). 1994. A systematic approach to building with trees. *Tree City USA Bulletin*. Nebraska City, NE: National Arbor Day Foundation. 8 pp.

Franklin, J., and C. Dyrness. 1984. *Natural Vegetation of Oregon and Washington*. Corvallis: Oregon State University Press.

International Society of Arboriculture, Western Chapter. 1992. *Species Classification and Group Assignment for Northern California*. Sacramento, CA: ISA Western Chapter. 23 pp.

Kunde, S. Kunde Company, Inc., St. Paul, MN. Personal communication. February 1997.

Matheny, N., and J. Clark. 1994. *A Photographic Guide to the Evaluation and Hazard Trees in Urban Areas*. 2nd ed. Savoy, IL: International Society of Arboriculture.

Muir, J. 1984. Silvicultural information to help select and manage native trees in urban or suburban developments. *Arboricultural Journal* 8:13–17.

Pleasant Hill, California, City of. 1989. An ordinance dealing with tree removal and preservation. Ordinance No. 626. 6 pp.

San Mateo, California, County of. 1991. Section 11000, San Mateo County Ordinance: Regulation of the removal of heritage trees. Redwood City, CA: Planning and Building Division. County of San Mateo. 9 pp.

United States Department of Agriculture, Forest Service. 1990. *Silvics of North America* (two volumes). Agricultural Handbook No. 654. Washington DC: USDA.

Vancouver (British Columbia), City of. Undated. Regulation of trees on private property. British Columbia: Planning Department, City of Vancouver. 2 pp.

Designing for Tree Preservation

Designing for tree preservation means that trees are considered an integral feature of the project from the first stage of planning. Project design is at first conceptual in nature and becomes more detailed as plans are refined. The consultant participates in the early stages of design by providing accurate, appropriate information about the trees and their needs for continued good health. The resource evaluation (see Chapter 5) provides the information from which the consultant makes those decisions in concert with the planning needs for the development.

The consultant facilitates early design efforts by translating the information gathered in the resource evaluation into recommendations about which trees are suitable for preservation and how much undisturbed space they need to remain viable. The consultant also provides the design team with specific guidelines regarding grading, drainage, trenching, etc. to avoid excessive damage to trees.

EVALUATING SUITABILITY FOR PRESERVATION

The goal of tree preservation is to have trees remain assets to the site for years to come. Trees that are preserved on construction sites, therefore, must be carefully selected to make sure that they will survive construction impacts, adapt to a new environment, and perform well in the landscape.

Evaluation of suitability of individual trees or stands for preservation is one of the most important tasks for the consultant. This analysis must take place early in the planning process. Considerable time and money can be wasted by designing projects around trees not suitable for preservation. An assessment of suitability for preservation evaluates tree health, structure, age, and species factors. It is the final evaluation of the potential for a tree or a stand to remain an asset to the site for many years.

Little quantitative information exists about factors that may influence the response of tree species to construction impacts. Therefore, assigning suitability for preservation is a qualitative process based upon the observations of tree response by consultants. Suitability for preservation is a relative rating, describing the tree potential as poor, moderate, or good (Table 6.1).

The following factors must be evaluated when making an assessment of suitability for preservation.

- **Tree health.**
Healthy, vigorous trees are better able than nonvigorous trees to tolerate impacts such as root injury, demolition of existing structures, changes in soil grade and moisture, and soil compaction (Photo 6.1). Moreover, healthy trees are better able to acclimate to the new site conditions that occur after development.

PHOTO 6.1 Low-vigor and declining trees are poor choices for retention on construction sites because they are less able than vigorous, healthy trees to acclimate to new site conditions.

- **Tree structure.**
Trees with defects such as decayed wood, poor crown structure, or codominant trunks with poor attachments are not suitable for preservation in areas where people or property could be injured or damaged (Photos 6.2a, b). Such defects cannot be treated and may lead to failure. Similarly, trees that have developed in dense stands with poor live crown ratios and/or high height: diameter ratios may be unstable when exposed to wind and precipitation. (Refer to Matheny and Clark 1994 for further discussion of tree structure.)

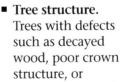

TABLE 6.1 Tree suitability for preservation rankings.

Good	Tree with good health and structural stability that has the potential for longevity at the site
Examples	26" diameter London plane (*Platanus* x *acerifolia*) in good health, structurally stable, and with high construction tolerance
	18" diameter honey locust (*Gleditsia triacanthos* f. *inermis*) in good health, structurally stable, and with high construction tolerance
Moderate	Tree with fair health and/or structural defects that can be abated with treatment; tree will require more intense management and monitoring and may have shorter lifespan than those in "good" category
Examples	30" diameter red pine (*Pinus resinosa*) (close to maximum size for this species), in good condition, but with limited longevity
	24" diameter coast redwood (*Sequoia sempervirens*) with codominant, upright trunks (a relatively minor structural defect for this tree), fair health, and good construction tolerance
Poor	Tree in poor health or with significant defects that cannot be mitigated; tree is expected to continue to decline, regardless of treatment; the species or individual may have characteristics undesirable for landscapes and is generally unsuitable for use areas
Examples	50" diameter live oak (*Quercus virginiana*) with extensive decay in the trunk that extends into the scaffold branches
	15" diameter red alder (*Alnus rubra*), intermediate in form, relatively short-lived with poor construction tolerance

- **Species.** Although all trees require protection to avoid injury, species vary widely in ability to withstand damage and changes in environment. Some trees tolerate a significant loss of roots, while others decline with much less interference (see Appendix B). Another species consideration is the potential to become an invasive weed. Norway maple (*Acer platanoides*) and tree of heaven (*Ailanthus altissima*) can be invasive and displace native taxa. A decision to preserve invasive species must balance the value of the individual tree against the measures needed to control seedlings or root sprouts.

PHOTO 6.2 Trees with structural defects such as extensive decay (a) or weakly attached codominant trunks —notice crack (b) are poorly suited for retention in areas where their failure could result in damage or safety problems.

- **Age and potential longevity.** Mature and overmature trees are less able to tolerate construction impacts and remain assets than are young and semi-mature individuals. This observation was supported by Anderson and Barrows-Broaddus (1989), who found that trees less than 10 inches in diameter had the best survival rates in new developments in Georgia.

A suitability evaluation provides others on the project team (especially the developer, architect, landscape architect, and engineer) with information about the potential for successful tree preservation. When combined with the basic tree survey information, the evaluation allows the project team and the governing agency to agree on the nature of the site's tree resource. Whether assigned to individual trees or to assemblages within a stand, the suitability for preservation evaluation is a key finding by the arboricultural consultant.

A variation on the term "suitability for preservation" is Safe Use Life Expectancy (SULE), a program developed by Jeremy Barrell (1995). It summarizes information on age, species lifespan, life expectancy, health, and structure in a context of management, impacts, and sustaining amenity. The resulting ranking, the Safe Useful Life Expectancy, is an assessment of the effective, safe, and useful lifespan of the tree resource. The SULE ranking does not consider the visual amenity value of the location of the trees.

Single Specimen Trees

The best candidates for retention as single trees are those that have developed as individual specimens because they typically have uniform canopies and well-tapered trunks. In some cases, dominant trees that have developed in stands also can be retained alone. For the most part, trees that have developed in stands, particularly intermediate and suppressed trees, will not function well as individuals. They have tall, poorly tapered trunks, high, irregularly shaped crowns, and are prone to failure and decline when their neighbors are removed (see Chapter 2). Not only are the trees unstable, but they contribute little to the appearance or landscape quality of the new project. They quickly become liabilities to the project rather than assets (Photos 6.3a–d).

When construction will occur within wooded areas, Coder (1995) recommends removing all trees within the construction zone—a 30-foot-wide area around the structure to be built—unless there are high-quality individual trees that can be adequately protected. Any trees within 60 feet of the structure must be protected from construction damage by barriers. No construction activity is allowed beyond that 60 feet, except for access corridors.

Anderson and Barrows-Broaddus (1989), in evaluating tree survival in developments in native pine/ hardwood forest in Georgia, advise against retaining only one or a few trees in narrow spaces between structures. Rather, they suggest identifying clumps of trees with at least 15 to 20 feet of protected area away from the construction. Trees larger than 10 inches in diameter within the 15- to 20-foot area should be removed, unless appropriate protection can be provided.

Peepre (undated) does not recommend retaining individual mature Douglas-fir trees from single-aged stands because of problems with windfall, although young trees with high live crown ratios could be selected.

Retaining Groups of Trees

Trees that develop in woodlands or forests are best retained in groups of sufficient size to maintain some of the integrity of the unit (Photo 6.4). Retaining small stands of mature single species of similar age is seldom effective. Increased exposure along the edges usually leads to structural failure and decline.

The minimum size of the remnant forest depends on

- species composition and sensitivity to impacts
- size and age of trees
- root and canopy conformations (as constrained by site features)
- structural stability of trees when new edge is formed
- development constraints
- habitat conservation concerns

When stands of trees will be retained, the consultant must evaluate those trees for their potential to fall out of the stand onto use areas. The frequency of failure of trees along a new forest edge is high for the first few years following clearing (Photo 6.5). In particular, the consultant should examine intermediate and suppressed trees, as well as codominant trees with trunk and branch defects that could lead to

(a) (b) (c) (d)

PHOTO 6.3 Trees that have developed as individual specimens (a) are better candidates for retention alone (b) because they are acclimated to sun and wind exposure, have well-tapered trunks and more uniform canopies. Trees that have developed in stands (c) are rarely successful when exposed (d). (Photo 'd' courtesy of Sandra Thorne-Brown)

PHOTO 6.4 Trees that develop in woodlands or forests are best retained in groups large enough to maintain some integrity of the group.

PHOTO 6.5 The frequency of failure of trees along a new forest edge is high for the first few years following clearing. Intermediate and suppressed trees, and those with significant defects, should be removed.

failure (Matheny and Clark 1994). Jim Barborinas (1995) has found that conifers with a live crown ratios less than 30 percent tend to break in winds when exposed, while those with live crown ratios greater than 50 percent are more stable (Photos 6.6a,b). Other potential targets (e.g., passive recreation, trails) of damage within the stand should also be considered when evaluating the trees.

Dunster (1995) describes the general failure of preservation efforts in second-growth coniferous forests in British Columbia, where dense, even-aged stands with little species diversity are typical. He suggests removing large trees while carefully protecting the land. The goal is "to retain an ecologically functional land base that is capable of growing trees well into the future." In this scheme, the understory plants and forest soil are protected. The protected area is planted with young trees the fall or early spring following completion of clearing and grading.

IDENTIFYING A TREE PROTECTION ZONE

The next step in the preservation process is for the consultant to provide the design team with guidelines for tree protection. This will allow the designers to plan for adequate space around trees from the beginning of the project, rather than trying to incorporate the trees later on. The consultant determines how much undisturbed space is needed for the trees to retain good health and vigor by identifying an optimal tree protection zone (Photo 6.7).

Tree protection is a seemingly straightforward effort: put up a fence to enclose the entire root area of the tree or group of trees and allow no construction activity within that area, including storage, dumping of excess materials, fires, etc. Under ideal conditions, the tree protection zone would include all of the tree's root area and crown. As land values rise, however, there is more pressure to encroach closer to the tree to gain usable space. We are not asked, "How much space does the tree require?", but rather, "How close to the tree can I build?"

The question of how close one can encroach on a tree is a difficult one to answer. It is commonly thought that a healthy tree tolerates removal of approximately one-third of its roots (Harris 1992, Helliwell 1985). Helliwell further states that a healthy, vigorous tree could withstand removal of up to 50 percent of

(a)

(b)

PHOTO 6.6 Live crown ratio is an important criteria for selecting codominant trees for retention in groups. Trees with less than a 30 percent live crown ratio in (a) have declined and/or failed. Trees with a live crown ratio greater than 50 percent (b) are the best candidates for preservation (photos courtesy of Jim Barborinas).

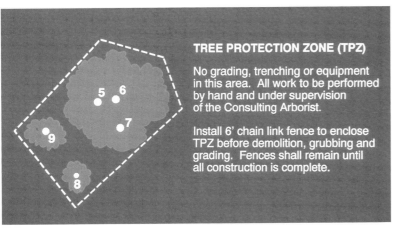

PHOTO 6.7 The tree protection zone is the area around the tree or groups of trees in which no grading or construction activity may occur.

its roots without dying, although there may be stability problems if all the roots on one side are severed.

Field application of this standard is limited by a significant unknown—what is the full extent of the tree's root system? Rooting patterns are highly variable, so it is difficult to know at what point 30 to 50 percent of the roots have been impacted.

A variety of guidelines have been suggested for determining the size of the protection zone for individual trees.

- **Dripline method.** Protect the area within the dripline for broad-canopied trees, or up to 1 1/2 times the dripline for narrow-canopied trees (Photos 6.8a, b).

- **Tree height method.** Protect a circular area with the radius equal to the height of the tree. Miller et al. (1993) recommend a "critical root radius" that is 40 percent of the height of the tree for trees in stands with narrow crowns.

- **Trunk diameter method.** For every inch of trunk diameter at 4 1/2 feet above grade, allow 1 to 1 1/2 feet of space from the trunk (Coder 1995, Harris 1992).

- **Site occupancy method.** Assign an "effective root colonization distance": predict the expected diameter of the tree in ten years. Multiply that diameter by 2.25 to yield the distance of protected area from the trunk (in feet) This method considers the tree's increasing need for root space as it grows (Coder 1995).

The dripline method is the most commonly used method to determine tree protection zones (Photos 6.8a,b). Based on a typical root structure, even limiting construction and grading to outside the dripline could still lead to removal of over half the tree's roots. Yet most vigorous, broad-canopied trees survive well if the area within the dripline is protected. Indeed, for some species, when the tree is in prime condition, it may be possible to encroach some distance within the dripline without extensive damage to the tree. That determination must be made by a qualified consultant familiar with the species and its response to construction.

Some problems arise when using the dripline as an indicator for the tree protection zone. Leaning trees whose trunks are located at one side of the canopy clearly have many support roots away from the lean and beyond the canopy. Obviously, narrow-canopied trees, such as Lombardy poplar (*Populus nigra* 'Italica') or Italian cypress (*Cupressus sempervirens*) would not be adequately protected, nor would narrow-crowned, closely spaced trees growing in stands.

The wide variation in root distribution and tree response (given the species, age, and size of the tree), as well as many site variables, means that general tree protection guidelines based on dripline or tree height are not very useful. The dripline can be successfully used in communities in which tree retention focuses on broad-canopied trees, such as oaks. A more appropriate

PHOTO 6.8 For broad-canopied trees, the dripline may represent an adequate tree protection zone (a). For narrow-canopied, codominant trees, however, the dripline may not provide a large enough tree protection zone (b). Given the size of the tuliptrees in (b), the tree protection zone, defined by the dripline, was inadequate.

guideline is trunk diameter because the size of the tree protection zone is adjusted for the size of the tree, independent of canopy conformation. Coder (1995) suggests that a minimum of 6 feet should be protected around a tree, regardless of its diameter.

The British Standards Institute (1991) developed tree protection guidelines, based on ranges in trunk diameter, that considered the age and vigor of the tree. That system acknowledges that old trees and those of low vigor are less tolerant of construction impacts and, therefore, need a larger protection zone. We adapted the BSI method to include species tolerance to impacts (see Appendix B for species list). The optimum tree protection zone is calculated based on the species tolerance to impacts (good, moderate, or poor) and the age of the tree (young, mature, overmature) (Table 6.2). This system acknowledges that a mature walnut can tolerate less disturbance than a young ash. The protection zone should be increased by 25 to 50 percent for low vigor trees, although retention of low vigor trees is discouraged.

This approach is intended to be a guide for planning adequate space around trees, not an absolute rule. It is a tool to help the design team. There certainly will be times when it is not possible to retain the optimum tree protection zone around each tree to be preserved. The consultant then must evaluate the minimum tree protection zone that would prevent the death, decline, or instability of the specific tree (see Chapter 8).

When young trees are retained, consideration should be given to the future needs of those trees for rooting space as they mature. Coder's (1995) site occupancy method described above can be used to estimate future space requirements.

Design Guidelines

The consultant further helps the design team by providing

CALCULATING THE OPTIMAL TREE PROTECTION ZONE

1. Evaluate the species tolerance of the tree: good, moderate, or poor (refer to Appendix B).

2. Identify tree age: young, mature, or overmature.

3. Using Table 6.2, find the distance from the trunk that should be protected per inch of trunk diameter.

4. Multiply the distance by the trunk diameter to calculate the optimum radius (in feet) for the tree protection zone.

Examples
A healthy 60-year-old, 30" diameter California black walnut (*Juglans hindsii*) (poor tolerance, mature age):

1.25' x 30" = 37.5' radius tree protection zone

A 15-year-old, healthy, 13" diameter Raywood ash (*Fraxinus* 'Raywood') (good tolerance, young age):

0.5' x 13" = 6.5' radius tree protection zone

Table 6.2 Guidelines for optimal tree preservation zones for trees of average to excellent vigor (modified from the British Standards Institute 1991). Refer to Appendix B for species tolerance.

Species tolerance	Tree age	Distance from trunk feet (per inch trunk diameter)
Good	Young (<20% life expectancy)	0.5'
	Mature (20–80% life expectancy)	0.75'
	Overmature (>80% life expectancy)	1.0'
Moderate	Young	0.75'
	Mature	1.0'
	Overmature	1.25'
Poor	Young	1.0'
	Mature	1.25'
	Overmature	1.5'

guidelines and standards for project planning. The following actions should be taken by the consultant during the design phase. Not all items are applicable to all projects.

1. Plot accurate trunk locations and driplines of all trees and/or tree stands to be preserved within development areas on all plans for the project. Include tree preservation notes on all plans. (Note: When stands of trees will be preserved well away from construction areas, it is not necessary to plot accurate trunk locations. The conformation of the stands and notes regarding their protection should be included.)

2. Identify a tree protection zone for each tree in which no soil disturbance, including stripping, is permitted. Specify that the natural grade shall be maintained within the tree protection zone. Specify that no storage, dumping of materials, parking, construction trailers, underground utilities, fires, etc. be allowed within the tree protection zone without approval of the consultant.

3. Require that any plan affecting trees be reviewed by the consultant. This requirement should include (but not be limited to) plans for demolition, erosion control, improvement, utility and drainage, grading plans, landscape, and irrigation.

4. Specify that special foundation, footing, and pavement designs be employed to minimize root interference when structures must be placed within the tree protection zone.

5. Require utilities (electric, gas, cable TV, telephone, water, drains, sewer) to be routed outside the tree protection zone.

6. Indicate that landscapes be designed to exclude trenching for irrigation lines within the tree protection zone and that no irrigation be applied within 5 feet of the trunks of protected trees. (Note: The irrigation limits will vary from project to project.)

7. State that any new plantings within the tree protection zone must be designed to be compatible with the cultural requirements of the retained tree(s), especially with regard to irrigation and nitrogen application. (Note: In locations where native trees are adapted to a period of summer drought, a requirement for no summer irrigation and exclusion of specific types of plantings such as turf or flower beds may be appropriate.)

8. If excavation must occur within the tree protection zone, specify that the consulting arborist will determine where tunneling, hand work, and root pruning are required. Require that root pruning be completed before grading begins. (Note: This is included to forewarn the design team and owners that nonroutine construction methods may be required to successfully retain the tree.)

9. Stipulate that surface drainage not be altered so as to direct water into or out of the tree protection zone unless specified by the consultant as necessary to improve conditions for the tree.

10. Require that site drainage improvements be designed to maintain the natural water table levels within tree retention areas, and that such improvements be designed to maintain the natural volume and seasonal distribution of water in tree retention areas. If water must be diverted, permanent irrigation systems should be provided to replace natural water sources for the trees.

SUMMARY

Design professionals typically do not know what it takes to keep trees alive; that information must be communicated by the consultant. The consultant works with the team to help develop a project that provides adequate space for trees that have a potential to be an asset to the site for years to come. That is accomplished by selecting trees suitable for retention based on several characteristics: tree health, tree structure, species ability to tolerate injury, and tree age and longevity.

To assist the design team in allowing adequate space around trees, the consultant identifies a tree protection zone in which no equipment, storage, dumping, grading, or excavation is allowed. The size and conformation of the tree protection zone depends on several factors including species sensitivity to impacts, health and age of the tree, root and crown conformation, and development constraints.

Finally, the consultant provides the design team with guidelines to help them plan the project while protecting trees. These guidelines require accurate trunk locations of specific trees, exclusion of structures and utilities from the tree protection zone, and sustaining normal water supply for trees. When these requirements cannot be met, the guidelines should indicate that special design considerations or construction techniques may be required.

Once the preliminary design is prepared, the consultant examines the plans for adherence to the guidelines, evaluates specific impacts to trees (Chapter 7) and prepares recommendations for design modifications, as needed (Chapter 8).

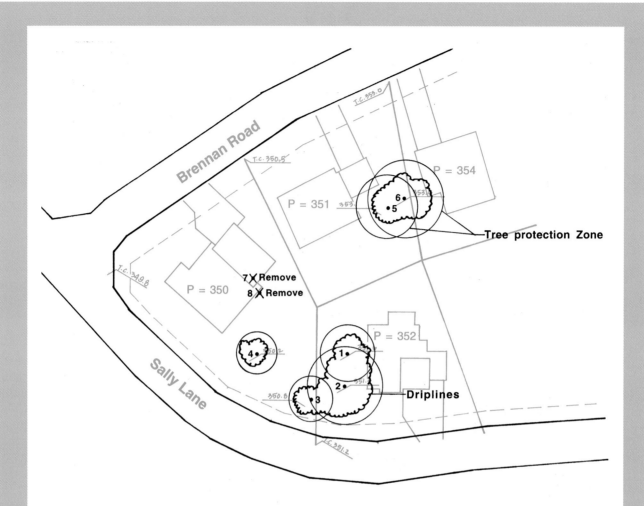

After completing the tree survey, the consultant determines which trees are suitable for retention. Trees #7 and #8 are not suitable due to poor health and structure. The tree protection zones for the trees to remain are determined and plotted. Using that information, the project designers attempt to place site improvements outside the tree protection zone. (Refer to Table 6.2 for tree protection zone guidelines. All trees in this example are mature.)

Tree#	Species	Trunk diameter	Construction tolerance	Tree protection zone (radius)
1	Douglas-fir	20"	Moderate	20'
2	Douglas-fir	30"	Moderate	30'
3	Western red cedar	24"	Good	28'
4	Red alder	12"	Poor	15'
5	Hemlock	18"	Poor	23'
6	Hemlock	28"	Poor	35'
7	Red alder	15"	unsuitable for retention; remove	
8	Red alder	4"	unsuitable for retention; remove	

REFERENCES

Anderson, L.M., and J. Barrows-Broaddus. 1989. Inexpensive ways to improve homebuilders' tree survival. *Journal of Arboriculture* 15(1):13–16.

Barborinas, J. 1995. Urban Forestry Services, Inc. Mt. Vernon, WA. Personal communication. May.

Barrell, J. 1995. Pre-development tree assessments. In *Trees and Building Sites*, G.W. Watson and D. Neely, eds. Savoy, IL: International Society of Arboriculture.

British Standards Institute. 1991. *Guide for Trees in Relation to Construction*. BS 5837:1991.

Coder, K.D. 1995. Tree quality BMPs for developing wooded areas and protecting residual trees. In *Trees and Building Sites*, G.W. Watson and D. Neely, eds. Savoy, IL: International Society of Arboriculture.

Dunster, J.A. 1995. Effective tree retention in new developments. In *Trees and Building Sites*, G.W. Watson and D. Neely, eds. Savoy, IL: International Society of Arboriculture.

Harris, R.W. 1992. *Arboriculture: Integrated Management of Landscape Trees, Shrubs and Vines*. 2nd ed. Englewood Cliffs, NJ: Prentice Hall. 674 pp.

Helliwell, D.R. 1985. *Trees on Development Sites*. Romsey, England: Arboricultural Association. 18 pp.

Matheny, N.P., and J.R. Clark. 1994. *A Photographic Guide to the Evaluation of Hazard Trees in Urban Areas*. 2nd ed. Savoy, IL: International Society of Arboriculture.

Miller, N.L., D.M. Rathke, and G.R. Johnson. 1993. *Protecting Trees from Construction Damage: A Homeowner's Guide*. NR-FO-6135-S. St. Paul, MN: Minnesota Extension Service. 13 pp.

Peepre, J.S. Undated. *Saving Native Trees in the Lower Mainland*. Vancouver, BC: J.P. Peepre & Associates.

Evaluation of Impacts to Trees

The goal of a tree preservation program is to hold construction impacts to a level the trees can tolerate. It is impossible to retain trees on a construction site without the trees incurring some degree of either injury or change in their environment. When anticipated impacts are too severe, the plans must be changed or the tree removed. The consultant's ability to determine the severity of impacts and to evaluate the tree's prospects for survival is key to successful tree preservation.

Evaluating impacts to trees involves two components. The first is determining what activity might occur around the tree based on the site development plans and specifications. The second is evaluating the effects of direct injury to individual trees, as well as sitewide changes that affect long-term health and structural stability. This information, in combination with knowledge of the tree resource, allows the consultant to determine the potential for preservation of each tree.

EVALUATING IMPACTS FROM DEVELOPMENT PLANS

The type of construction that will occur around existing trees and how it will be executed have a great influence on tree survival and growth. By thoroughly examining construction plans and specifications, communicating with the project's design professionals, and corroborating the information in the field, the consultant can obtain a clear picture of what changes to the site will occur. In fact, the consultant must understand and be able to communicate those changes long before construction begins. Once plans are finalized, limited opportunity exists to significantly reduce impacts around trees.

To evaluate the impacts that will occur to trees, the consultant must examine all of the plans and specifications that describe the activities that will take place during development, from demolition and site clearing to postconstruction maintenance (Table 7.1) (also see Chapter 4). Applicable items may include

- demolition plans
- site plans
- improvement plans
- grading plans
- drainage and erosion control plans
- landscape construction, planting, and irrigation plans
- utility plans
- construction plans and documents
- geotechnical (soil) reports and maps

Sections

The ability to draw and explain sections is a valuable skill for evaluating the impacts of development on trees. Sections are drawings that translate the plan view (looking down) onto a vertical view (looking from the side) (see Chapter 4, Figure 4.2a,b). A section is drawn by plotting distance along a section line on the plan onto a horizontal scale and the elevation onto a vertical scale (Figure 7.1).

Sections are helpful for visualizing and communicating the cumulative impacts on trees (Figure 7.2). The sections should include any trenches that will be dug to install utilities or other underground improvements and should show their intended depth. Similarly, over-excavation to prepare subgrade for roads or footings, keyways at the toe of slopes, etc. should be shown. Several types of plans, details, and drawings may need to be studied to compile all the necessary information onto a section. When construction will occur all around a tree, more than one section may be required.

Pavement

When evaluating impacts from pavements, refer to details and sections that describe what the pavement section will be. The primary factors to evaluate are the thickness of the pavement section and the

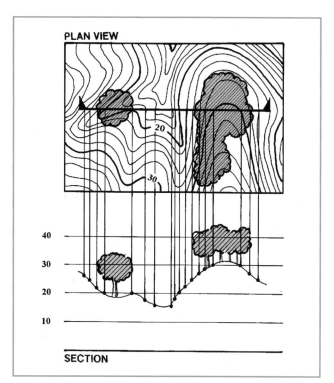

FIGURE 7.1 Sections (bottom) translate the plan view drawing (top) onto a vertical view. First draw a straight line through the portion of the plan to be examined. Starting at one end of the section line, plot the elevation of the contour that intersects the line onto the vertical axis of the section drawing. The contour interval on this topographic plan is 2 feet. Using a scale, measure the distance between the first contour and the next. Measure that distance on the section and place a dot at the appropriate elevation. Continue measuring and plotting each successive contour along that line. When all points have been measured and plotted, connect the points with a line. This shows natural ground along that line. Locate tree canopies and plot them. Note that the width—but not the height, number of trees, or trunk locations—can be estimated from the plan. That information must be collected in the field and can then be plotted onto the section.

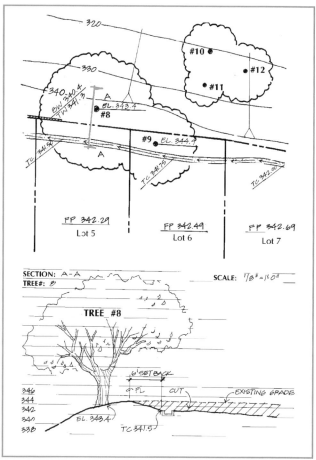

FIGURE 7.2 Sections are helpful for visualizing and communicating the cumulative impacts that will occur to trees. Determine where the section will be drawn. The section line (A-A) should go through the tree trunk and intersect the area of greatest impact at right angles. The arrows at the ends of the section line point in the direction of the view. Plot the natural ground as described in Figure 7.1. Then, using the same procedure, plot future grades. Where spot elevations are given, interpolate between the points (e.g., the bottom of the swale at the section line is between 341.5 and 341.75). Measure the distance from the trunk to the pad and plot its elevation (342.29). The difference between existing grade and finished pad shows the amount of cut required.

compaction necessary to prepare the subgrade (see "Pavement" in Chapter 4). The thickness of the pavement section is determined by adding the thickness of each layer (surface, base, subbase, and subgrade). The section depth can be subtracted from the finish elevation of the pavement to determine the depth of cut to prepare the pavement. For example, a residential street with a finish surface flush with the surrounding ground still will have to be cut 18 to 24 inches below grade (Photo 7.1). Even if the pavement is placed on a fill, roots in that area will be cut as the native soil and fill are processed (see "Creating a Stable Building Base" in Chapter 4).

Utilities

The degree of impact from underground utility installation depends on the depth of excavation and the distance from the edge of the trench to the tree. Improvement plans usually show the location of water, storm water, power, cable, and sewer lines (Figure 7.3). The lines on the plan indicate the center line of

the pipe. To accurately assess impacts, estimate the width of the installation trench. Note the locations of drain inlet features and the corresponding surface elevations. Also determine where the manholes and outfalls will be and the excavation required to construct them. Refer to street improvement and profile plans for that information. Discuss with the installing contractor the width of the trenches and how they will be dug.

Be sure to consider splice box proximity to existing trees. Often, the locations of these structures can be adjusted if this issue is addressed early in the design phase.

For utilities that will be installed by tunneling under tree roots, determine the size and location of launching and recovery pits (holes dug to place tunneling equipment at appropriate depth) and pot holes. This information will not be on the plans, but must

TABLE 7.1 Sources of site development and construction information for evaluating impacts to trees.

Type of impact	Plans to inspect
Pruning	Architectural drawings, elevations showing structure height Construction plans and details Fire department clearance requirements Contractor equipment and clearance requirements Utility plans (for overhead clearance requirements)
Grade changes	Site/improvement plans Grading plans Landscape plans
Excavation and compaction, engineered fills	Site/improvement plans and details Geotechnical report Grading plans and details Utility plans and details
Roads, pavement	Site/improvement plans and details Street profile plans and details Geotechnical report
Changes in water table	Drainage plans Geotechnical report Grading plans Site/improvement plans Landscape and irrigation plans
Diversion of streams	Grading plans Site/improvement plans Topographic map
Increased exposure	Demolition plan Grading plan Site/improvement plan

PHOTO 7.1 Although the grade of this street was designed to be the same as the tree, extensive impacts were incurred because a 2-foot-deep cut was required for the pavement section (pavement + base rock + compacted subbase). To allow room for construction, the cut is made approximately 12 inches from the back-of-curb.

be obtained from the installing contractor.

If utilities are to be placed above ground, consider the location of power poles, how they will be installed, and clearance requirements from adjacent trees for installation equipment as well as to maintain clearance for the lines.

ASSESSING DIRECT INJURY TO TREES

After the impacts have been fully described, the next step is to evaluate the effects of those changes on tree health and stability. When development occurs close to trees, some injury will be incurred. To estimate the amount of damage, the consultant must consider the architecture of the tree—both above and below ground—and ask two questions: How much of the crown and roots will be removed or damaged in the construction process? If the optimum tree protection zone cannot be maintained, will the impacts be too severe for the tree to survive? (See "Identifying a Tree Protection Zone" in Chapter 5.)

Assessing Changes to the Tree Crown

Site development may require pruning tree canopies to avoid conflicts with structures or access. While any tree retained in use areas should be pruned to clean the crown and minimize the potential for structural failure, additional pruning may be required as well. Common requirements include pruning to:

- **Raise the crown for vertical clearance over streets and walkways.** Roads and driveways with emergency vehicle access usually require at least 14 feet of clearance; for pedestrian use, at least 8 feet of clearance.

- **Raise the crown for vertical clearance for construction equipment.** Ask the construction contractor what equipment will be used under the tree and how much clearance is required. In some cases it may be possible to tie back branches to provide temporary clearance without pruning off limbs.

- **Provide clearance for a structure.** Estimates can be made from elevation drawings of the structure.

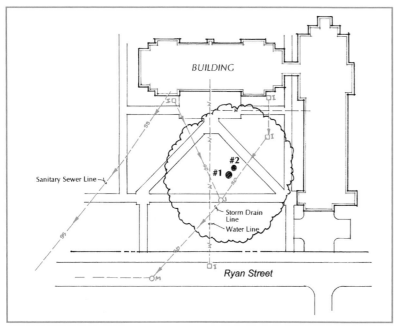

FIGURE 7.3 It is imperative to examine placement of water (W), sewer (SS), storm drains (SD), inlets (I), junction boxes (J), and manholes (MH), as well as other utilities when evaluating impacts to trees. Although the site plan for this project considered the trees (#1 and #2), the utility placement clearly did not. The consultant should offer suggestions to the site engineer and designer to avoid trenching close to trees, such as alternate routes and/or tunneling under roots.

Estimates should be confirmed once the footing is staked in the field. Measure from the finish floor elevation, not natural ground. Consider what equipment will be used, whether construction scaffolding is necessary, and any additional clearance required. Also determine chimney and vent locations and the need for clearance zones for safety.

■ **Provide line-of-sight for street signs, lights, satellite dishes, etc.**

Trees vary in their responses to pruning. Nevertheless, the greater the amount of foliage removed and heartwood exposed from pruning, the greater the impact to the tree. When extensive pruning is required, consider the effects the reduced leaf area, increased exposure to sun, and change in weight distribution will have on the tree. For trees that must be pruned heavily, a thick, corky bark provides greater protection than thin bark from subsequent sunburn and dieback.

Assessing the Extent of Injury to Tree Roots

When excavating close to trees, it is important to know how much root damage will occur, not only from a standpoint of tree survival, but also for stability. Assessing the extent of root injury is a seemingly simple task of overlaying the root pattern with the grading and construction plans and estimating what will be removed. Unfortunately, root systems are neither symmetric in form nor entirely predictable in their depth.

The general conformations of root systems is described in Chapter 2. For an isolated tree growing in a uniform, favorable soil, the roots generally extend great distances—as much as two to three times the diameter of the crown. Typically, most roots are within the top 3 feet of soil, and most of the fine roots active in water and nutrient absorption are in the top 12 inches. Some species form vertical sinker roots that grow downward from larger horizontal roots near the trunk of the tree (usually within 8 to 12 feet). These roots explore deeper layers of aerated, moist soil and are particularly important in water absorption when surface soils are dry. Sinker roots are not usually present in shallow or poorly aerated soil.

These are only general patterns, however. Experience excavating roots has taught us that roots deviate from that "typical" form quite often. Frequently we are surprised to dig along one side of a mature tree and encounter no woody roots. In another situation, we may be some distance away and find many large roots. Root depth in uniform soils is particularly difficult to predict. Contrary to the root model, we sometimes see large roots (greater than 4 inches diameter) deeper than 3 feet. Roots are opportunistic and grow in soil fractures where oxygen is present.

Root patterns are affected by topography, characteristics of the soil or substrate, and underground obstructions. Certainly, trees growing adjacent to building foundations or in plazas have different rooting conformations than those in dense forests, open savannas, or along creeks. We have seen 6- to 8-inch-diameter roots of riparian trees 8 feet below the ground surface in deep, gravely loam soils. In contrast, Tipton and Barba (1997) found roots of two desert tree species confined to the top 16 inches of soil, even though the soil was deep and uniform. Trees growing on shallow soils on fractured bedrock may have heavy fans of roots in the rock fractures at great depth. Trees in areas with high water tables may have shallow roots above the saturated soil.

On previously developed sites, the highly variable nature of soils in urban areas and the presence of underground obstructions make it even more difficult to predict root spread. Large roots are often found in the interface between pavement and base material (Photo 7.2). Root spread and depth can be limited by layers of compacted soils, underground utilities, foundations, and other features (Photo 7.3). The most important rooting characteristic to consider is that, in most situations, roots are shallow and asymmetrical in spread. Therefore, developing a

The impacts to roots remaining under engineered fill have yet to be quantified. No research has been conducted to evaluate root and tree growth following compaction of fill soils to engineering standards. At this point, we assume that in most cases, roots under engineered fill will gradually die and not be replaced at similar densities because of disruptions to normal air exchange and moisture. When either a cut or fill occurs near trees, therefore, the root system is immediately reduced. Furthermore, the soil area available for root growth is permanently restricted.

Fill soil placed around tree trunks is very damaging for many species, particularly if an irrigation system is part of the landscape plan. The fill holds moisture around the trunk and alters normal gas exchange. Some trees develop adventitious roots in the fill soil that keep the tree green and alive. Over time, however, disease and decay may develop in the original root crown and buttress roots. The tree becomes structurally unstable and is prone to failure. These are responses that may not be fully expressed for many years following construction (Photos 7.7a,b)

The consultant must communicate clearly with the geotechnical engineer to determine how all fills and compacted areas will be prepared. Requirements vary widely depending on the specific characteristics of the site soil, import fill material, the structure to be supported, and construction design and techniques.

Surface Soil Compaction

Surface soils often are compacted on construction sites as a consequence of equipment moving over the soil. The most severe damage occurs in the top 4 to 6 inches of soil (Craul 1994), but soil structure can be affected deeper as well. The degree of compaction depends on several factors: amount and type of pressure and vibration applied, presence and depth of surface organic litter, soil texture and structure, and the soil moisture level (Adams and Froehlich 1981). Compaction is maximized on soils with a wide range in particle size (e.g., loamy), with weak structure, and with a moisture level at field capacity on which a heavy, vibrating weight is applied in a small area. The greatest increase in soil density occurs during the first few equipment passes over the soil (Adams and Froehlich 1981).

Compacted soils affect tree growth by restricting root activity and development. When macropores that allow air and water movement are collapsed, a larger proportion of micropores are left through which air and water move slowly. The result of the increased density is slow water infiltration, reduced drainage, poor aeration, and increased potential for erosion. The tree response is reduced root activity, increased resistance to root penetration, less mycorrhizal activity, and increased susceptibility to root diseases (Harris 1992). Furthermore, dense soils present a physical impediment to root elongation.

Pavement

The negative effects most commonly attributed to pavements over roots are decreased exchange of gases and moisture. Actually, most pavements, even concrete and asphalt, are somewhat porous because of expansion joints and the multitude of small cracks that form. Under low load-bearing pavements where the pavement section is thin and subgrade compaction is minimum, root growth actually may be enhanced. Wagar and Franklin (1994) found warmer temperatures and higher soil moisture under concrete sidewalks than in adjacent turf. Certainly the significant problems with tree roots displacing sidewalks, curbs, patios, parking lots, and roads attest to the roots' ability to grow and proliferate beneath some pavements.

Nevertheless, when pavement is installed over existing tree roots, significant injury occurs as soil is excavated and compacted to build the pavement section (see "Pavement" in Chapter 4). The immediate impact of pavement installation is water stress from root removal. The long-term effect is chronic stress from a reduced root system. The soil for some depth under the pavement is compacted and new roots are

PHOTO 7.7 Placing fill soil around the trunk of mature trees can lead to disease and decay in the root crown. This tree (a) had been buried in 18 inches of fill for 20 years before symptoms of decline in the crown led an arborist to remove the fill and examine the base of the tree. Over 80 percent of the circumference of the root crown below the fill had been killed by the root rot *Armillaria* (b).

unlikely to develop in it, although they may grow in the interface between the subgrade and the base, or between the base and the surface material. The ability of new roots to grow under the pavement depends on several factors, including specific soil density, moisture, drainage, aeration, and species root growth characteristics.

Excavation

Excavation is performed when installing footings, foundations, irrigation lines, lights, underground structures, etc. Under normal excavation procedures, when soil is removed, so are roots (see Chapter 8 for alternatives). An immediate reduction in water absorption and possibly reduced stability result. Long-term effects may be chronic water and nutrient stress.

Often building codes and worker safety standards require that shoring be installed in an excavation, or that excavations be sloped to the angle of repose during construction. These requirements are not shown on plans but must be determined in consultation with the contractor.

Irrigation Systems

The impacts from irrigation installation can be both beneficial and detrimental. Installation of irrigation systems can cause extensive damage to trees during excavation of trenches to place pipes underground. The effects of the altered soil moisture regime can also have a negative impact on trees. Native trees that are adapted to a summer dry period often develop root diseases if irrigated during warm months. On the other hand, irrigation can be beneficial for trees that have permanently restricted root systems or for species that require more water than is provided seasonally through rainfall or during dry periods in humid climates.

ASSESSING INDIRECT IMPACTS TO TREES

Indirect impacts to trees are the result of changes to the site that may cause tree decline, even when the tree is not directly injured. It is important to consider large-scale alterations to the area as well as the specific changes that will occur around trees. Sitewide changes that may affect trees include diverting runoff and storm water, creating retention and detention ponds, relocating streams or making improvements to streams, lowering or raising water tables, altering the capacity for soil moisture recharge, removing vegetation, and damming underground water flow. In considering these types of site changes, it is necessary to compare the natural vegetation and drainage patterns as depicted on the topographic map with the overall site changes that are shown on the conceptual or rough grading map.

Hydrology, soil science, geology, and topography are at the core of evaluating sitewide changes. Consultants need to know enough about these disciplines and how they interact to ask the right questions of the appropriate professionals. Predicting how individual trees and stands will respond to indirect impacts of site development often is quite difficult for several reasons. First, the interactions among soils, geology, hydrology, and topography are complex and intimately tied. Alter one component and others may be affected. Second, adequate information about the soil profile and ground water may not be available, so reliable assessments may not be possible. Third, localized variations in geology and hydrology can lead to problems that may not be revealed in the geotechnical sampling. Finally, sites primarily are engineered to protect structures, not vegetation. Additional planning and engineering may be required to protect biologic systems.

Diversion of Runoff

Runoff is surface water from rainfall, snow melt, or irrigation. Runoff often is diverted into a storm drainage system and is lost as a water source to recharge soil moisture. Vegetation that relies on surface water for its moisture supply can, therefore, be affected. On the other hand, diversion of water towards trees can be detrimental. Trees intolerant of increased soil moisture may decline, develop root diseases, and eventually die (Photo 7.8).

Most communities have specific requirements regarding treatment of runoff. For instance, in some areas, runoff must not be directed from one property onto another. To protect from erosion of slopes, water may be collected at the top, at benches, or at

PHOTO 7.8 Changes in water supply can have long-term effects on trees. This V-ditch is designed to divert runoff into the storm drain system. In the process, the water supply to the downhill trees is changed.

the toe of the slope. Vegetation downslope would then receive less water than normal.

Drainage outfalls also should be considered. If water is collected on site, transported in a storm drainage system, and then released at one or more points into a natural water feature (e.g., stream or river), the effects on the riparian vegetation should be considered. Construction impacts would occur to the vegetation near the outfall where bank protection must be installed (Photo 7.9).

PHOTO 7.9 Installing culverts and stream bank protection requires cutting into the bank. Large tree roots often parallel the banks and are quite shallow. The presence of roots and the amount of bank disturbance required for construction should be evaluated.

Where and how runoff is collected and outfall locations should be shown on grading and/or site plans. From that information, the effects of diversion on the vegetation can be evaluated.

Water that runs over streets, parking lots, and industrial-use areas may accumulate de-icing road salt, organic solvents, heavy metals, or other materials that could affect life downstream. In most cases, the concerns are for animal life rather than effects on vegetation. Plants may accumulate heavy metals, nitrites, and nitrates in the foliage and fruit that can affect animals feeding on them but may not harm the plant. Filtering systems or devices often are required to remove specific impurities.

In some locations, runoff must be contained on site either temporarily (detention) or permanently to recharge the ground water (retention). This may require construction of ponds, or above- or below-ground reservoirs. Siting of the ponds is influenced largely by natural topography, soils, and hydrology. Effects of detention or retention on adjacent vegetation also depend on those factors. For example, if retention ponds are placed in areas that do not allow percolation, the water table can rise and kill existing trees. If properly located, however, there should be no ill effects because the water table would not be altered significantly. Detention ponds that store

water during seasons when water tables normally are high and when the trees are dormant would not be detrimental. Conversely, detaining water next to trees in leaf during a naturally dry season could kill them.

Detention and retention ponds that take advantage of natural features, for instance low-lying areas and existing ponds or lakes, and also maintain the normal water-table levels and seasonal soil moisture, will have the least negative impacts to existing vegetation. Furthermore, they can enhance wildlife habitat.

Diversion of Streams

Small streams and creeks are sometimes diverted to facilitate site construction. Altering the course of waterways will affect vegetation receiving its water supply from the stream. Realigning a channel, for example, to cut off an oxbow would isolate the vegetation in the oxbow from the water source (Photo 7.10). Similarly, intercepting creek flow upstream and diverting the water into a storm drainage system would affect trees downstream. Identifying this impact early in the design process provides the option to alter the design or provide alternative methods of supplying adequate water to the downstream trees.

Stream Improvement

Installing drop structures, placing road fills over streams, and changing the stream gradient all have the potential to alter water movement and cause erosion and siltation within a riparian system. Those changes affect the long-term health and survival of vegetation dependent on the stream. The interactions are often complex and may not be fully expressed for many years. Some specific situations include the following.

- Culverts in road fills must be placed to accommodate low flows, which may be below the

PHOTO 7.10 During development, the creek was realigned, cutting off this oxbow from the channel. Because the natural source of water for these trees was removed, they had to be irrigated during dry months.

ground surface. If the culvert is placed too high, water will back up behind the fill, slowing down water movement and increasing siltation behind the fill and possibly damaging surrounding vegetation.

- Drop structures may be installed to slow water movement. Small ponds may be created behind the structures, increasing siltation behind the structure and decreasing it downstream.

- Increasing stream gradient by lowering the grade downstream usually will either increase downcutting (incising) of the stream or increase stream bank erosion. Either of these actions may decrease tree stability in the area if roots are undercut.

- Deepening channels may lower the surrounding water table and affect adjacent vegetation.

Changes in Water Table

The water table is the upper surface of the zone in which macropores are saturated with water; water tables may vary seasonally. Rather than a flat, static surface, the water moves down a gradient. Its depth varies, depending on the structure of the soil and rocks through which it flows. In uniform soils, the water table generally conforms to the surface topography, but the slopes are more gentle and uniform (Sowers and Sowers 1951). A perched water table may form in soils that have impermeable strata (Figure 7.4). Swamps are created where the water table intersects level ground.

Sites with high water may have to be drained to allow construction (Figure 7.5). Retention of native vegetation rarely is compatible with drained sites. Trees usually decline quickly and become a liability to the owner. A better solution is to retain the native vegetation in areas where normal water levels can be maintained.

Utility trenches can cause localized drops in the water table if the bottom of the trench is below the water table (Yingling et al. 1979). Water will flow through the gravel layer at the bottom of the trench.

A spring or seep is formed where the water table intersects the surface on a hillside (Sowers and Sowers 1951). These may be drained for development by intercepting the flow before it reaches the surface. Any vegetation that relies on that groundwater may be adversely affected (Figure 7.6).

Most mature trees will tolerate some fluctuation in water level, and can even withstand a permanent drop of a few feet.

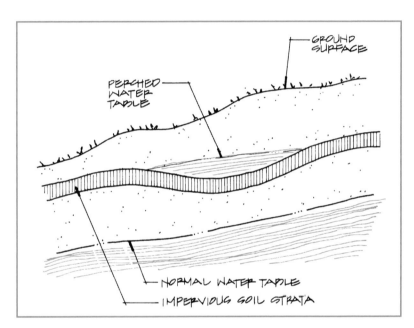

FIGURE 7.4 Water tables are underground "streams," or zones of saturation, that move downhill. They generally conform to the ground topography but slope more gently. Perched water tables can form in the depressions underlain by impervious soil strata.

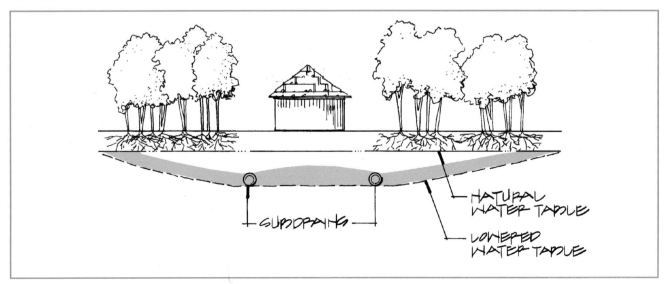

FIGURE 7.5 Survival and regeneration of retained trees may be compromised if site development requires lowering the water table.

Natural reproduction of the vegetation, however, may require higher water tables during establishment and early growth. If water tables are affected to the extent that the vegetation will not reproduce, a group of trees might be retained for a few years, but the resource has not been conserved. An active planting program that includes introduction of species tolerant of the new water regime would be necessary to maintain vegetation in that location.

Change in Capacity for Soil Water Recharge

In most locations, native vegetation relies on precipitation to recharge the soil moisture in the root zone. Several site changes may adversely affect that process:

- covering the soil with pavements or other impervious materials
- capturing runoff and diverting it into storm drains
- compacting soils, thereby reducing their ability to absorb precipitation
- removing leaf litter and vegetation that slows water movement and enhances percolation

Removal of Vegetation

Partial removal of vegetation can have several effects on remaining trees. First, exposure to wind and sun of the remaining trees is increased, and humidity within that stand will be lower. The trees may be more prone to sunscald, drought, and heat stress—chronic stresses that are usually expressed in slower growth, dieback, decline, and increased susceptibility to some pests and diseases. Furthermore, trees that develop in stands with tall crowns and thin, poorly tapered trunks will be more likely to fail when support of their neighbors is eliminated and their potential for trunk and root failure will increase (see "Tree Growth in Forests and Woodlands" in Chapter 2).

Another effect of vegetation removal is erosion hazard of unprotected soil. Siltation of streams and associated impacts to riparian vegetation can occur.

Damming Underground Water Flow

Underground structures such as footings, basements, subterranean buildings, and retaining walls at cuts may intercept impermeable layers in the soil on which water perches. If adequate drainage is not provided, the water table uphill may gradually rise and interfere with tree roots (Figure 7.7). This type of damage usually takes a period of time to be recognized and diagnosed. Even shallow road fills and pipelines placed in wetland forests will alter water tables on either side of the road and cause tree death (Boelter and Close 1974).

The best way to assess underground flow is to thoroughly review the geotechnical reports. Pay particular attention to sites with highly layered soils with impermeable layers. Consult with the geotechnical engineer or hydrologist about the effects construction may have on underground water flow.

DETERMINING TREE RESPONSE TO IMPACTS

The final step in assessing impacts is to evaluate how the tree will respond biologically to the changes

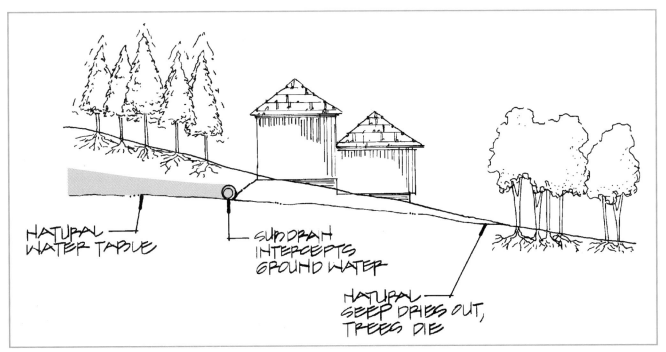

FIGURE 7.6 Seeps or springs can be drained by intercepting water flow uphill. Vegetation supported by the seep would be adversely affected.

FIGURE 7.7 Building roadways, retaining walls, basement foundations, and other underground structures can intercept underground water flow. As the water level rises, trees may be damaged.

imposed. Will it survive with adequate health and structural stability to be an asset to the site, or will it become a liability?

Assessing Cumulative Impacts to Trees

One of the guiding principles of tree preservation during development is "impacts to trees are cumulative." Rarely does the tree experience just one impact that affects its growth. Rather, a series of changes and site manipulations occur to which the tree must respond and adapt. First, roots are injured and the site microclimate altered by clearing. Then further changes occur during grading and installation of improvements. Construction of adjacent structures causes another series of impacts. Finally, finish grading and landscaping further alter the tree's environment. The consultant must anticipate and protect the tree from a multitude of events and impacts.

The challenge for the consultant is to determine when impacts will be too severe for the tree to survive, not only in the short term, but also in the long term. Although there are no quantitative methods to calculate that critical level, the ability to predict how a given tree will respond is developed with experience. As a starting point, the consultant should compare planned activity with the optimum tree protection zone for each tree (see Chapter 5). Knowledge of the species in general, combined with specific information about the individual tree's age and condition, will lead to the best determination.

Factors Affecting Tree Response to Impacts

Trees vary widely in their ability to tolerate injury and changes in their environment. Some trees with more than half of their major buttress roots severed

survive, while others with a seemingly small amount of root damage die. There are a number of factors that influence how trees respond to impacts, including species, age, health, and structural development.

Species Tolerance to Impacts

There is great variation in construction tolerance among species. Unfortunately, these variations have not been tested, so the consultant must rely on experience to guide evaluation of species response to a given impact (see Appendix B for species tolerance lists). In northern California, for example, coast live oak (*Quercus agrifolia*) and London planetree (*Platanus x acerifolia*) have relatively good construction tolerance, while California black walnut (*Juglans hindsii*) and southern magnolia (*Magnolia grandiflora*) do not (Table 7.2).

Some of the factors that appear to influence species tolerance to impacts are the ability to restrict water loss; tolerate periodic water stress; generate new roots; develop roots in dense, poorly aerated soils; compartmentalize decay; alter relative growth of roots, shoot, and trunk; tolerate heavy pruning; and resist stress-related pests.

Influence of Age and Longevity

Many tree preservation efforts focus on old heritage trees. While these have the greatest visual impact and emotional appeal to the public, significant constraints affect their successful, long-term retention.

As trees age, several biological changes occur that affect their ability to respond to injury and site changes (see "Tree Development Over Time" in Chapter 2). Growth slows and the capacity for efficient compartmentalization is reduced. Young, vigorous trees are better able to generate new tissue and adapt to a new environment than old trees. Helliwell (1985) described the difference clearly:

> When lifted from the ground in the nursery, trees often lose as much as 75 percent of their root system, and yet they survive and grow. At the other end of the scale, the loss of even 5 percent or 10 percent of the root system of a fully mature tree which has reached its maximum size is likely to result in some dieback in the crown and make the tree more prone to attack by pests and diseases.

Influence of Health and Vigor

Recovery from construction injury requires energy. Healthy, vigorous trees have greater carbohydrate reserves to generate new roots, compartmentalize wounds, and quickly react to pest attack than declining trees have. For these reasons, healthy trees are

TABLE 7.2 Sample matrix comparing retention decisions for a relatively tolerant species (London planetree, *Platanus* x *acerifolia*) with those for a sensitive species (California black walnut, *Juglans hindsii*).

	Tree condition		
Intensity of impact	Poor	Moderate	Good
For London planetree:			
Low	Remove	Preserve	Preserve
Moderate	Remove	Preserve	Preserve
Severe	Remove	Redesign/preserve?	Redesign/preserve?
For California black walnut:			
Low	Remove	Preserve?	Preserve
Moderate	Remove	Remove	Redesign/preserve?
Severe	Remove	Remove	Remove

better able to tolerate a given impact than weak or otherwise stressed trees.

Influence of Time of Year

The time of year that impact occurs could influence tree response. Immediate water stress from root injury certainly would be less severe during the fall or winter than during the summer because of lower transpiration demand. Given our knowledge of tree biology, it may be helpful to avoid impacts when carbohydrate reserves are low. Svihra (1997) recommends avoiding wounding trees and root pruning during the late spring and early summer when new leaves are expanding and wood is forming. Recovery may be quicker if root disturbance occurs between late summer and late winter when carbohydrate reserves are at their highest.

In practice, the consultant rarely has control over when grading and construction occur. Most often, in fact, construction must take place when weather is favorable, which usually coincides with the tree's period of active growth.

Ability to Ameliorate Impacts

Finally, the mitigation of adverse impacts should be considered. If a high level of maintenance (such as irrigation, fertilization, and pest and weed control) can be provided, a tree might tolerate more root removal than one that must depend upon natural rainfall and compete with other vegetation. Similarly, irrigation will help a tree that has had roots removed, but little can be done to help a tree that has had half its foliage removed to provide clearance for a building (see Chapter 10).

Because limited treatments exist to ameliorate construction injury, the best treatment is to protect rather than to repair.

TREE SURVIVAL

Projects that consider trees early in the design process and during construction rarely cause short-term tree death. The exceptions have been when significant mistakes were made in design (e.g., grades on plans were incorrect) or when construction activities were careless or negligent.

Rather than dying quickly, trees may decline gradually and eventually reach the point that removal is required (see Chapter 10). This pattern is typical when impacts are indirect and cause chronic stress to which the tree never adapts. The tree ultimately may be killed by insects or diseases that successfully attack it. Examples of site changes that can cause chronic stress include:

- changes in hydrology of site
- changes in soil quality
- changes in soil surface (crusting, hydrophobia, erosion, etc.)
- restrictions in soil area available for root development
- addition of toxic materials to the soil
- direct injury to root system
- increased exposure to sun and/or wind
- excessive reduction in leaf area, such as from heavy pruning
- large mechanical wounds, which interrupt sap flow and lead to decay

Long-term survival, over a period of years and decades, involves interaction of several biological, physical, and environmental factors. In many cases, survival appears to involve the tree's tolerance to periodic water stress and ability to generate new roots. Another important characteristic is the ability of the tree to compartmentalize decay that develops

IMPACT TOLERANCE

How much impact a tree can tolerate depends on many factors.

The specific tree
  age
  health
  structure
  species tolerance
  previous exposure to wind, sun
  vigor

Changes that will occur
  amount of root injury
  degree of restriction of root area
  amount of reduction in leaf area
  degree of change in soil structure,
    moisture, and drainage
  new exposure to sun, wind
  change in microclimate
  exposure to toxic chemicals
  competition with other plants
  number and depth of mechanical wounds

Ability to ameliorate impacts
  possibility for irrigation
  potential for reducing compaction
  potential for increasing soil aeration
  potential to protect from stress-related
    insects and diseases
  potential for improving drainage

TREE IMPACT EVALUATION CHECKLIST

Tree characteristics
  Species tolerance to impacts
  Tree age/longevity
  Tree health and vigor
  Root depth and extent
  Conformation of canopy
  Structural stability

Site development
  Disturbance that will occur within rooting area
    Distance from trunk and depth of
      excavations (e.g., grade changes,
      underground utilities, pavement
      section, footings, foundations)
    Root area exposed to compaction
    Root area covered by pavement
    Pruning requirements (e.g., clearance,
      overhead utilities)
    Irrigated landscape (compatibility
      with tree, trenching for system)
    Removal of adjacent vegetation (root
      damage, changing microclimate,
      exposure)

  Disturbance to overall site that could affect tree
    Diversion of runoff (to or from tree)
    Installation of subdrains or drainage
      swales (lowering water table)
    Altered drainage patterns that increase
      erosion
    Altered drainage patterns or vegetation
      removal that increases siltation
    Walls or foundations damming
      underground water flow
    Road fill over streams and check dams that
      alter water flow and sedimentation
    Change in capacity for soil water
      recharge

from construction-related wounds. A tree may survive the short-term changes adequately but become structurally unstable over a period of years as decay develops in the roots, trunk, or crown.

SUMMARY

Evaluation of impacts requires considering both the specific changes that will occur on the site and the response of the tree. The consultant examines construction plans and specifications, communicates with the project's design professionals, and corroborates information in the field when assessing impacts. Factors to consider are:

- Direct Injury to the Tree
  - changes to the crown, primarily from pruning to provide clearance and access
  - the extent of injury to roots caused by creation of a stable building base, excavation, grading, and installation of pavement, utilities, and irrigation systems

- Indirect Injury to the Tree
  - diversion of runoff
  - diversion of streams
  - stream improvements
  - changes in water table
  - change in capacity for soil water recharge
  - removal of adjacent vegetation
  - damming of underground water flow

Tree response to a given impact varies widely depending on the species, age, and condition. That variability makes it difficult to develop quantitative measures for tree survival that are applicable to a wide range of species and site conditions. The consultant must combine knowledge of tree biology, site influences, and construction practice to evaluate impacts to trees. If the impacts are determined to be too severe, the plans must either be redesigned to reduce injury, or the tree removed. The next chapter discusses specific design techniques to help minimize impacts to trees.

REFERENCES

Adams, P.W., and H.A. Froehlich. 1981. *Compaction of Forest Soils*. Pacific Northwest Extension Publication. (Oregon State University, Washington State University, and University of Idaho). PNW 217. 13 pp.

Boelter, D.H., and G.E. Close. 1974. Pipelines in forested wetlands. *Journal of Forestry* 72:561–563.

Craul, P.J. 1994. Soil compaction on heavily used sites. *Journal of Arboriculture* 20(2):69–74.

Harris, R.W. 1992. *Arboriculture: Integrated Management of Landscape Trees, Shrubs and Vines*. 2nd ed. Englewood Cliffs, NJ: Prentice Hall. 674 pp.

Helliwell, D.R. 1985. *Trees on Development Sites*. Romsey, England: Arboricultural Association. 18 pp.

Majeskie, G. 1993. Milwaukee, WI. Personal communication.

Mann, G. 1990. Redwood City, CA. Personal communication.

Tipton, J., and J. Barba. 1997. The root systems of planted southwestern trees. In *Turf and Ornamentals Research Summary*. Tucson: University of Arizona Agricultural Experiment Station.

Sowers, G.B., and G.F. Sowers. 1951. *Introductory Soil Mechanics and Foundations*. New York: Macmillan.

Svihra, Pavel. 1997. *Time Tree Care Practices to the Advantage of the Tree by Synchronizing Treatments with Annual Variation of Stored Carbohydrates*. University of California Cooperative Extension, unnumbered leaflet.

Wagar, J.A., and A.L. Franklin. 1994. Sidewalk effects on soil moisture and temperature. *Journal of Arboriculture* 20(4):237–238.

Yingling, E.L., C.A. Keeley, S. Little, and J. Burtis, Jr. 1979. Reducing damage to shade and woodland trees from construction activities. *Journal of Arboriculture* 5(5):97–105.

CHAPTER

8

Minimizing Impacts
and Preparing Specifications

Up to this point in the development process, the consultant has evaluated the resource, identified trees or stands suitable for preservation, provided planning input, and evaluated potential impacts to trees. The design team has used this information to prepare preliminary site plans. The consultant has a clear idea of the activity that will occur near each tree and has estimated whether or not the trees will acclimate.

The next step, modifying preliminary designs to reduce impacts to trees, is the subject of this chapter. The design modification phase is closely linked to evaluating impacts. As the consultant reviews the development plans, conflicts between the design and tree preservation are identified. The consultant discusses those areas of concern with the design team, conveying what the trees need to survive. The design team responds with revised drawings, and the consultant determines if the changes are adequate for tree preservation. Design changes to plans normally are prepared by the project engineer, architect, or landscape architect—not the consultant.

Once the design has been finalized, plans are prepared that include specifications for how the work is to be performed during demolition, grading, and construction. All treatments, protective devices, work procedures, and other measures to protect trees must be included in the specifications.

MODIFYING DESIGN TO REDUCE
IMPACTS TO TREES

As the consultant evaluates impacts to trees, he or she should consider design alternatives to reduce overall effects (Table 8.1). Options often exist for foundation design, utility alignment and installation, and grade transitions. The consultant can help the design team select the option that best allows the required construction, yet minimizes injury to trees.

To be effective in considering design alternatives, the consultant must be familiar with grading and construction techniques and practice. Refer to Chapter 4 for a discussion of common terms and designs.

Grade Transitions

How grade transitions are handled can significantly affect root disturbance. Several common techniques, requiring different amounts of excavation, can be employed. Most commonly, natural grade is sloped to finish grade, usually at a 2:1 or 3:1 slope (see Chapter 4, Figure 4.9). The soil must be compacted to engineer standards (usually 95 to 98 percent compaction) to a specified depth. The slope can be covered with plants to protect it from erosion. If the slope is finished with stone riprap or concrete cribbing, excavation into the slope is required to anchor the materials.

An alternative is to construct retaining walls to reduce the horizontal distance for the grade change (Figure 8.1). Retaining walls are expensive to build and can require considerable site disturbance to construct, so the consultant should be confident of the benefit before recommending their use. For small grade changes (1 to 2 feet), it often is less damaging to slope to natural grade rather than to construct a retaining wall. For larger grade changes, however, the wall can increase the distance natural grade is maintained by several feet (Photos 8.1a–c).

Retaining walls require footings to support them. Wall design dictates the amount of excavation required to construct the footing and wall. If the excavation for the footing will be into the root area, additional impacts will be imposed on the tree. In some cases, particularly when fills will be retained, impacts can be reduced by designing the wall with a discontinuous footing using piers (see Chapter 4, Figure 4.12e). The size and spacing of the piers must be

TABLE 8.1 Major construction impacts, construction activities, and methods to minimize tree damage (adapted from Matheny 1989).

Impacts to tree	Construction activity	Methods/treatments to minimize damage
Root loss	Stripping site of organic surface soil before grading; clearing unwanted vegetation; demolishing existing structures	■ Restrict stripping of topsoil around trees. ■ Install fences to protect trees from injury. ■ Any woody vegetation to be removed adjacent to trees to remain should be cut at ground level and not pulled out by equipment; otherwise, root injury to remaining trees may result. Arborist may be needed for adjacent tree removal if crowns are intertwined.
	Lowering grade, scarifying, preparing subgrade for fill and structures	■ Before grading, root prune tree at edge of excavation to depth required. Spoil beyond cut face can be removed by equipment sitting outside the dripline of the tree. ■ Use retaining walls with discontinuous footings to increase the distance that natural grade is maintained from trunk.
	Preparing subgrade for pavement	■ Use paving section requiring a minimum amount of excavation (e.g., reinforced concrete instead of asphalt). ■ To minimize thickness of pavement section, design traffic patterns to avoid heavy loads adjacent to trees. ■ Increase strength of pavement to reduce reliance on subgrade for strength (e.g., use extra reinforcement in concrete, geotextile under base material).
	Excavation for footings, walls, foundations	■ Avoid continuous footings adjacent to trees. ■ Use pier foundations with grade beam above grade instead of slab foundations. ■ Orient piers to avoid major roots. ■ Excavate by hand, bridging roots where possible. ■ Where roots must be removed, cut cleanly with appropriate equipment (e.g., rock saw). Do not use equipment that pulls and shatters roots (e.g., backhoe, trencher).
	Trenching for utilities, drains	■ Avoid open trenching in root area. ■ Tunnel under roots, if possible. If not, within root area, dig trench by hand, bridging roots greater than 1 inch diameter. ■ Consolidate utilities into one trench.
Wounding crown of tree	Injury from equipment	■ Fence trees to enclose low branches and protect trunk. ■ Clean up wounds as soon as possible.
	Creating clearance for building, traffic, construction equipment	■ Prune to minimum height required prior to construction. ■ Consider minimum height requirements of construction equipment and emergency vehicles over roads. ■ All pruning should be performed by a Certified Arborist and conform to ANSI pruning standards.

TABLE 8.1 (continued)

Impacts to tree	Construction activity	Methods/treatments to minimize damage
Unfavorable conditions for root growth; chronic stress from reduced root systems	Compacted surface soils	■ Fence trees to keep traffic and storage out of root area. ■ Provide a storage yard and traffic areas for construction activity well away from trees. ■ Where traffic cannot be diverted, protect soil surface with thick mulch or steel plates.
	Spills, waste disposal (e.g., paint, oil, fuel)	■ Fence trees to exclude dumping. ■ Clean up accidental spills immediately.
	Soil sterilants (herbicides) applied under pavement	■ Use herbicides safe for use around trees. Adhere to label requirements.
	Impervious pavement over soil surface	■ Minimize use of pavement within dripline.
Inadequate soil moisture	Rechannelization of stream flow; redirecting runoff; lowering water table; lowering grade	■ Consider system to allow low flow through normal stream alignments and provide bypass into storm drains for peak flow. ■ Provide supplemental irrigation in similar volumes and seasonal distribution as would normally occur.
Excess soil moisture	Underground flow backup; raising water table	■ Fills placed across drainage courses must have culverts placed at the bottom of the low flow so that water is not backed up upstream. ■ Study the geotechnical report for ground water characteristics to see that walls and fills will not intercept underground flow.
	Lack of surface drainage away from tree	■ Where surface grades are to be modified, make sure that water will flow away from the trunk (i.e., that the trunk is not the lowest point). If tree is in low point, design drain system with least impact to roots.
	Irrigation of exotic landscape	■ Match irrigation requirements of tree and understory landscape to avoid over irrigation.
Increased exposure	Thinning stands, removal of undergrowth	■ Retain forest trees in groves rather than singly. ■ Maintain natural undergrowth.
	Reflected heat from surrounding hard surfaces	■ Minimize use of hard surfaces around trees. Monitor moisture needs where water use is expected to increase.
	Pruning	■ Avoid severe pruning where previously shaded bark would be exposed to sun. Where pruning is unavoidable, provide protection to bark from sun.

Zoning, grading, and construction standards and requirements may inadvertently restrict tree preservation efforts. Flexibility in applying standards can improve conditions for trees. Some examples follow.

Policies/requirements	Modifications to enhance tree preservation
Maximum allowable slope 3:1	Allow steeper slope (e.g., 2:1) next to trees to increase tree protection zone
Street width requirements (e.g., 30 feet)	Reduce street width (e.g., 24 feet)
Street pavement section requirements	To minimize excavation into root zone, use thinnest pavement section possible
Placement of utilities in right-of-way	Where there are conflicts with trees, allow placement of utilities in street
Large pad overbuild requirements (e.g., 5 to 7 feet) for slab foundations	Reduce pad overbuild to minimum possible (e.g., 2 to 3 feet)
Large turn-around areas for fire truck access	Consider alternative methods of providing emergency services, such as placing fire hydrants at entrance and end of cul-de-sacs
Zoning density requirements	Allow flexible density over site, such as higher density in areas without trees in exchange for retaining trees in open space
Structure setback requirements from property lines	Allow flexible setbacks to provide adequate space where needed for trees
Storm water runoff requirements	Allow credits in runoff calculations when trees are retained on site
Requirement that irrigation lines be placed underground with 8-inch minimum cover	When within the tree protection zone, allow placement of lines on surface with mulch covering
Sidewalks placed at back of curb or at specified distance from curb	Allow sidewalk width and alignment to vary to minimize impact to trees or place sidewalk on only one side of street, opposite tree(s)

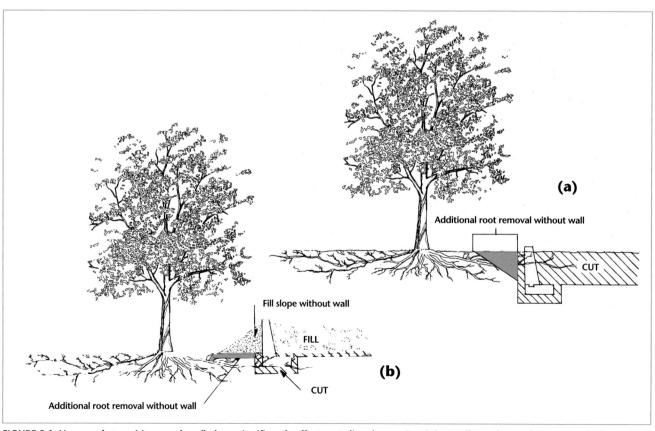

FIGURE 8.1 How grade transitions are handled can significantly affect root disturbance. Retaining walls can be used to reduce the horizontal distance for grade changes for a cut (a) or a fill (b).

When evaluating the benefit of discontinuous footing for walls, consider:
     rooting depth of the tree
     excavation required to construct footing
     size and spacing of piers
     equipment clearance and access
          requirements

PHOTO 8.2 Retaining walls can be stepped down the slope to reduce the mass of a single wall.

PHOTO 8.1 Retaining walls can increase the distance retained at natural grade around trees. A variety of materials can be used to construct the wall including wood (a), concrete block (b), and rock (c).

PHOTO 8.3 A vertical cut can be retained with a system of "soil nailing." (Photo courtesy of Spence Rosenfeld.)

considered when evaluating soil and root disturbance. Also consider the type of equipment that will be used to drill the holes for the piers and what the clearance requirements will be if operating under the tree canopy. If the wall retains a cut, there is no benefit from a discontinuous footing where the cut extends below the root zone.

Where the grade is raised, excavation towards trees is minimized with L-type footings when the footing extends towards the fill; in cuts, towards the cut (see Chapter 4, Figure 4.12a). For grade changes over 5 feet, two or more small walls can be stepped down the slope to reduce the mass of a single wall (Photo 8.2). Typically, walls more than 4 to 5 feet in height must be designed by an engineer.

Another method of retaining a cut is by "soil nailing" walls (Photo 8.3). The wall is built from the top down without disruption of the area behind the wall, so vegetation beyond the cut is not disturbed. The technique uses steel tendons grouted into drilled holes to reinforce the ground. Pneumatically applied concrete (shotcrete) supports the excavation's face between the soil nails.

Most arboriculture literature emphasizes the importance of retaining natural grade around the base of the tree. Where the grade will be raised, a common treatment is to build a wall a few feet from the trunk to create a well around the tree. An aeration system composed of pipes in a wagonwheel design is placed on natural grade (beneath the fill) and connected to vertical pipes extending through the fill to the new soil surface. We question the utility and effectiveness of this treatment. The aeration systems are expensive to construct, and to date there is no scientific evidence that it has a positive effect on the tree. Furthermore, the resulting "aerated fill" is unstable from an engineering perspective, so it is an unsuitable base for any structure. If the fill will not support a structure, why is it there? On the other hand, if the fill is constructed to engineering specifications, not only will existing roots be destroyed, but it is unlikely that the aeration system will help new roots establish (see Chapters 4 and 7 for further discussion). A better solution for the tree, project economics, and site design would be to consider the following options.

- Adjust surrounding grades to match the base trunk elevation as closely as possible.

- Where the grade must be raised, determine the location of the structure on fill, plus required overbuild. If working within the tree protection zone, consider placing a retaining wall at that location.

- If the tree will be in a low area that will collect water, install a drain as far from the tree as possible (near the retaining wall). If necessary, fine-grade by hand to create flow to the drain.

- If an adequate tree protection zone cannot be retained, consider removing the tree, creating the required grade changes, and planting appropriate trees for that location.

Pavement

Most arborists consider pavements harmful to trees because they restrict movement of water and air in the root zone. Many tree protection guidelines recommend use of pervious rather than impervious pavement under trees.

Where impervious pavements are used, some type of venting or aeration system often is recommended. A simple design is to cut 1-to-2-inch-diameter, regularly spaced holes through the pavement once it has set (Photo 8.4). Another design lays a base of gravel, topped by sections of PVC pipe standing on end, with the pavement poured around it. After the concrete is set, the pipe is cut off at finish grade, filled

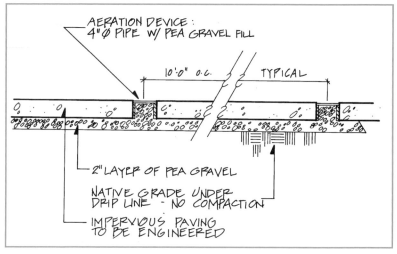

PHOTO 8.4 Several methods have been designed to increase the permeability of concrete paving. In this case, the concrete was laid on 2-inch pea gravel. Holes were cored through the concrete and filled with pea gravel (inset).

with gravel, and capped with a grate (Figure 8.2). A linear or grid pattern can be created with aeration strips, which are narrow gaps between sections of concrete that are filled with gravel. This design might cause problems with pedestrian footing. Placing many expansion joints in the pavement would accomplish the same thing.

There is no scientific evidence that these treatments improve conditions for tree growth. Actually, most pavements are reasonably porous, particularly after they have aged. Both asphalt and concrete develop many small cracks that allow water and air to penetrate. Concrete pavements are designed with expansion joints that create gaps. The soil under pavement is usually moister than that exposed to the air, and roots of many planted trees certainly have no trouble growing under it—hence, the problems with root heaving and cracking pavements.

FIGURE 8.2 Detail of an aeration system for concrete paving. It is unknown whether this and similar treatments actually improve conditions for root growth. We consider it more important to minimize subbase excavation and compaction.

The most important impacts to minimize are root removal and soil compaction that occur as the area is prepared for installation of the pavement. Where pavement must encroach within the tree protection zone, consider the amount of excavation required to create the pavement section and the degree of compaction required for the subbase. To the extent that pavement designs can minimize those stresses, impacts to trees can be reduced. This may be accomplished in several ways (also see Chapter 4).

- Use the pavement type requiring the thinnest section. Concrete usually requires a thinner section than asphalt or interlocking pavers.

- Place heavy-load corridors that require a thicker pavement section away from trees.

- Adjust finish grades so that the pavement section is built on top of natural grade, using a "no-dig" design (Figure 8.3). Some edge treatment will be necessary to retain the pavement section. The pavement will be higher than the surrounding grade. If the grade differential is a concern, mulch can be placed on the soil surface to meet the grade of the pavement.

- Increase the strength of the paving material so that is does not rely on a compacted subbase for strength. This is usually accomplished by putting extra reinforcing material in the surface layer.

- To reduce subbase compaction requirements, place a geotextile fabric at the bottom of the pavement section to protect from displacement into soft soil.

Heavily reinforced concrete requires the thinnest pavement section and least amount of subbase compaction, but it is expensive. Brick or interlocking pavers on sand are usually considered the best pavement under trees because they are more pervious than concrete or asphalt, although frost can heave these in cold-weather areas (Figure 8.4). Pavers may require more excavation to install than concrete unless a no-dig design is used for above-ground installation. Preparation of a compacted base usually is required. Pavers are more subject to displacement by roots and soil movement than concrete, although repair is easier because small sections can be removed and replaced. (See Case Study #4).

The amount of pavement a tree can safely tolerate depends on how much root interference occurs during installation and the potential for the tree to re-establish roots under the pavement. If the driveway and parking area on a residential lot can be installed simply by

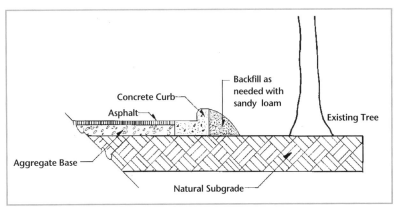

FIGURE 8.3 A "no-dig" type of pavement places the pavement section atop natural grade, thereby minimizing root disturbance and soil compaction. Extra reinforcement in the pavement and use of a geotextile under the base material may be needed to increase the stability of the pavement. (Adapted from a detail provided by Mary Ann Beale, City of Charlotte, North Carolina.)

smoothing and hand-tamping the surface soil, then it may be possible to cover a portion of the optimum tree protection zone. On the other hand, pavements for major streets that require 2 to 3 feet of excavation for subbase preparation, curb, sidewalk, and perhaps underground utilities, must be more respectful of the tree.

Curbs require excavation for construction (see Chapter 4, Figure 4.10). Rolled curbs require the least amount of excavation. Where significant root injury would occur to install the curb, it may be possible to place the curb on top of the pavement (Photo 8.5). A steel bar holds the curb in place (Figure 8.5). A gutter is not constructed.

Footing and Foundation Design

The amount of soil excavation and compaction required varies greatly with footing and foundation type and, therefore, affects the degree of impact to adjacent trees. The consultant should discuss design options with the engineer to determine which design would have the least impact to trees.

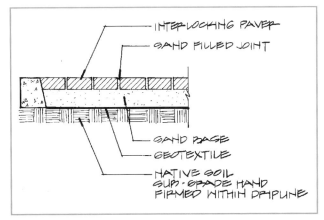

FIGURE 8.4 Brick or interlocking pavers on sand often are recommended as pervious paving. Use of geotextile under the sand and hand-firmed subgrade can minimize root impacts.

PHOTO 8.5 Excavation into the roots of this tree was avoided by placing the pavement section on top of existing grade and constructing the curb on top of the pavement (see Figure 8.5 for construction detail). (Photo courtesy of Howell Beach, Robert E. Marvin & Associates.)

PHOTO 8.6 Footings can be designed to span over tree roots, as shown with this brick wall. A metal plate spans the distance between footings (inset) (see also construction detail, Figure 8.6).

Where structures must be placed close to trees, some alternative footing designs may be considered.

- Use custom footing (designed by an engineer) in the vicinity of the tree that bridges over the roots (Photo 8.6; Figure 8.6).
- Cantilever the structure, so the building extends outwards from the footing.
- Install a raised foundation with discontinuous footing (piers).

Sometimes the least disruptive method is the pier foundation with grade beams placed above grade (see Chapter 4, Figure 4.11e). The diameter, depth, and spacing of the piers, as well as the size and weight of the equipment needed to drill the piers, define the potential for root injury. Compared to other foundation types, this design may provide little benefit to trees if piers are large and closely spaced. If the pier is

end supported, the excavation must be as wide or wider than the base of the footing. If the beams are not specified to be above grade, a trench will be dug, usually to 18 inches, to construct it, potentially severing many roots.

Structure Design

Several factors about the design of structures adjacent to trees should be considered in order to minimize impacts to the tree. This primarily involves minimizing pruning requirements by considering potential interference of the tree's canopy with the structure—both in the present and with future growth.

- Make allowances for future growth of the tree in trunk girth and canopy height and spread.
- Locate fireplaces to avoid chimneys near canopies or locations where tree litter will accumulate. Local requirements for clearance may vary.
- Consider window location for desired views. Close views would be enhanced by mature trees, while distant views may place the tree in conflict with the view and lead to excessive pruning.
- If the structure will be within the dripline, consider limiting the height of the structure to avoid excessive pruning.
- Consider placement of solar panels or passive solar heating relative to trees.
- Consider line-of-sight for communication devices (e.g., satellite dishes).

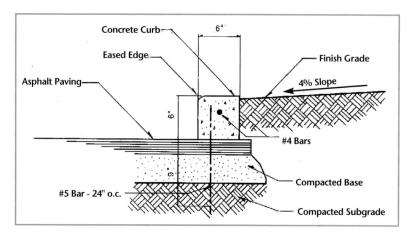

FIGURE 8.5 Placing the curb on top of the edge of pavement may reduce excavation into the root system compared to a typical curb detail. The curb is held in place with steel bars. (Adapted from detail provided by Howell Beach, Robert E. Marvin & Associates.)

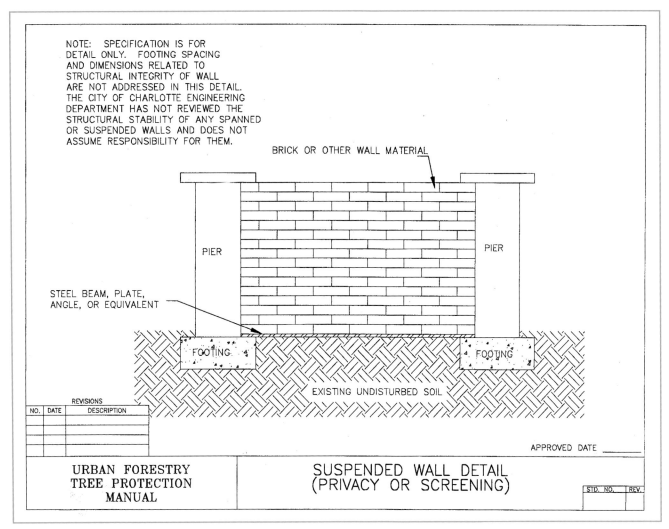

NOTE: SPECIFICATION IS FOR DETAIL ONLY. FOOTING SPACING AND DIMENSIONS RELATED TO STRUCTURAL INTEGRITY OF WALL ARE NOT ADDRESSED IN THIS DETAIL. THE CITY OF CHARLOTTE ENGINEERING DEPARTMENT HAS NOT REVIEWED THE STRUCTURAL STABILITY OF ANY SPANNED OR SUSPENDED WALLS AND DOES NOT ASSUME RESPONSIBILITY FOR THEM.

BRICK OR OTHER WALL MATERIAL

PIER

PIER

STEEL BEAM, PLATE, ANGLE, OR EQUIVALENT

FOOTING

FOOTING

EXISTING UNDISTURBED SOIL

REVISIONS
NO.	DATE	DESCRIPTION

APPROVED DATE _____

URBAN FORESTRY TREE PROTECTION MANUAL	SUSPENDED WALL DETAIL (PRIVACY OR SCREENING)	STD. NO.	REV.

FIGURE 8.6 Detail of a wall suspended between piers. (Detail provided by Mary Ann Beale, City of Charlotte, North Carolina.)

Utilities and Services

The consultant must work with the designer and engineer to devise utility installation methods and alignments that minimize tree impacts while allowing the contractor to complete the job. The ideal situation would exclude all service and utility lines within the tree protection zone. This ideal is not always possible to attain.

Locations of electrical distribution lines and water, sewer, and storm drain main lines are usually included on plans. Less frequently, service line locations are shown. Often the route of the service lines from the service drop to the structure is determined by the installing contractors while in the field. Usually the utility contractor plots the alignment in the field by running the service drop lines from the connection point off the distribution line to the structure being serviced with the shortest, straightest line possible. Line placement may need to be adjusted to avoid existing trees. When the location of lines is important to tree protection, the consultant should make sure project plans and specifications include all utilities.

The number of trenches required to install utilities can be reduced by placing multiple lines in joint trenches. When utilities must go through a grove, place all lines through a single corridor. Because service lines are installed by different contractors (e.g., telephone, cable TV, electric, gas), joint trenches must be accessible when each is at the site.

Water, storm drain, and sewer lines require specific amounts of separation (see "Utilities and Services" in Chapter 4) and must tie into existing systems, so the possibilities for relocation are limited. The main lines usually are placed in the street. If trees are along the street edge, lines might be placed closer to the opposite side. It is usually more difficult and expensive to tunnel main lines under root systems than under service lines because of the depth and large diameter of the pipes.

Utility junction boxes, splice boxes, and manholes require extensive excavation and large equipment to install. They should be placed outside the tree protection zone.

MODIFYING CONSTRUCTION PROCEDURES TO MINIMIZE IMPACTS TO TREES

A number of construction work procedures can help protect trees from unnecessary damage. The care with which work should be performed around trees should increase the closer the encroachment to trees. Appropriate work procedures therefore will vary depending on the type or methods of construction and distance from the tree (Table 8.2).

Clearing and Demolition

Clearing, grubbing, and demolition activities usually involve very large equipment that moves across the land, removing everything in its path. If trees, soils, and other resources are to be preserved, methods must be devised to accomplish the clearing tasks without damaging that which is to remain. Those methods often increase the amount of time necessary to clear the site, so the contractor should be aware of the requirements before the job begins. This means having adequate specifications when the contract is let.

Construction specifications should include any special protection or work procedures needed during clearing operations (see "Preparing Specifications" later in this chapter). Additionally, the consultant should meet with the clearing contractor to discuss and agree on haul roads, access routes, stockpile locations, and equipment operation methods. Large equipment requires plenty of space in which to maneuver. If the operator cannot safely move within the allotted space, the equipment should be downsized.

Damage to trees often occurs during the clearing and demolition phases. The best procedure is to have tree protection measures in place before any equipment enters the site. All trees should be fenced, enclosing any understory as well (Photos 8.7a–d). Then the contractor can safely perform the work. The understory can be cleared or groomed by hand at a later date. This procedure works well where trees are widely spaced, and when preserving groups of trees.

For sites with dense vegetation, or when vegetation or structures to be removed are close to trees that will remain, it may not be possible to fence before clearing. In this situation, we have had the best results with a combination of clearing by arborists and demolition contractors, using both equipment and hand labor. We remain on site most of the time to help make decisions about operations and ensure that work proceeds according to plan. The following procedure has been effective.

1. The engineer stakes the edge of grading and the construction zone.

2. The consultant walks the edge of the grading, painting trees to be removed and flagging trees to remain along the line. Trees that should be removed by an arborist rather than the demolition contractor are marked a different color.

3. The consultant meets with the demolition contractor and arborist to review work procedures, haul routes, stockpile locations, and work areas.

4. The arborist removes vegetation, placing brush and wood in designated locations for disposal

TABLE 8.2 Work procedures vary with extent of impact. The greater the amount of intrusion into the optimum tree protection zone, the greater the care that must be taken (see Table 6.2 to determine optimum tree protection zone).

Location of tree protection zone	Work/design procedures
Optimum tree protection zone maintained	No restriction of activity outside tree protection zone.
One-third or less of optimum tree protection zone impacted	Pruning needed for clearance must be determined. Special designs (e.g., discontinuous footings and foundations, reinforced pavement to reduce pavement section and span soft soil) may be recommended to minimize root interference. Where excavation will occur, roots should be pruned at the edge of excavation before soil removal. Consultant may determine that the tree is unlikely to survive or will become unstable and, therefore, recommend removal.
One- to two-thirds of area within optimum tree protection zone impacted	Improvements staked in the field and reviewed by consultant. Location of major roots in direction of improvement determined by consultant. Special designs are required in order to minimize root interference. Roots cut either by hand or with appropriate equipment before excavation, per consultant's recommendation. Consultant may determine that the tree is unlikely to survive or will become unstable and, therefore, recommend removal.

PHOTO 8.7 All trees to be preserved should be fenced prior to demolition or clearing. Fencing may be orange plastic on flanged posts (a), wood (b), or wire. Six-foot chainlink with posts sunk into the ground provides the greatest protection (c). Signs indicating that fences are not to be disturbed and who to contact are helpful (d).

by the demolition contractor. The arborist grinds tree stumps 12 inches below grade.

5. The arborist prunes trees to be retained, according to specifications.

6. For structures, including pavement, that will be demolished within the tree protection zone, temporary trunk protection devices are installed. The contractor uses the smallest equipment possible to accomplish work. The consultant remains on site to monitor work.

7. The consultant identifies the location of tree protection fencing. Fencing is installed.

8. The demolition contractor proceeds with work outside fenced areas.

WHO SHOULD CLEAR UNWANTED VEGETATION AROUND TREES THAT WILL REMAIN?

Site clearing usually is performed by clearing and demolition contractors. They use large equipment (with a big turning radius) that gouges and compacts the soil, damaging trees to be preserved. Such equipment must stay outside the tree protection zone.

Removal of vegetation and structures within the tree protection zone can be accomplished by clearing contractors, if they use methods that will not damage the trees or soil. In most cases, this means use of hand tools only; no vehicles are allowed within the tree protection zone. The clearing contractors should demonstrate experience in vegetation removal and tree felling without damaging protected plants.

When the canopies of trees to be removed are entwined with those of trees to be retained, a qualified arborist should remove the trees. A qualified arborist will avoid damage to remaining trees by first removing the intertwining branches and "piecing down" the tree. The arborist should clear an area adequate to allow maneuvering of contractor's clearing equipment without damaging trees to be preserved.

When construction occurs in woodland situations, trees should be cleared some distance back from the developed area. Coder (1995) recommends removing trees within 30 feet of planned construction because trees in that zone are subject to damage. Trees that lean into the development and declining trees should be removed. For cuts, Yingling et al. (1979) recommend removing trees within a distance of 1 foot back from the top of the cut for each foot depth of cut. Our experience in California oak woodlands is that it is difficult to predict which trees adjacent to cuts will survive and which will die. Most of the death was limited to trees within 5 feet of the cut, even when cuts exceeded 20 feet in depth. It should be noted that desiccation of the soil at the cut face is a significant factor, and the California oaks are adapted to drought conditions. In less drought-tolerant species, a greater distance may be required.

In fill situations, similar guidelines can be used because the fill will first require a cut into natural grade. Desiccation of the cut face is not a factor after fills are placed.

Root Pruning

When excavation will occur near trees, the roots should first be pruned to sever them cleanly. Soil excavation equipment pulls, rips, and shatters roots, causing unnecessary damage for some distance towards the tree.

Root pruning is most efficiently accomplished with root pruning equipment specifically designed for that purpose. Large circular saws used to cut concrete, and rock saws also are effective. The saws must cut through the woody roots to the depth of the required excavation. Root pruning equipment designed primarily for curb and sidewalk repair may cut only 8 to 12 inches deep. Where excavation must occur very close to trees, it may be necessary to dig the soil away with a shovel, then cut the exposed root with a saw. The following procedure is recommended.

1. Stake the edge of excavation.
2. Cut with root pruning equipment 6 to 12 inches outside the staked line towards the tree.
3. If root pruning equipment cannot be used, dig a trench along the staked line. Equipment such as a backhoe can be used until roots larger than 1 inch in diameter are encountered. Then, dig with a shovel.
4. When a root is encountered, expose it by removing soil by hand, and cut it cleanly with a saw at the outside edge of the trench (towards the tree) (Photo 8.8). Cut to a lateral root when possible. Do not paint the cut root end. If excavation is for installation of underground utilities, leave the root intact and thread the lines underneath.

PHOTO 8.8 To root prune by hand, excavate a narrow trench with a backhoe until roots greater than 1 inch in diameter are encountered. Then dig by hand to expose the roots and cut them cleanly with a saw.

5. Replace soil in the trench.
6. Place tree protection fencing at the edge of excavation.
7. Allow grading equipment to operate freely outside the fence area.

Trenching and Tunneling

Trenches should be routed outside the tree protection zone. Soil removed from the trenches should be placed on the side away from trees and replaced as soon as possible. The sides of deep trenches are laid back at an angle for stability (Photo 8.9a). To reduce the width of the trench, the walls could be shored rather than sloped (Photo 8.9b).

Utility trenches should be backfilled with good quality soil within the root area of trees. Geotechnical specifications require compaction to a given percentage. City of Milwaukee trenching guidelines (1995) do not allow concrete, slurry, gravel, stone, sand, or other such materials within the top 4 feet of excavations in the tree border between the curb and sidewalk/property line.

The method by which trenches are routed across root systems of trees can greatly reduce the percentage of roots severed (Table 8.3). For electric, gas, telephone and cable TV, as well as service drops for water and sewer, an alternative to open trenching is tunneling. Tunneling under root systems can greatly reduce both damage to the tree and the cost to repair landscape and other features destroyed in the trenching process.

There are a number of guidelines for determining the distance at which trenching should be replaced with tunneling. The Maryland Forest Service (Yingling et al. 1979) recommends tunneling as soon as roots 1 inch in diameter are encountered. For trees less than 7 inches in diameter, no trenching should occur under the dripline. Helliwell (1985) recommends bridging roots greater than 1½ inches in diameter. Morell (1984) suggests specific distances depending on trunk diameter (Table 8.4). The City of Milwaukee (undated) dictates a minimum tunnel depth of 3 feet for trees less than 8 inches in diameter and a minimum of 4 feet for larger trees.

Tunneling can be accomplished by hand for short distances. A backhoe can be used to dig a trench until roots over 1 inch in diameter are encountered. Excavation is then performed with shovels to expose the roots. Joseph McNeil (1997) had

PHOTO 8.9 Deep trenches are much wider at the top than at the bottom (a). To reduce the width of the trench, the sides can be shored (b).

TABLE 8.3 Underground utility installation methods and their impacts to trees (adapted from Goodfellow 1995).

Installation method	Procedure	Impacts to trees
Cable plow	Heavy knife or plow is drawn through the soil, from the surface to the cable depth. Cable is fed into the void. Most appropriate in rural, open areas where there are few underground obstructions.	Plow severs roots in path. Impact depends on proximity of line to tree.
Open trench	Trench excavated with backhoe or similar equipment, cables placed, and trench backfilled.	Excavation severs roots. Degree of impact depends on trench width, depth, and proximity to tree.
Wheel trench	Narrow trench is cut with a rock-saw trencher in the street or at the shoulder of the road.	Potential for root shattering is reduced because roots are cut, not pulled. Degree of impact depends on proximity and depth of trench.
"Unguided" trenchless techniques	A pneumatic "mole" or steel rod hammers horizontally through the soil, compressing displaced soil out of the way. Conduit or cables are pulled in the void. Requires excavation of launching and recovery pits at both ends of the tunnel. Suitable for short distances.	Minimal impacts to trees as long as as bores are below roots and if launching and recovery pits are outside the root area.
"Guided" trenchless techniques	Similar to "unguided" techniques, except that the tunnel is bored and soil removed, usually by a mechanical cutting head or high-pressure jet. Requires excavation of launching and recovery pits. Standard practice is to "pot hole," or excavate at sites where head encounters obstructions or existing utilities. Impractical in rock.	Minimal impacts if bores are below roots and if launching and recovery pits are outside the root area.

TABLE 8.4 The distance for augering in each direction if trench is located within a particular radius (Morell 1984).

Tree diameter (dbh)	Auger distance from face of tree
0–2"	1'
3–4"	2'
5–9"	5'
10–14"	10'
15–19"	12'
over 19"	15'

success tunneling under the roots of trees to install a 20-inch PVC sewer line at a depth of 10 feet. An open trench was dug 8 to 12 feet from the tree on opposite sides. The backhoe was then used to dig under the trees to connect the trenches, leaving the top 3 feet of soil and roots intact. The pipe was threaded through the tunnel.

There are times, however, when tunneling is not a reasonable alternative. Very rocky soils and slopes are difficult to tunnel. Trees that have large roots extending deep into the soil still will be injured. Sometimes these factors cannot be adequately evaluated during the design phases; final decisions about methods are made during construction. Specifications should indicate that the contractor will be required to use tunneling under certain circumstances so that appropriate costs and equipment are figured into the contract.

Soil Protection

Soil compaction on construction sites is a ubiquitous problem. Soils are compacted intentionally to create stable building bases (see "Grading" in Chapter 4). However, soils also are compacted unintentionally as a consequence of equipment moving across the site. Alakukku (1996) reports that one pass with a high-axle load compacted clay soil to a depth of 16 inches, although Harris (1992) indicates that the most serious compaction typically occurs at a depth of 6 to 8 inches. Turning, starting, and stopping increase the force of the equipment on the soil (Harris 1992). The decreased soil porosity and permeability and increased soil strength limit root growth and function (Craul 1992).

Restoring soil structure is a difficult and slow process, especially when tree roots are present, which means that tilling is not an option (see Chapter 10 for further discussion). The best solution is to protect the soil from becoming compacted; the potential for compaction is eliminated if no traffic is allowed within the root zone.

Sometimes it is necessary for equipment to move across root areas. In such cases, applying a surface mulch can help distribute the weight of the load and minimize soil compaction. Lichter and Lindsey (1994) tested the effects of several surface treatments to minimize compaction from eight passes with a front-end loader. They found that 6 inches of wood chips or 4 inches of ¾-inch crushed gravel placed over the soil surface significantly reduced compaction at depths up to four inches, compared to the unprotected soil. Compaction under plywood sheets (¾-inch construction grade) was not significantly lower than unprotected soil. Placing geotextile under the mulch or gravel did not further reduce compaction but may facilitate cleanup when the temporary road is no longer needed. Depending on future use, it may be possible to leave the mulch in place.

PRECONSTRUCTION TREATMENTS

Before construction starts, a number of activities may be implemented to invigorate trees and thereby increase their tolerance of construction impacts. The applicability of each to a given situation depends on the amount of time available for treatment and tree response before construction begins, as well as the condition of the tree, its history of care, and its potential to respond to treatment. The goal is to maximize stored carbohydrates and the effectiveness of growth regulators in the tree to quickly produce new root, shoot, and adaptive growth and to compartmentalize wounds.

Appropriate treatments should be applied as early as possible because mature trees take time to respond. For example, a full year before construction began, we were able to irrigate, fertilize, and prune a mature turkey oak that had little care previously (see Case Study #4). The tree had a fuller crown, along with better annual shoot growth and color after construction than before.

Irrigation

Providing supplemental irrigation for trees under water stress probably is the single most important treatment. Irrigations should be designed to wet the soil within the tree protection zone to the depth of the root system and to replace that water once it is depleted. Light, frequent irrigations should be avoided.

Early in the project, there may be no ready access to water on the site. One way to irrigate in that situation is to create a 6-inch-high berm around trees, at the edge of the tree protection zone, and fill the basin from a water truck. Alternatively, water could be injected into the soil using a pressure system from a truck-mounted holding tank, although care must be taken to apply water shallowly where roots are present. Irrigations should wet the top 2 to 3 feet of soil.

Fertilization

The need for supplemental fertilization depends on the history of care of the tree. In general, fertilizing is recommended if the tree has been growing slowly or has poor color, or if leaf litter has been removed. Harris (1992) notes that, in most cases, nitrogen is the only element required. Kim Coder (1997) recommends applying ¼ to ½ pound of nitrogen per 1,000 square feet of open surface area within the tree protection zone. Nitrogen can be applied to the soil surface and irrigated in, or injected into the soil as a liquid.

Although fertilizer may be beneficial if applied the season before construction, fertilization of trees during and for at least one year following construction is not advised.

Pest Control

Pests that significantly affect tree health should be controlled both before and during construction. For example, diseases or insects that would defoliate the tree and stimulate production of new leaves at the expense of stored carbohydrates should be controlled. Thresholds for pest populations should consider effects on stored carbohydrates.

Pruning

Pruning should be performed to clean the crown of dead, diseased, crossing, weak, and dead wood, and to provide adequate clearance for equipment and construction. All pruning should be performed by qualified arborists and in accordance with the International Society of Arboriculture's *Tree-Pruning Guidelines* (1995) and/or the ANSI A300 Pruning Standard (1995). In most cases no more than 20 percent of the live foliage should be removed from the tree. Consider the time of year of pruning and the tree's susceptibility to insect and diseases (Table 8.5). General specifications for pruning are provided in the section on preparing specifications.

Brush can be chipped and spread under the tree for mulch to help protect against surface compaction, to ameliorate soil temperatures, and to conserve soil moisture. Beware of using fresh chips of highly allelopathic species. Toxicities have been reported for uncomposted or unleached eucalyptus sawdust and leaves, redwood and cedar sawdust, Douglas-fir, larch, and spruce bark (Harris 1992). Do not chip herbicide-killed plant material.

WHAT IS A QUALIFIED ARBORIST?

An arborist is a specialist in the care of individual trees. To ensure that trees receive proper care, it is critical to employ a trained, technically competent arborist. The following are criteria that might be used to evaluate the qualifications of the arborist who will be working on your trees.

Is the arborist licensed?
Some states require that companies providing tree care services be licensed.

Does the arborist hold membership in professional organizations?
The International Society of Arboriculture and National Arborist Association are the professional organizations of tree care professionals.

Is the arborist certified?
ISA Certified Arborists have passed a comprehensive examination covering all aspects of tree care and continue to update their education and skills through continuing education.

Does the arborist have adequate insurance?
Request proof of liability and workers compensation insurance. Ask about the limits of coverage.

Will the arborist provide references?
Request references and contact them.

Does the arborist follow accepted practices?
Review the planned work with the arborist. Do not accept recommendations to top a tree, climb with spikes, or remove an excessive amount of foliage.

Will the arborist provide a written contract?
Reputable arborists will have clients sign a prepared contract.

(Adapted from *Why Hire an Arborist?*, prepared by the International Society of Arboriculture. For more information, contact ISA at P.O. Box 3129, Champaign, IL 61821-3129 or visit their web site at www.ag.uiuc.edu/~isa.)

PREPARING SPECIFICATIONS

Specifications are a critical component of tree preservation because they describe work procedures and standards. Without specifications, no special care will be taken, and trees will be damaged unnecessarily. Specifications are part of the contract documents and should be included with all construction plans.

Specifications should describe requirements clearly, rather than use general phrases that are difficult to interpret. Some examples of statements to avoid are "use all reasonable methods," or "contractor to take necessary steps to preserve tree." It is the consultant's

TABLE 8.5 Relationship of pruning time to pest susceptibility for selected tree species.

Plant group	Period to prune	Reason for timing
Alnus rhombifolia	November–March	Pruning during growing season attracts flatheaded borer (Svihra and Koehler 1989).
Betula spp.	fall–winter	Pruning during growing season attracts bronze birch borer (Ball 1992).
Cornus spp.	late fall–winter	Pruning during spring and summer attracts dogwood borer (Potter and Timmons 1983).
x *Cupressocyparis leylandii*	summer or winter	Pruning during rainy or foggy weather increases potential for cypress canker disease (McCain and Hamilton 1977).
Eucalyptus spp.	winter–early spring	Pruning during growing season attracts eucalyptus long-horned borer (California Department of Forestry and Fire Protection).
Fraxinus spp.	winter	Pruning during spring and early summer attracts ash and lilac borers. Pruning during summer and fall attracts clearwing borer (Potter and Timmons 1983).
Olea europaea	summer	Pruning during rainy season allows transport of oliveknot bacteria to wounds (Van Steenwyck et al. 1983).
Pinus spp.	November–mid-December	Pruning from mid-January to mid-October increases susceptibility to bark beetles, sequoia pitch moth, western gall rust, and pitch canker disease (Koehler 1991).
Prunus spp.	Late fall–winter	Pruning during spring and summer attracts peachtree and lesser peachtree borer (Potter and Timmons 1983).
Quercus spp.	Late summer–fall	Avoid pruning from February through May, when oaks are most susceptible to inoculation with oak wilt (Appel et al. 1987).
Quercus spp.	Fall–winter	Prune when attack by picnic beetles and infection by oak wilt is least likely (Minnesota Department of Agriculture 1989).
Quercus agrifolia, Q. lobata	November–January	Prune when infection by *Diplodia* is least likely (Costello et al. 1989).
Quercus rubra, Q. palustris	Fall–winter	Pruning during spring and summer attracts oak borer (Potter and Timmons 1983).
Rosaceae	Summer–winter	Avoid pruning during spring rains when fire blight bacteria are active (McCain 1981).
Ulmus spp.	November–January	Prune during fall and winter when bark beetle activity (which spreads Dutch elm disease) is reduced (Byers et al. 1980).

Note: Pruning times may be region and species specific. Check with Cooperative Extension staff in your area for precise information on pest biology.

job to tell the contractor what those steps and methods are. Having clear specifications serves the best interests of all parties: the consultant, the owner, the public agency, and the contractor, as well as the tree.

The following are typical specifications we use for design, demolition, and construction on projects for which trees are to be protected. These specifications should be adjusted to suit the site and type of construction to occur. Not all items are applicable to all projects. Factors that should be adjusted for a specific project are underlined, while additional notes are enclosed in brackets.

Sample Specifications for Demolition and Site Clearing

The following work must be accomplished before any demolition or site clearing activity occurs <u>within 100 feet of trees</u> [(or some protected area designated by other means, such as map or aerial photo)]:

1. The demolition contractor is required to meet with the consultant at the site prior to beginning work to review all work procedures, access and haul routes, and tree protection measures.

2. The limits of all tree protection zones shall be staked in the field.

3. Tree(s) to be removed that have branches extending into the canopy of tree(s) to remain must be removed by a qualified arborist and not by demolition or construction contractors. The qualified arborist shall remove the tree in a manner that causes no damage to the tree(s) and understory to remain.

4. Any brush clearing required within the tree protection zone shall be accomplished with hand-operated equipment.

5. Trees to be removed shall be felled so as to fall away from tree protection zones and to avoid pulling and breaking of roots of trees to remain. If roots are entwined, the consultant may require first severing the major woody root mass before extracting the trees. This may be accomplished by cutting through the roots by hand, with a vibrating knife, rock saw, narrow trencher with sharp blades, or other approved root-pruning equipment. [Note: If possible, show areas where root cutting is required on the demolition plan.]

6. Trees to be removed from within the tree protection zone shall be removed by a qualified arborist. The trees shall be cut near ground level and the stump ground out.

7. All downed brush and trees shall be removed from the tree protection zone either by hand or with equipment sitting outside the tree protection zone. Extraction shall occur by lifting the material out, not by skidding it across the ground.

8. Brush shall be chipped and placed in the tree protection zone to a depth of 6 inches.

9. Structures and underground features to be removed within the tree protection zone shall use the smallest equipment possible [or specify equipment], and operate from outside the tree protection zone. The consultant shall be on site during all operations within the tree protection zone to monitor demolition activity.

10. All trees shall be pruned in accordance with the provided Pruning Specifications.

11. A 6-foot chainlink fence with posts sunk into the ground shall be erected to enclose the tree protection zone

12. Any damage to trees due to demolition activities shall be reported to the consulting arborist within 6 hours so that remedial action can be taken. Timeliness is critical to tree health.

13. If temporary haul or access roads must pass over the root area of trees to be retained [indicate specific locations if known,] a road bed of 6 inches of mulch or gravel shall be created to protect the soil. The road bed material shall be replenished as necessary to maintain a 6-inch depth.

Sample Pruning Specifications

[Note: Specifications for individual trees, indicated by tree tag number, and describing which branches should be pruned and how, may be needed. Also consider requirements for crown reduction and crown raising where structures will be close to trees. Pruning requirements in stands should consider local needs for fire safety.]

1. All trees within the project area shall be pruned to:

    a. clear the crown of diseased, crossing, weak, and dead wood to a minimum size of 1½ inches diameter;

    b. provide 14 feet of vertical clearance over streets and 8 feet over sidewalks;

    c. remove stubs, cutting outside the woundwood tissue that has formed around the branch;

    d. reduce end weight on heavy, horizontal branches by selectively removing small diameter branches, no greater than 2 to 3 inches, near the ends of the scaffolds.

2. Where temporary clearance is needed for access, branches shall be tied back to hold them out of the clearance zone.

3. Pruning shall not be performed during periods of flight of adult boring insects because fresh wounds attract pests. Pruning shall be performed only when the danger of infestation is past.

4. All pruning shall be performed by a qualified arborist. [Note: In California, common practice is to specify an ISA Certified Arborist or Tree Worker. Furthermore, arborists are required to have a State of California Contractors License for Tree Service (C-61/D49) and provide proof of workers compensation and general liability insurance. Other states may have different regulations.]

5. All pruning shall be in accordance with the *Tree-Pruning Guidelines* (International Society of Arboriculture) and/or the ANSI A300 Pruning Standard (American National Standard for Tree Care Operations) and adhere to the most recent edition of ANSI Z133.1.

6. Interior branches shall not be stripped out.

7. Pruning cuts larger than 4 inches in diameter, except for dead wood, shall be avoided.

8. Pruning cuts that expose heartwood shall be avoided whenever possible.

9. No more than 20 percent of live foliage shall be removed within the trees.

10. While in the tree, the arborist shall perform an aerial inspection to identify defects that require treatment. Any additional work needed shall be reported to the consultant.

11. Brush shall be chipped and chips shall be spread underneath trees within the tree protection zone to a maximum depth of 6 inches, leaving the trunk clear of mulch.

Sample Construction Specifications

[Note: The following specifications should be included on all construction plans. If no site demolition or clearing was required, specifications regarding fencing and pruning should be included here.]

1. Before beginning work, the contractor is required to meet with the consultant at the site to review all work procedures, access routes, storage areas, and tree protection measures.

2. Fences have been erected to protect trees to be preserved. Fences define a specific protection zone for each tree or group of trees. Fences are to remain until all site work has been completed. Fences may not be relocated or removed without the written permission of the consultant.

3. Construction trailers and traffic and storage areas must remain outside fenced areas at all times.

4. All underground utilities and drain or irrigation lines shall be routed outside the tree protection zone. If lines must traverse the protection area, they shall be tunneled or bored under the tree.

5. No materials, equipment, spoil, or waste or washout water may be deposited, stored, or parked within the tree protection zone (fenced area).

6. Additional tree pruning required for clearance during construction must be performed by a qualified arborist and not by construction personnel.

7. Any herbicides placed under paving materials must be safe for use around trees and labeled for that use. Any pesticides used on site must be tree-safe and not easily transported by water.

8. If injury should occur to any tree during construction, it should be evaluated as soon as possible by the consultant so that appropriate treatments can be applied.

9. Any grading, construction, demolition, or other work that is expected to encounter tree roots must be monitored by the consulting arborist. [Note: Specific locations or tree tag numbers should be identified.]

10. All trees [or indicate tag number of specific trees] shall be irrigated on a schedule to be determined by the consultant [schedule should be included here if possible]. Each irrigation shall wet the soil within the tree protection zone to a depth of 30 inches.

11. Erosion control devices such as silt fencing, debris basins, and water diversion structures shall be installed to prevent siltation and/or erosion within the tree protection zone.

12. Before grading, pad preparation, or excavation for foundations, footings, walls, or trenching, Tree No. [specify tag #] shall be root pruned 1 foot outside the tree protection zone by cutting all roots cleanly to a depth of 24 inches [specify depth of adjacent excavation, to the maximum depth of root penetration, usually 3 feet]. Roots shall be cut by manually digging a trench and cutting exposed roots with a saw, vibrating knife, rock saw, narrow trencher with sharp blades, or other approved root-pruning equipment.

13. Any roots damaged during grading or construction shall be exposed to sound tissue and cut cleanly with a saw.

14. If temporary haul or access roads must pass over the root area of trees to be retained [indicate specific locations of roads affecting trees, if known], a road bed of 6 inches of mulch or gravel shall be created to protect the soil. The road bed material shall be replenished as necessary to maintain a 6-inch depth.

15. Spoil from trenches, basements, or other excavations shall not be placed within the tree protection zone, either temporarily or permanently. [Indicate appropriate place for stockpiling or disposal.]

16. No burn piles or debris pits shall be placed within the tree protection zone. No ashes, debris, or garbage may be dumped or buried within the tree protection zone.

17. Maintain fire-safe areas around fenced areas. Also, no heat sources, flames, ignition sources, or smoking is allowed near mulch or trees.

SUMMARY

After the consultant evaluates the impacts that may occur to trees, the design is re-evaluated to determine how impacts could be reduced. Some design options are:

- using retaining walls for grade transitions
- adjusting paving sections, finish grades, and paving materials to minimize root interference
- modifying footing and foundation design to reduce excavation in the root zone
- considering canopy conformations when locating fireplaces, windows, and structures

- locating utilities and services (including lines, junction boxes, and splice boxes) away from trees, and consolidating lines into joint trenches

A number of construction work procedures can help protect trees from unnecessary damage. Such procedures include planning the clearing, grubbing, and demolition with tree protection in mind, root pruning before excavating near trees, tunneling under roots rather than trenching through them, and protecting the soil from surface compaction from equipment. Postconstruction treatments for trees also help ensure survival. These may include irrigation, fertilization, pest control, and pruning.

How these operations should occur is defined in the plans and specifications and part of the contract documents.

REFERENCES

Alakukku, L. 1996. Persistence of soil compaction due to high axle load traffic, I: Short-term effects on the properties of clay and organic soils. *Soil and Tillage Research* 37:211–222.

American National Standards Institute. 1995. *Standard Practices for Tree, Shrub, and Other Woody Plant Maintenance*. ANSI A300. Washington, DC: ANSI.

Appel, D., R. Peters, and R. Lewis. 1987. Tree susceptibility, inoculum availability and potential vectors in a Texas oak wilt center. *Journal of Arboriculture*. 13:169–173.

Ball, J. 1992. Response of the bronze birch borer to pruning wounds on paper birch. *Journal of Arboriculture*. 18:29–297.

Byers, J., P. Svihra, and C. Koehler. 1980. Attraction of elm bark beetles to cut limbs of elm. *Journal of Arboriculture*. 6:24–246.

California Department of Forestry and Fire Protection. Undated. *Eucalyptus Longhorn Borer: Stop the Spread*. Sacramento: California Department of Forestry and Fire Protection.

Coder, K.D. 1997. Nitrogen prescriptions for trees. http://www.forestry.uga.edu/docs/for97-016.html.

Coder, K.D. 1995. Tree quality BMPs (best management practices) for developing woodland areas and protecting residual trees. In: *Trees and Building Sites*. G. Watson and D. Neely, eds. Savoy, IL: International Society of Arboriculture. pp. 111–124.

Costello, L., E. Hecht-Poinar, and J. Parmeter. 1989. *Twig and Branch Dieback of Oaks in California*. University of California Cooperative Extension Leaflet 21462. Berkeley: University of California. 4 pp.

Craul, P. 1992. *Urban Soil in Landscape Design*. New York: Wiley. 396 pp.

Harris, R.W. 1992. *Arboriculture: Integrated Management of Landscape Trees, Shrubs and Vines*. 2nd ed. Englewood Cliffs, NJ: Prentice Hall. 674 pp.

Helliwell, D.R. 1985. *Trees on Development Sites*. Romsey, England: Arboricultural Association. 18 pp.

International Society of Arboriculture. 1995. *Tree-Pruning Guidelines*. Savoy, IL. 14 pp.

Koehler, C. 1991. Tree injuries attract borers. *Growing Points*. 27:2.

Lichter, J.M., and P.A. Lindsey. 1995. The use of surface treatments for the prevention of soil compaction during site construction. *Journal of Arboriculture*. 20(4):205–209.

Matheny, N. 1989. Preserving trees affected by development. In *A Technical Guide to Community and Urban Forestry in Washington, Oregon, and California*. R. Morgan, ed. Portland, OR: World Forestry Center. pp. 34–41.

McCain, A., and D. Hamilton. 1977. *Cypress Canker*. University of California Cooperative Extension Leaflet 2997. Berkeley: University of California. 2 pp.

McCain, A. 1981. *Fire Blight of Ornamentals and Fruits*. University of California Cooperative Extension Leaflet 2715. Berkeley: University of California. 3 pp.

McNeil, J. 1997. Pleasant Hill, CA. Personal communication.

Milwaukee, City of. Undated. *Preventing Construction Damage to Municipal Trees*. City of Milwaukee, Department of Public Works. 27 pp. plus appendices.

Minnesota Department of Agriculture, Oak Wilt Program. 1989. *Oak Wilt Control and Prevention on Construction Sites*. St. Paul, MN: Minnesota Department of Agriculture. 2 pp.

Morell, J.D. 1984. Parkway tree augering specifications. *Journal of Arboriculture* 10(5):129–132.

Potter, D., and G. Timmons. 1983. Biology and management of clearwing borers of woody plants. *Journal of Arboriculture*. 9:145–150.

Svihra, P., and C. Koehler. 1989. *Flatheaded Borer in White Alder*. University of California Cooperative Extension Leaflet 7187. Berkeley: University of California. 2 pp.

Van Steenwyck, R., B. Teviotdale, and M. McHenry. 1983. *Control Guide for Olive Pests and Diseases*. University of California Cooperative Extension Leaflet 21370. Berkeley: University of California. 4 pp.

Yingling, E. L., C.A. Keeley, S. Little, and J. Burtis, Jr. 1979. Reducing damage to shade and woodland trees from construction activities. *Journal of Arboriculture* 5(5):97-105.

The Construction Phase

One of the guiding principles is "Trees preservation cannot wait until construction." By this point in the development process, plans and specifications have been finalized. If trees have not been considered during the preparation of these documents, it is difficult to incorporate adequate protection during construction. In carrying out the plans, trees may be irreparably damaged or killed. In this chapter, the consultant's tasks and responsibilities during building are discussed.

THE CONSULTANT'S ROLE DURING CONSTRUCTION

As discussed in the previous chapter, tree preservation has its greatest opportunity for success during the early stages of a project's design. Attempts to create preservation programs during construction are largely doomed. The critical design decisions are made before construction begins.

Nonetheless, activities during construction and post-construction phases are critical to successful preservation. Most important, the consultant must help ensure that the tree protection treatments and designs specified in the tree preservation plan are implemented.

The people involved often change as the project moves from design to construction. The consultant can provide important continuity during these changes. Whereas earlier in the project, the consultant's primary contacts were designers, planners, and engineers, once construction begins, the primary contacts are the project superintendent, various contractors and, in many cases, city inspectors or other representatives from regulatory agencies.

The consultant has six major responsibilities during the construction phase.

- **Maintain the tree protection zone.** Maintaining the integrity of the tree protection zone is the single most important factor in protecting trees from excessive damage. Space often is at a premium on construction sites and the open areas defined by the tree protection zone are attractive locations for all types of activities that can cause damage to trees, including storing materials, parking vehicles, and dumping waste (see "Identifying a Tree Protection Zone" in Chapter 6).

- **Assist with changes in the field.** Few projects proceed without changes in the field. This occurs for a variety of reasons. Plans and field situations may not match, and work must occur closer to the tree than planned. Alternatively, an item may have escaped notice or was not discovered until construction. The consultant must participate in the decisions that could affect trees.

- **Monitor tree health and conditions and specifying appropriate treatments.** Sometimes, even with a comprehensive tree protection plan, trees are accidentally damaged. The consultant must be available to recommend mitigations and appropriate actions when damage has occurred. Similarly, changes in water status, pest populations, etc. must be identified early so treatments can be applied.

- **Communicate with the project superintendent and contractors.** In our experience, one of the most critical factors in the success of a tree preservation project is the commitment of the project superintendent who manages all on-site construction activity. The superintendent's interest and willingness to support tree preservation actions (for example, honoring the tree protection zone) is vital. The consultant must acknowledge the range of demands for time and money facing the superintendent in completing the project and establish an effective means of communication and cooperation at the site.

- **Help identify appropriate work procedures around trees.** The consultant should talk with the project superintendent and contractors to identify work procedures that are effective for all parties and minimize impacts to trees. The consultant can help identify locations for haul roads that avoid trees while providing adequate turn and back-up zones for equipment.

- **Facilitate completion of the project.** Once a project is approved and construction begun, one of the consultant's responsibilities is to help complete the project in a timely manner. This is not done at the expense of adequate tree protection, but in a spirit of cooperation.

Communicating with Construction Personnel

The consultant's role during construction is to advise and facilitate. Working as part of a team, rather than in a policing role, fosters cooperation on the construction site. The consultant should report problems, lapses, and failures to the client. Focus comments on what needs to be done to improve the situation and to avoid problems in the future.

Holding a preconstruction meeting with contractors is an effective means of making sure everyone understands the tree preservation program. During the meeting the consultant should emphasize the shallow nature of tree roots, their susceptibility to damage from digging or compaction from traffic, and inability to repair bark injury. The importance of tree protection fencing should be discussed, and it should be understood that no dumping, storage, or activity will be allowed within that area. Any fines or other penalties for disturbing the tree protection zone or moving fencing should be explained. The chain of command, the authority of the consultant, and the procedure for evaluating and approving field changes should be described. Emphasize the importance of the contractors' operations to tree survival and invite them to be advocates of the tree preservation program, too. Ask what you can do to help them work efficiently around the trees.

Work procedures have a significant effect on the extent of impact to trees. Equipment must be able to move around the site, hauling necessary materials. Discuss hauling, access, and equipment turning requirements with the operators to designate routes least disruptive to tree roots and canopies. When it is important that equipment not intrude into an area, define the access routes with snow fencing or similar temporary material. When soil compaction is of concern, some protection can be provided by placing 6 inches of mulch or gravel on the surface (see "Modifying Construction Procedures" in Chapter 8).

One example of an extensive effort at educating construction personnel occurred during expansion of the McDonald's corporate headquarters in Oak Brook, Illinois. Every construction person was required to view a video describing the tree protection program before being allowed to work on the site. After the worker viewed the video, a sticker was placed on his or her hard hat. No one was allowed on the site without a sticker.

CONSTRUCTION PHASE MONITORING

The purposes of monitoring are threefold:

1. to ensure that all regulations and requirements imposed on the project are being met
2. to identify any existing or developing tree-related problems that require treatment
3. to discuss any new design or work procedures with the project superintendent and/or contractors

The amount of time the consultant should spend on the site during construction varies widely. If, for instance, large tree protection zones have been established and defined with sturdy fencing, there may be little need for the consultant to be at the site. On the other hand, if equipment must maneuver close to trees, the consultant may need to be present to help determine appropriate work procedures and protection measures.

In some cases, the governing agency or other regulatory body may dictate the requirement for and frequency of construction monitoring. Schedules and reporting requirements may be defined in the conditions of approval, the environmental impact report (EIR), or other project documents.

When monitoring is not required by the governing agency, the consultant can include a general statement regarding monitoring in the specifications (see "Preparing Specifications" in Chapter 8), such as:

> Any grading, construction, demolition or other work that is expected to encounter tree roots must be monitored by the consultant. (Note: Specific locations or tree tag numbers should be identified.)

During the final stages of design, the consultant attempts to anticipate all possible activities and operations on the site and prepare specifications to describe how that work will be performed. In reality, changes always occur, things happen that were not planned, and adjustments must be made in the field. The consultant should listen carefully to the description of what work needs to occur, then work with the contractor or job superintendent to accomplish the task in the least damaging way for the trees. Refer to "Modifying Design to Reduce Impacts to Trees," "Modifying Construction Procedures," and "Preparing Specifications" in Chapter 8 for guidelines in making those decisions.

What to Look for During Monitoring

- Ensure the integrity of the tree protection zones.
  - tree protection fences intact
  - no storage of materials

- no parking
- no dumping
- no evidence of soil or understory disturbance in protected area

■ Note any tree injury that occurred.
- damaged branches from equipment
- cut, injured, or exposed roots

■ Look for unusual changes in tree appearance and make treatment recommendations.
- leaf color, density
- wilting
- checking, bleeding on bark
- pest activity

■ Confirm that previously recommended treatments have been applied.
- irrigation
- pruning
- mulching
- fencing
- root pruning

■ Address new questions and problems.
- unapproved activity near trees
- additional pruning for clearance
- design changes
- work procedure or design changes

■ List new action items
- tree treatments
- fence repair
- soil projection

A construction monitoring form, such as shown in Table 9.1, is a convenient way to record observations and recommendations. These can be filled out in the field and left with the project superintendent. Comments may be general, such as "Irrigate all trees to wet the soil in the top 3 inches," or specific, such as "Trees #499 and 500 were injured by vehicles today."

PROVIDING TREATMENTS DURING CONSTRUCTION

The primary treatments that may be required during the construction phase are irrigation, pest management, and wound cleaning. Although trees should have been pruned before construction (see "Preconstruction Treatments" in Chapter 8), additional pruning may be required if clearance requirements were underestimated or if field changes increase clearance needs.

Irrigation

Irrigation frequency and depth should be based on tree need. Trees with significant root removal may require irrigation every three to four weeks, in the absence of adequate rainfall. Drought-tolerant trees with minimal disturbance may not require any irrigation. Regardless of irrigation frequency, applications should be of sufficient volume to wet the soil to at least 3 feet deep (adjust as necessary for specific site conditions). Application can be made by creating a 6-inch berm and filling the basin with a water truck, letting a hose run, or injecting into the soil.

Treating injuries

The most common type of injuries encountered on construction sites are bark wounds and broken branches.

Bark Wounds

If the cambium is still moist, torn bark often can be replaced. Harris (1992) recommends the following treatment:

1. Remove any shredded bark and debris from the wound face.
2. Place the loose bark onto the wound, pressing firmly against the cambium.
3. Hold the bark to the wound with a few small lacquered nails or duct tape.
4. Cover the wound with a moist cloth, paper towel, or peat.
5. Wrap a sheet of polyethylene film around the wounded area and secure it to tree with tape.
6. Inspect the wound in a week or two. If the bark has not reunited with the trunk, remove the dead bark and leave it exposed to air.

For wounds in which the cambium has dried and the bark will not reunite, Harris (1992) recommends the following treatment:

1. Remove loose, dry bark from the wound.
2. Cut away loose and torn bark cleanly to the edge of firmly attached bark, taking care not to increase the width or depth of the wound (Photo 9.1). Use a sharp wood chisel to cut at right angles to the wound surface. It is not necessary to shape the wound. Leave any peninsulas of live bark in the wound to speed callusing.
3. If the wood is torn, smooth it over without unnecessarily enlarging the wound.
4. Leave the wound exposed to air. It is not necessary to paint the wound with wound dressing.

Broken Branches

Branches in trees sometimes are broken when inadvertently struck by equipment. Broken branches

TABLE 9.1 Example of a construction monitoring form to record observations in the field and recommend treatments.

OAK ESTATES
Tree Preservation Monitoring

INSPECTION SUMMARY

Inspection Date:	Dec. 29, 1997	**Development Stage** ☐ Preconstruction ☐ Tree care
Inspector:	Ed Brennan, Consultant	☐ Trenching ☐ Demolition/stripping ☐ Rough grading
Also present:	Vern Smart, Project superintendent Steve Cool, Utility contractor	■ Streets/utility/drainage ☐ Building/construction ☐ Fine grading/landscaping ☐ Other:

General comments:
We walked the alignment of the joint trench in Phase 1 to determine impacts to trees.
Location of service drops will be discussed as house locations are determined.

SITE CONDITIONS

Tree No.	Conditions/concerns	Treatment required
1590	Two junction boxes near trunk	Move boxes south towards edge of dripline. Tree has been root pruned on west side along alignment of the joint trench.
1655	Trench will be within tree protection zone	Move trench to the outside of the fence.
1542	Trench will be within tree protection zone	Move trench to the outside of the fence.
1593, 1576	Trench 7' from trees	Tree has already been root pruned for street excavation. No further work needed at this time.

RECOMMENDATIONS AND FOLLOWUP

The following trees need to be irrigated to compensate for root impacts:

#1542, 1574, 1583, 1576, 1593, 1658, 1604–1607, 1912

Irrigation can occur either by placing a berm just inside the fence and filling the basin with a water truck, or by soil injection. A second irrigation will probably be needed the end of September.

Repair fence at tree #1526.

PHOTO 9.1 Bark injuries should be treated promptly. When cleaning the wound, remove loose bark, but avoid widening or deepening the wound. Cut broken roots back to sound tissue.

should be pruned back to an appropriate lateral branch or removed at the point of origin. Any repair pruning should be performed by a qualified arborist and adhere to ISA Pruning Standards (see "Pruning Specifications" in Chapter 8).

Pest Management

Any pests identified during monitoring that can significantly affect the long-term health of the tree should be controlled. Trees impacted by construction are predisposed to certain insects and diseases such as bark beetles, borers, *Botryosphaeria* canker, *Phytophthora* root rot and *Armillaria* root rot (Clark and Matheny 1994). In some cases, the thresholds for action should be lowered to account for the reduction in vigor that trees experience on construction sites.

SUMMARY

The construction phase is one of intense activity, involving many contractors intent on completing their part of the project. To be effective, the consultant must visit the site regularly and respond promptly to questions relating to trees. Primary responsibilities include:

- maintaining the tree protection zone
- interpreting and explaining specifications relative to trees
- assisting with changes in the field
- monitoring tree health and condition and specifying appropriate treatments
- communicating with the project superintendent and contractors
- helping identify appropriate work procedures around trees
- facilitating completion of the project

Treatments that might be necessary during construction include irrigation, pest management, and wound treatment. Although trees should have been pruned prior to construction, additional pruning may be required if clearance needs were underestimated or if field changes increased clearance needs.

Establishing an effective means of communication and operating in a spirit of cooperation help the project be completed with appropriate tree protection. Visiting the site regularly is important to maintaining communication and observing site and tree changes.

REFERENCES

Clark, J.R., and N.P. Matheny. 1994. The special needs of trees. In *Handbook of Integrated Pest Management for Turf and Ornamentals*. A.R. Leslie, ed. Boca Raton: LA. Lewis Publishers. pp. 17–28.

Harris, R.W. 1992. *Arboriculture: Integrated Management of Landscape Trees, Shrubs and Vines*. 2nd ed. Englewood Cliffs, NJ: Prentice Hall. 674 pp.

Postconstruction Management

There comes a point in every project when construction ends. The buildings are completed; the details of landscape installation are finished. The project, or one phase of the project, moves into the postconstruction period. This is a transitional period for tree management. The development team is phasing out of the project and the new owners are assuming direct management. In the meantime, the trees remain in place, acclimating to the changes that have occurred.

Many postconstruction programs of tree care focus on correcting physical damage that occurred during development. In reality, arboricultural treatments have limited ability to cure mechanical injury and other impacts from construction; therefore, the goal of a tree preservation program is to prevent injury to trees (Photo 10.1). When this is not possible and injury has occurred, the approach of postconstruction care is to maintain tree health and structural stability as the tree recovers. Put another way, the focus of postconstruction care is on "restoration of tree functions and values" (Coder 1995).

PHOTO 10.1
Arboricultural treatments are limited in their ability to cure declines in health and structure due to construction impacts. Once trees are this far along the mortality spiral, little can be done to prevent either death or structural failure.

During the postconstruction period, the development team, new owners, public agency, and consultant must work together to continue the tree preservation program that was initiated prior to construction. The recommendations for postconstruction tree maintenance must be communicated to new owners and initiated. The consultant plays a significant role in providing continuity through this transition and in determining appropriate tree care.

This chapter focuses on the time following construction when the trees are acclimating to new site conditions. The chapter describes treatments and programs to care for trees and remnant forests impacted by development activities.

THE TRANSITION PERIOD

As a project is completed, the personnel involved on the job (contractors, project team, etc.) usually changes. Because the goal is to allow trees both to survive construction and thrive in the future, keeping the consultant involved during the transfer of responsibility for trees ensures that some continuity will occur.

The way in which responsibility for trees is transferred varies among development projects. Some common options include:

- **Residential**

  - **Transfer from developer directly to new owner.** This holds true even when the developer provides site improvements but does not build the homes.

  - **Transfer from developer to builder, then from builder to new owner.** Developer may provide site improvements but sell ownership of individual lots to a builder, who then sells the completed home to a new owner.

  - **Transfer from developer to a community association.** In some planned communities, particularly multifamily, occupants do not own the land upon which their home is built.

121

Instead a community corporation owns and is responsible for the land. The developer usually maintains responsibility for management until a certain percentage of the homes are sold. Then there will be a gradual reduction in responsibility as management falls to the association or other governing body. Often, the community association contracts with a professional property manager to oversee day-to-day operations. The developer may create protective covenants as a vehicle for ensuring continuity of care. Using such agreements to protect trees during development and transfer has become more common in recent years (Petit et al. 1995). Covenants may include provisions against removing preserved trees without consent of the community association (Meyer and Carlisle 1991).

- **Transfer from developer to property owner and community association.** In some residential projects (particularly large, planned communities), ownership is divided among homeowners and the community association. The association is most often responsible for land held in common (e.g., parks, greenbelts). Transfer of management is similar to that described above: after a certain percentage of homes are sold, the association assumes a more active and dominant role.

■ **Commercial and Institutional**

- **Transfer from developer directly to new owner.** In this situation, the developer sells the new property following construction, with direct transfer of ownership.

- **No transfer.** Ownership of many commercial (e.g., office and retail) and all institutional projects does not change. Rather, the owner may act as the developer in building the project, either taking occupancy upon completion or making space available on a lease/rental basis. In many cases, property managers are employed to assist in operations.

THE GUARANTEE PERIOD

The developer frequently is required to maintain the installed landscape for some period of time, usually one to two years following occupancy. When completion of a project occurs over several phases, the requirements for maintenance may also be linked to phasing. Trees preserved during construction are not usually included in those requirements. Unless there is a specific mention of preserved trees in the community tree preservation ordinance, the project's conditions of approval, or an ownership transfer agreement, there might be no provisions for maintenance of trees retained during construction. When postconstruction maintenance is specified, the tasks and time periods vary depending on the policies of individual communities and the nature of the project.

One approach to ensuring continued care of preserved trees is to require the developer to post a bond prior to the start of construction. The size of the bond is determined in one of two ways: paying a set amount per tree (e.g., $500), or establishing the value of trees to be preserved using the methods described in the *Guide for Plant Appraisal* (Council of Tree and Landscape Appraisers 1992).

The goal of such a bond is to ensure that the developer complies with the conditions of approval for tree preservation during the construction phase. If trees die during construction, part of the bond is forfeited. Communities with requirements for bonding often stipulate that release of the bond occurs some time after completion of the project, with 18 to 24 months being typical (Bassert 1996). Julian Dunster (1996) has set the postconstruction period as two years.

Following the period of postconstruction maintenance by the developer, responsibility for the trees transfers to the new owners. We know of few, if any, projects in which new owners are required by ordinance to continue a program of maintenance for preserved trees. In communities with strict covenants, conditions, and requirements (CC&Rs), there may be limitations on the ability of individual property owners to remove trees. Moreover, there is often a communitywide contract for tree care in which individual owners take part.

At the time of ownership transfer, there is usually a site inspection. When trees preserved during construction are inspected, a list of remedial actions required to be undertaken may be created. Items to be addressed may include final cleanup of debris and removal of protective fencing. Completion of these tasks is usually the last action taken by the developer with respect to trees.

EDUCATING THE NEW OWNERS

Buyers of residential property, lessors of commercial properties, and even commercial property managers may not know how to adequately care for preserved trees (Vander Weit and Miller 1986). One way to communicate maintenance requirements and provide continuity from development to property transfer is for the project consultant to prepare a "homeowner's guidebook to tree care" specific for the project and individual lots. Such a manual might describe the trees present on the property and their maintenance requirements. The manual should also include guidelines for common homeowner improvements: landscaping, irrigation and drainage systems,

OUTLINE FOR HOMEOWNER'S GUIDE TO CARING FOR PRESERVED TREES

I. Background and Overview
   A. Introduction to project and the tree preservation program
   B. Community regulations and policies regarding trees, their care, and removal
II. Description of Trees
   A. Species found on the lot
   B. Description of tree and its parts
   C. Characteristics of individual trees
III. Maintenance Requirements
   A. General requirements for each species
       1. Environmental
       2. Cultural
       3. Pest and disease
   B. Specific maintenance tasks
       1. Pruning
       2. Irrigation
       3. Fertilization
       4. Mulch
       5. Pest management
       6. Fire fuel management
IV. Guidelines for Continued Protection of Trees
   A. Installation of drain lines
   B. Installation of irrigation and lighting
   C. Construction of patios, deck, and walkways
   D. Installation of pools, spas, and ponds
   E. Construction of swales, berms, and mounds
   F. Construction of fences, walls, and structures
   G. Soil management
   H. Planting (including lists of species-compatible plants as required)
V. Summary

approval. Alternatively, a homeowners' association may request an evaluation of preserved trees sometime after transfer.

In any case, if the person providing the postconstruction evaluation also performed the predevelopment resource evaluation (covered in Chapter 5), specific information on preserved trees can be updated. If the consultant has no previous experience with the site, he or she must first evaluate the changes that have occurred around the trees, the condition of the trees, and how they may respond over the long term (see Chapter 7). If development plans and/or the tree report are available, they will form the basis for the assessment and should be reviewed. If not, the consultant must evaluate the trees and site characteristics and assess the impacts from construction.

Inspection for Health and Vigor

A postconstruction evaluation must be concerned with the health and vigor of trees impacted by development. In the ideal case, the information contained in the predevelopment tree report can be compared to that found in a postdevelopment evaluation. At this time, trees that have declined in health may be targeted for remedial treatments such as pruning and irrigation.

and decks and patios. Alternatively, developers and consultants may obtain and distribute public information brochures prepared by organizations such as the International Society of Arboriculture, a conservation group such as the California Oak Foundation, and/or the local Cooperative Extension Service.

THE SITE INSPECTION: CARE OF TREES FOLLOWING CONSTRUCTION

An essential step in providing tree care following construction is to evaluate the condition of the trees. This may occur either before or after transfer of ownership. A developer will be required to meet any preservation and planting components of the conditions of

Inspection for Structural Stability

Trees impacted by construction may become unstable and prone to failure. Two patterns are common. First, failure may occur as a result of the increased exposure associated with site clearing. Second, trees may decline in health over a longer period of time and become prone to failure.

In conducting the postconstruction inspection for structure, the consultant must consider both of these possibilities. Some defects in structure (e.g., dieback of twigs and branches, branch attachments, weight distribution) can be corrected before they increase failure potential. Factors such as live crown ratio, weight distribution, soil stability, and trunk taper may be useful in assessing the potential for failure.

TYPICAL SYMPTOMS OF TREE STRESS FROM CONSTRUCTION INJURY

Short annual elongation
Small, yellow leaves
Thin foliage
Leaf scorch
Wilting
Early fall coloration and defoliation
Epicormic shoots
Heavy seeding
Twig dieback
Branch dieback
Irregular wounds from equipment damage on trunks and lower branches
Attack by borers and other stress-related pests
Death

Consultants should refer to *A Photographic Guide to the Evaluation of Hazard Trees in Urban Areas* for guidelines on inspecting trees for structural defects (Matheny and Clark 1994).

Evaluation of Construction Impacts

In addition to assessing tree health and structure, a postconstruction evaluation should also consider the degree of such construction impacts as fill soil and mechanical injury. The interaction of impacts with tree species and health affects the potential for the tree to survive and remain an asset to the site. When impacts are severe, the prudent course may be to remove a tree before it begins to decline and/or become unstable (Photo 10.2a). Impacts such as broken branches and exposed roots can be corrected with treatment (Photo 10.2b). The intensity of impacts may be

reduced by removing fill soil (Photo 10.2c), supplying supplemental irrigation, or providing similar treatments.

Coder (1996) describes a process of evaluating impacts from construction that considered both the tree and its environment. In addition, he offers techniques for the evaluation, suggesting that the following areas be addressed:

- destruction of the general root system, particularly loss of rooting area
- damage to the root collar and structural roots
- mechanical injury and damage to the stem
- changes in soil structure such as compaction, fills, erosion, and loss of organic matter
- changes to wind loading in the crown, which is particularly related to potential for failure
- damage to branches
- decline in overall health
- obstructions

Whatever the form of the postconstruction evaluation, the compiled results of inspections for health, structure, and impacts will form the basis for the future management of trees in the new community.

PHOTO 10.2 Impacts from construction are assessed during the inspection. In some cases, impacts may be deemed too severe and the tree recommended for removal (a). In other cases, remedial actions such as pruning of broken branches (b) and removal of fill soil (c) will be appropriate.

THE MAINTENANCE PROGRAM: CARE OF TREES FOLLOWING CONSTRUCTION

The management of preserved trees following construction must encompass the needs of both individual trees and the forest remnants they comprise.

Caring for Individual Trees

The program of postconstruction care for individual trees focuses on the normal goals of any tree management effort: maintenance of vigor and structural stability. For trees to remain assets to the community, they must remain in good condition with low potential for failure. We address these goals by treating the tree itself (pruning, pest management) and the environment around the tree (mulch, irrigation). Overall, we strive to avoid any factors that predispose the tree to attack by pests and loss of wood through decay.

The most common remedial actions recommended for trees impacted by construction include the treatments described below.

Irrigation

Trees that have suffered loss of roots may not be able to exploit as large a soil volume as they did before injury. Alternatively, changed patterns of drainage across a site may divert water into new drainage patterns, away from trees. In either case, trees may benefit from supplemental irrigation. The following are general guidelines.

- The amount of water applied must be appropriate to the needs of the individual species.

- Light, frequent irrigations should be avoided. Irrigation should wet the entire root zone and be allowed to dry before another application.

- Excess irrigation from new landscapes should be avoided. Runoff from plantings should be minimized and/or directed away from trees.

- Wetting the trunk should be avoided.

Another approach is to reduce water loss by misting the canopy. In this technique, fine sprays of water are applied throughout the canopy on regular, relatively continuous intervals. The mist appears to raise humidity and reduce air temperature within the canopy, thereby reducing water loss. Schrader (1996) considered this treatment instrumental in the survival of transplanted oaks in Florida.

Pruning

Trees on construction sites should be inspected annually to determine pruning requirements. Pruning may be required for one of two reasons. First, crowns may need to have dead, dying, diseased, broken, and otherwise structurally weak branches removed. This pruning may also involve reducing the size of the crown where dieback is extensive. Second, crowns may be thinned to reduce the amount of canopy exposed to wind and to balance weight among branches.

Arborists have long debated the value of pruning the crown as a way of compensating for loss of roots; however, there is no scientific evidence to support this practice. Watson (1991) notes ". . . no research has been published to demonstrate the effectiveness [of crown reduction pruning] on mature trees." Harris (1992) notes, "As with most things, moderation would appear to be wise in caring for root-damaged trees." Our recommendation is that arborists not attempt to balance root loss by reducing the size of the crown. Rather, we recommend that the health and structure of the tree be monitored and appropriate pruning actions be applied.

In proscribing pruning treatments, the general guidelines described in the section on pruning specifications in Chapter 8 should be followed.

Mulch

Trees preserved on construction sites generally will benefit from having a 4- to 6-inch layer of organic mulch beneath the canopy. The mulch will reduce loss of moisture from the soil, protect against compaction, and moderate soil temperatures. It also has been demonstrated that the addition of mulch reduces soil compaction over time (see section on remedial soil treatment).

We normally specify that brush from pruning be chipped and spread under the crown. Mulch depth should be adjusted so that only 1 to 2 inches is placed against the trunk of the tree.

Fertilization

Arborists are not in agreement about the value of supplemental fertilization to trees preserved on construction sites. A consistent benefit to such treatment has not been demonstrated by scientific research. Because trees growing in forests settings do not usually exhibit any symptoms of nutrient deficiency, we might surmise that mineral elements are not lacking in the soil and, therefore, supplementing those nutrients following root injury is not necessary. Although applications of supplemental fertilizer have resulted in increased growth of trees in forest stands, trees preserved on development sites are no longer strictly forest trees. Historical patterns of nutrient cycling are disrupted as soil, litter, and woody debris are removed; mycorrhizal associations are altered; and patterns of water movement through the profile and across the site are changed. Moreover, we expect trees in landscape settings to be healthier than those in woodland environments.

In addition, there is significant anecdotal evidence regarding the benefits of supplemental fertilization. We assume that the ability of trees on construction sites to absorb water and mineral nutrients has been reduced due to injury and root compaction. Providing supplemental fertilization, therefore, allows the trees to absorb necessary elements with a limited root system. Trees that were previously growing in urban landscapes or without maintenance may benefit from fertilization.

We concur with Harris (1992) who suggests that "modest amounts of nitrogen [1 pound per 1,000 square feet] applied to . . . injured . . . roots should benefit both root and top growth." Harris also recommends applying fertilizer in the late autumn. We suggest consultants evaluate each situation on its own merits.

Pest Management

Tree death often follows a pattern of weakening by predisposing stresses, such as injury from construction, followed by attack from opportunistic pests and pathogens. For example, the two-lined chestnut borer attacks oak trees that have been weakened by biotic or environmental stress (Dunn et al. 1990). Oak trees that have been mechanically wounded are predisposed to attack by *Armillaria* (Svihra 1991). Construction activity has been associated with decline of white pine (Weaver and Stipes 1988) and with increased occurrence of oak wilt (Miller et al. 1993).

Pest management is an important part of a post-construction maintenance program. Developing pest management programs for preserved trees involves

- knowledge of the tree species and its pattern(s) of decline and death
- treating the tree to enhance vigor and/or avoid predisposition (e.g., supplemental irrigation, timing of pruning)
- monitoring for the presence of pests
- applying preventive control treatments

Because trees impacted by construction are more susceptible to pests, managers need to be vigilant about pest management programs. Particular attention must be paid to monitoring for pests and to application of control procedures. Thresholds for treatment may be more conservative on infested trees than for undisturbed trees. Under normal circumstances, the action threshold for control procedures might be defoliation of 30 percent of the crown. For trees impacted by development activity, a threshold of 15 to 20 percent defoliation would be more appropriate.

Tree Removal

Trees that have died or become structurally unsound are no longer assets to the community and should be removed. A thorough structural inspection will identify trees in either condition. In proscribing tree removal operations in use areas, several general guidelines should be followed.

- Local requirements for tree removal must be met. These may take the form of removal permits, payment of fees, requirements for replanting, etc.
- Removal operations should be performed by a licensed tree care contractor carrying proof of workers compensation and general liability insurance.
- Removal should be performed by a qualified arborist.
- Tree removal operations must adhere to the most recent of the American National Standard for Tree Care Operations (ANSI Z133.1).

Removing Fill Soil

In situations where grades have been raised within the dripline, the fill soil should be removed to original grade. If the entire root area cannot be cleared of fill, a minimum 5-foot radius around the trunk should be returned to natural grade. In some cases, a small retaining wall may be necessary. Drainage must be provided to ensure that water does not collect at the base of the trunk. Removal of fill soil should occur by hand, especially within 10 feet of the trunk.

Remediation of Soils Damaged During Construction

The structure of soils on development sites is often altered during the construction process. Soils are compacted to provide a stable base for structures, as vehicles move across the site, and when utilities and other improvements are installed. Miller et al. (1996) noted, however, that "compaction" is often used as a catch-all term for soil disturbances including kneading, churning, rutting, and displacement. By whatever means it is accomplished, compaction results in increased soil density and decreased porosity. It is an unfavorable environment for roots as well as soil microflora.

Consultants are frequently asked to recommend treatments that will quickly reduce compaction and improve structure. Rolf (1992a), Day and Bassuk (1994), and Smiley (1996) reviewed possible amelioration treatments. Solutions such as tillage and subsoiling are not appropriate on development sites where large trees are already present. In postconstruction situations, four treatment options are available.

- Holes and fractures can be created to increase air space. This is accomplished by injecting high-pressure water or air and physically augering openings. In some cases, voids are filled with porous material such as sand or gravel, a process known as vertical mulching.
- Soil is removed from radially oriented trenches and replaced with porous soil material (Photo 10.3). Removal may be achieved either by backhoe and other mechanical methods or by hydroexcavation (Gross 1995).

- Organic mulch can be placed around the tree beneath the canopy.
- The tree can be treated with growth regulators such as paclobutrazol (Watson 1996).

The experimental results from examining the effectiveness of the numerous possible remediation treatments are ambiguous (Table 10.1). However, three treatments appear to provide clear benefits. First, mulching the soil beneath the canopy with organic mulch is beneficial. Smiley (1996) notes ". . . the most dramatic results I have ever seen in a soil compaction experiment came from using mulch by itself." Smiley (1996) also demonstrated improvement in trunk growth of crepe myrtle and Callery pear trees in a compacted soil setting. Second, the soil removal and replacement technique has resulted in clear improvements in tree growth (Watson et al. 1996, Watson 1996, Smiley 1996). In Watson's work, however, the soils involved were not described as compacted at the start of the project. Third, Watson (1996) demonstrated increased root development of declining white oak trees from application of paclobutrazol.

Other experiments using vertical mulching (drilling holes in the soil and filling them with mulch material) of all types, treatment with biostimulants, aeration, and other methods have yielded either inconsistent or negative results for either soil characteristics or tree health. The exception to this has been the work of Rolf (1992b and 1994), which focused on remediation treatments in improving growing conditions of new plantings.

It is clear that prevention and avoidance are the key elements in dealing with soil compaction and related degradations in structure on development sites. Consultants have limited ability to provide effective long-lasting treatments. As Rolf (1992a) noted, "There are no perfect methods for aeration around trees in limited spaces and where vegetation is already established."

PHOTO 10.3 Soil removal and replacement is a promising treatment for alleviating soil compaction around established trees. Trenches are either hydro- or mechanically excavated. Compacted soil is removed and replaced with high-quality material. (Photo courtesy of Gary Watson, The Morton Arboretum.)

Caring for Remnant Forests

Remnant forests are pieces and fragments of preexisting woodland retained during development. They are often described as buffer areas, greenbelts, natural areas, wildland parks, and open space. Following development, these parcels may be deeded to the community or neighborhood association.

The need for management of forest remnants is not always recognized either by the owners or the community at large. Remnant forests usually are viewed as natural, able to function without outside intervention. A commonly held view expects that a remnant forest will retain the natural processes and functions of an intact forest.

The process of opening forest stands for development, however, disrupts the natural dynamics of that assemblage and reduces the ability of the stand to perform these functions. In urban areas, the primary driving forces of succession and stand development, such as fire and wind, are absent. The impacts of humans on the health and structure of these fragments are profound, leading to extensive damage to vegetation (Matlack 1993). These impacts are particularly acute near the forest edge and footpaths.

Remnant forests require management. Duntemann (1993), Hoesterey (1991), and Miller (1993) emphasize this point and come to the same conclusion: active management must substitute for the loss of natural processes. Acceptance of this biological reality by the new owners is an important challenge; however, the need is clear. Miller (1993) suggests that a program of education, particularly about the historical development of local forests, will allow management treatments to be applied.

The application of tree and stand management practices to remnant forests occurs as a function of size (small versus large) and form (long or linear versus unfragmented), as well as the existing forest structure, age, and species composition. In addition, management must consider the inevitability of change over time (Agee 1995). Miller (1993) notes that the successional path a forest stand will follow depends on the intensity of tree removal operations. Removing single trees will create a different result from cutting larger numbers of trees.

Given these considerations of size, form, and change, management of remnant forests must be site specific and have well-defined goals for the future. Because these remnants are often the focal point of neighborhood activity and attention, it is critical that there be some consensus about both the process of management and its end results. Some examples of broad management goals for forest remnants are

- maintaining existing character, species diversity, structure, and individual trees by arresting succession or change

TABLE 10.1 Comparison of treatments recommended for improving soil structure and tree growth in compacted soil.

Treatment	Results
Augering 2" diameter holes, 18" deep, 2' on center throughout root area, with and without vertical mulching (1:1 sand:milled fir bark)	Two years after treatment, no significant differences in tree growth among treatments. Soil was compacted sandy loam (Pittenger and Stamen 1990).
Mulch	Hardwood and softwood chips applied around recently planted trees in compacted soil. Trunk diameter after 2 years improved over controls in Callery pear. Improved visual appearance (Smiley 1996).
Vertical mulching (Perlite)	No effect on tree growth or water status (Kalisz et al. 1994).
Vertical mulching (Isolite)	No improvement in trunk diameter of 2 species (Smiley 1996).
Vertical mulching with peat moss and fertilizer	No improvement in trunk diameter of 2 species (Smiley 1996).
Water-jetting holes throughout root area	Two years after treatment, no significant differences in tree growth compared to controls (Pittenger and Stamen 1990).
Liquid fertilizer injected in soil	No improvement in trunk diameter of 2 species (Smiley 1996).
Installing perforated 4" diameter PVC pipe, backfilled with gravel	No statistically significant improvement in shoot elongation (Day et al. 1995) or trunk diameter (Pittenger and Stamen 1990).
Installing drainage mats (e.g., Enkadrain) in vertical openings to create aeration panels	No statistically significant improvement in shoot elongation (Day et al. 1995).
Fracturing soil with pressurized air (e.g., Grow Gun, Terralift)	Increased oxygen diffusion rate at fissures only. No effect on soil bulk density. No improvement in tree growth (Smiley et al. 1990, Smiley 1996)
Fracturing soil with pressurized air (Terralift)	In sandy loam: Decreased bulk density; increased porosity, saturated hydraulic conductivity, and air permeability (Rolf 1992b). In loam over clay loam: Decreased bulk density and porosity; no change in hydraulic conductivity; slight increase in air permeability (Rolf 1992b). In clay loam over clay subsoil: No change in bulk density; no consistent increase in tree growth (Smiley et al. 1990, Smiley 1994).
Humic acid solution	No improvement in trunk diameter of 2 species (Smiley 1996).
Tillage	In loam and clay loam soils over loam, and in silt loam subsoils: Assessed survival of seedlings planted in treated skid roads in Pacific Northwest forests. Early response in growth and survival was lost by year 8. Resulted in greater trunk diameter than controls for recently planted pear trees (Smiley 1996).
Removing and replacing soil in radial trenches around the tree; soil removed by either trenching or hydroexcavation	Improved root density and depth. Reversed declining health of *Tilia* and *Platanus*. Soils not noted as "compacted" (Watson et al. 1996). Resulted in greater trunk diameter than controls for recently planted crepe myrtle trees (Smiley 1996).

TABLE 10.1 (continued)

Treatment	Results
Removing and replacing soil in radial trenches around the tree; soil removed by either trenching or hydroexcavation (continued)	Used sandy loam backfill. Improved root and shoot growth of Callery pear trees over control (Day et al. 1995).
	Used soil/compost mix in trenches around declining white oaks. Improved root density and visual appearance over untreated controls (Watson 1996).
Treatment with growth regulators	Treated declining white oak trees with paclobutrazol, alone and in combination with soil replacement. Improved root density and visual appearance of over untreated controls. A combination of soil replacement and trenching did not produce significantly better results than either treatment alone (Watson 1996).

- fostering change through natural processes such as succession, prescribed disturbance, and/or stand structure
- enhancing specific features of the remnant (e.g., wildlife habitat, species diversity, riparian character, fishery resource, or herbaceous understory)
- producing timber or other forest products
- providing for public safety
- directing the composition and structure to some specified purpose (e.g., in the southeast United States, loblolly pine plantations are sometimes converted to oak and hickory forests; the East Bay Regional Park District of the San Francisco Bay area is converting some existing eucalyptus stands to oak woodland)

Once management goals have been established, their implementation usually involves some combination of arboriculture and forestry techniques. Both individual trees and the stand itself are considered. The city of Bellevue, Washington, incorporates pruning, removal, thinning, recreational enhancement, wildlife enhancement, and reforestation activities into its greenbelt management program. In addition to the treatments previously described, management of forest remnants may have the goals or concerns described in the following sections.

Regeneration of Desired Species

The successful regeneration of desired species, both woody and herbaceous, generally depends on at least four factors.

- **The existing stand structure.** Many forests have a complex structure of canopy dominants and emergents. As the dominants and overstory species are lost, new species may fill the gaps created by this loss.

- **The capacity for reproduction within the existing forest conditions.** There must be a sufficient capacity to produce seed or propagules.

- **The capacity for recruitment into the stand.** Any impacts from construction that affect germination or seedling and sapling growth must be considered. Alterations in patterns of runoff and drainage may alter the hydrologic balance within a remnant and prevent the successful development of an individual species. Similarly, the requirement of some species for a ground-clearing fire may be mimicked by mechanical clearing.

- **Competition.** The ability of natural vegetation to successfully compete with exotic species that may invade from adjoining landscapes must be considered.

When these features are lacking, successful regeneration of desired species may require interventions such as planting stock and/or removal of undesired species.

Weed Control

By definition, forest remnants are surrounded by development and planted landscapes; therefore, they are particularly vulnerable to invasion by exotic landscape species (Reichard 1994). These may outcompete native vegetation, both woody and herbaceous, and eliminate them from the remnant. Active weed-control programs must become part of a postconstruction maintenance program. This may involve traditional integrated pest management techniques of exclusion, prohibiting use of known invasive species, monitoring, sanitation, and application of control treatments. An excellent source for information is *Invasive Plants*, an encyclopedia recently published by the Brooklyn Botanical Garden (Randall and Marinell 1996).

Fire Fuel Management

In many forests, fire is a natural component of the ecosystem, playing an essential role in forest development and regeneration. In developed areas, however, fire generally cannot be tolerated. At the interface between developed and natural areas, there may be conflicting feelings about the presence of fire and its role in the ecosystem processes. Managers of remnant forests face two divergent concerns: preventing the spread of fire into, and out of, human use areas; and using fire as a tool in forest management.

In areas where fire is common and can be expected to occur, management may focus on preventing fire from either reaching homes or escaping from homes into natural forests (Photos 10.4a,b). Most guidelines focus on creating "defensible space" around use areas. When preserved trees are located within defensible space areas, postconstruction treatments are aimed at reducing the buildup of flammable fuels. Pruning to eliminate fuel ladders, thinning stands of trees, and clearing understory and ground cover vegetation are three common activities. In addition, removal of species particularly prone to fire, known as pyrophytes, should occur.

PHOTO 10.4 In areas with frequent fires, management of remnant stands will include fire management. Several common components include creating and maintaining defensible spaces around homes (a), as well as reducing the amount of fuel by tree pruning and removal (b). In some cases, prescribed burning may be used.

A second concern regarding fire involves the ability of the forest to sustain itself. In forests adapted to fire, prevention disrupts the natural dynamics, particularly regarding regeneration. Management options range from controlled burning to mimicking fire with mechanical treatments. Duntemann (1993) describes the use of controlled burning in management of a remnant forest in Illinois.

Pest Management

Pest management is no less a concern in remnant forests than it is with individual trees. In a small remnant forest, the presence of root diseases such as laminated root rot and oak wilt, soil-borne decay fungi such as sulfur fungus, and insects such as the eucalyptus longhorn borer may have devastating consequences. Because remnant forests are located adjacent to developed properties, any pest problem that compromises structural stability must be evaluated for control procedures.

Water and Hydrology

Any management plan for forest remnants must consider the impact development has had on site hydrology. Construction that alters existing hydrological processes across a site has significant consequences to existing vegetation as well as on the potential for new vegetation to emerge. For example, when flows along riparian corridors are regulated by dams, the effects on downstream vegetation can be dramatic. Not only may the historic patterns of flow be changed, but the processes of soil deposition and scour are also altered.

Hazard Tree Management

Because remnant forests exist adjacent to developed areas, management must include assessment of the potential risk posed by tree failures. This is particularly important along new forest edges and in any areas where the public is invited, such as paths, picnic sites, and other use areas.

SUMMARY

Postconstruction management begins with a comprehensive evaluation of trees preserved during the construction process. In most cases, postconstruction care builds upon the existing health and structure of the trees. When health and structure are good, arboricultural treatments can enhance and maintain them. When health and structure are poor, arboricultural treatments have limited value. With this in mind, it is even more essential that trees preserved on development sites be selected with care and protected throughout construction. As Schoeneweiss (1982) observed, "Construction damage is much easier to prevent than to try to correct later."

REFERENCES

Agee, J. 1995. Management of greenbelt and forest remnants in urban forest landscapes. In *Urban Forest Landscapes: Integrating Multidisciplinary Perspectives*. G. Bradley, ed. Seattle: University of Washington Press. pp. 128–138.

American National Standards Institute. 1988. *American National Standard for Tree Care Operations* (ANSI Z133.1). Washington, DC: American National Standards Institute.

Bassert, D. 1996. National Association of Home Builders. Washington, DC. Personal communication.

Coder, K.D. 1995. Tree quality BMPs (best management practices) for developing wooded areas and protecting residual trees. In *Trees and Building Sites*. G. Watson and D. Neely, eds. Savoy, IL: International Society of Arboriculture. pp. 111–124.

Coder, K.D. 1996. *Construction Damage Assessments: Trees and Sites*. University of Georgia Cooperative Extension Service. Forest Resources Unit. FOR96-39. Athens: University of Georgia. 24 pp.

Council of Tree and Landscape Appraisers. 1992. *Guide for Plant Appraisal*. 8th edition. Savoy, IL International Society of Arboriculture. 103 pp.

Day, S., and N. Bassuk. 1994. A review of the effects of soil compaction and amelioration treatments on landscape trees. *Journal of Arboriculture*. 20:9–17.

Day, S., N. Bassuk, and V. van Es. 1995. Effects of four compaction remediation methods for landscape trees on soil aeration, mechanical impedance and tree establishment. *Journal of Environmental Horticulture*. 13:64–71.

Dunn, J., D. Potter, and T. Kimmerer. 1990. Carbohydrate reserves, radial growth and mechanisms of resistance of oak trees to phloem-boring insects. *Oecologia*. 83:458–468.

Dunster, J. 1996. Dunster and Associates. Bowen Island, BC. Personal communication.

Duntemann, M. 1993. Natural area restoration. In *Proceedings of the Sixth National Urban Forestry Conference*. C. Kollin, J. Mahon, and L. Frame, eds. Washington, DC: American Forests. pp. 199–202.

Gross, R. 1995. Construction applications of hydraulic soil excavation. In *Trees and Building Sites*. G. Watson and D. Neely, eds. Savoy, IL: International Society of Arboriculture. pp. 177–184.

Harris, R.W. 1992. *Arboriculture: Integrated Management of Landscape Trees, Shrubs and Vines*. 2nd edition. Englewood Cliffs, NJ: Prentice Hall. 674 pp.

Hoesterey, R. 1991. The ecosystem strategy. In *Proceedings of the Fifth National Urban Forestry Conference*. P. Rodbell, ed. Washington, DC: American Forests. pp. 135–137.

Kalisz, P., J. Stringer, and R. Wells. 1994. Vertical mulching of trees: Effects on roots and water status. *Journal of Arboriculture*. 20:141–145.

Matheny, N., and J. Clark. 1994. *A Photographic Guide to the Evaluation of Hazard Trees in Urban Areas*. 2nd edition. Savoy, IL: International Society of Arboriculture. 85 pp.

Matlack, G. 1993. Sociological edge effects: Spatial distribution of human impact in suburban forest fragments. *Environmental Management*. 17:829–835.

Meyer, H., and H.C. Carlisle. 1991. Environmentally sensitive construction. In *Proceedings of the Fifth National Urban Forestry Conference*. P. Rodbell, ed. Washington, DC: American Forests. pp. 141–142.

Miller, R. 1993. Greenbelt silviculture. In *Proceedings of the Sixth National Urban Forestry Conference*. C. Kollin, J. Mahon, and L. Frame, eds. Washington, DC: American Forests. pp. 194–196.

Miller, N., D. Rathke, and G. Johnson. 1993. *Protecting Trees from Construction Damage: A Homeowner's Guide*. University of Minnesota Cooperative Extension. Publication No. NR-FO-6135-S. St. Paul: University of Minnesota. 13 pp.

Miller, R., W. Scott, and J. Hazard. 1996. Soil compaction and conifer growth after tractor yarding at three coastal Washington locations. *Canadian Journal of Forest Research*. 26:225–236.

Petit, J., D. Bassert, and C. Kollin. 1995. *Building Greener Neighborhoods: Trees as Part of the Plan*. Washington, DC: American Forests and the National Association of Home Builders. 117 pp.

Pittenger, D., and T. Stamen. 1990. Effectiveness of methods used to reduce harmful effects of compacted soil around landscape trees. *Journal of Arboriculture*. 16:55–57.

Randall, J.M., and J. Marinelli, eds. 1996. *Invasive Plants*. Brooklyn, NY: Brooklyn Botanical Garden. 112 pp.

Reichard, S. 1994. *Assessing the potential of invasiveness in woody plants introduced in North America*. Ph.D. Dissertation. University of Washington. Seattle, WA.

Rolf, K. 1992a. A review of preventative and loosening measures to alleviate soil compaction in tree planting areas. *Arboricultural Journal*. 18:431–448.

Rolf, K. 1992b. Soil physical effects of pneumatic subsoil loosening using a Terralift soil aerator. *Journal of Arboriculture*. 18:235–240.

Rolf, K. 1994. Soil compaction and loosening effects on soil physics and tree growth. In *The Landscape Below Ground*. G. Watson and D. Neely, eds. Savoy, IL: International Society of Arboriculture. pp. 131–148.

Schoeneweiss, D. 1982. Prevention and treatment of construction damage to shade trees. *Journal of Arboriculture*. 8:169–175.

Schrader. 1996. American Tree. Panama City, FL. Personal communication. 9 November.

Smiley, T. 1994. The effects of soil aeration equipment on tree growth. In *The Landscape Below Ground*. G. Watson and D. Neely, eds. Savoy, IL: International Society of Arboriculture. pp. 207–210.

Smiley, T. 1996. Treating soil compaction near trees. Manuscript submitted to *Grounds Maintenance*.

Smiley, T., G. Watson, B. Fraedrich, and D. Booth. 1990. Evaluation of soil aeration equipment. *Journal of Arboriculture*. 16:118–123.

Svihra, P. 1991. A practical guide for diagnosing root rot in ornamentals. *Journal of Arboriculture*. 17:294–297.

Vander Weit, W., and R. Miller. 1986. The wooded lot: Homeowner and builder knowledge and perception. *Journal of Arboriculture*. 12:129–134.

Watson, G. 1991. Attaining root:crown balance in landscape trees. *Journal of Arboriculture*. 17:211–216.

Watson, G. 1996. Tree root system enhancement with paclobutrazol. *Journal of Arboriculture*. 22:211–217.

Watson, G., P. Kelsey, and K. Woodlii. 1996. Replacing soil in the root zone of mature trees for better root growth. *Journal of Arboriculture*. 22:167–173.

Weaver, M., and R. Stipes. 1988. White pine decline: A case study from Virginia landscapes. *Journal of Arboriculture*. 14:109–120.

Preparing Reports and Plans

Providing timely, useful, accurate information about the tree resource and the effects of development upon it is the most important contribution a consultant can make to a project. As the person with special knowledge about trees, the consultant must convey that information to others on the project team, to the governing agencies, and to the public. Maps and reports are important means of conveying such information. This chapter describes the ways in which maps and reports are prepared. Appendix A describes the basic supplies and equipment suggested to produce maps, plans, and details.

PREPARING REPORTS

Preparing summary reports is an integral part of the consultant's role in the tree preservation process. Readers may wish to refer to Abeyta (1995) for guidelines on preparing reports as consulting arborists.

Throughout the tree preservation process, several types of reports may be produced, depending upon the stage of planning and the purpose (Table 11.1). The most common types of tree preservation reports are

- Tree stand delineation
- Tree inventory or survey
- Tree report
- Tree preservation plan
- Homeowner's tree maintenance manual

The goal is to convey the necessary and pertinent information in a professional manner. Several standard presentation formats are used: text, tables, and plans (Table 11.2). Reports may contain supplemental attachments and inserts, such as

- **Photographs.** Photographs supplement text and table information by illustrating specific items (Figure 11.1). Photo prints may either be pasted onto the page or scanned into the computer and inserted into the text. Use of digital cameras allows importing the image directly into the

computer. Color copies can substitute for original photographic prints, provided they are clean and of high quality. Text can be added directly onto a photograph or copy to call attention to a specific detail. For example, a consultant preparing pruning specifications could use arrows drawn or pasted on the photograph to indicate specific branches. Alternatively, acetate sheets can be laid over the photograph and text information added atop it.

- **Details.** Details are portions of plans or construction drawings. They are used to clarify or emphasize particular portions or aspects of the plan or design, such as specific impacts to a tree (Figure 11.2) or placement and configuration of tree protection fencing. The details can be drawn by hand, scanned from an existing plan, or cut out of a plan and pasted into the document and photocopied. The source of the drawing should be identified.

- **Other information.** Information that is appropriate to the reader and that addresses related issues can be combined into a workable format. For instance, when preparing information for a subdivision composed of custom lots, it is helpful to display data regarding trees on each lot separately, because each will have a different owner (Figure 11.3).

PREPARING MAPS AND PLANS

Maps, plans, sections, and details are integral to the development process. It is safe to say that development could not occur without them. Visual representations of conceptual, design, and construction information is the lingua franca of development.

Most development professionals expect a high level of skill with graphic materials. Therefore, the consultant must be able to create graphics on par with other professionals, or team with design professionals, landscape architects, graphic artists, or draftspeople who can. The final product should communicate the arboricultural consultant's professionalism.

Strive for simple and clean graphics. "Simple" means remembering that the goal of the plan is to present tree information in a readable manner. Too many lines, words, and overlapping numbers create confusion. "Clean" means creating straight, even lines and lettering that are free of smudges, and completely removing mistakes and alterations. Use high-quality reproduction. Meeting a goal of clean and simple can be facilitated by using quality pens, paper, and tapes (Appendix A), by paying attention to visual details such as adequate margins, and by limiting visual clutter. Unnecessary information on the base map can be cut out, erased, or covered.

The consultant may find it helpful to develop a consistent map format, although no one layout will work well for every map. However the information is arranged, there are several basic requirements for all maps (Figure 11.4):

- **Title block:**
  - Name of project
  - Site location
  - Name of consultant (company logo, address, phone)
  - Date

- **Legend or key:** Description of symbols used on plan

- **Notes:** Additional information, conditions, and/or requirements (varies from project to project)

- **Scale:** The scale at which the plan is drawn (see "Drawing Scale" in Chapter 4). If the plan will be reduced or enlarged, use a graphic scale.

- **North arrow:** Convention places north towards the top of the page. Sometimes that orientation is awkward for the layout, and north is rotated.

- **Information tables:** In some cases, it is helpful to include summary tables with relevant data about each tree.

Maps and plans may be drawn by hand, generated on a computer, or created with a combination of the two. Appropriate methods vary with the type and quality of base maps available, the type and use of the map to be produced, and the tools and equipment available for production. The process of creating maps and plans can be summarized as follows. (Examples of this process are shown in Figures 11.5 through 11.8).

1. **Visualize the final product.** The first step is to develop a clear image of the final product. What information will be included and how will it be arranged on the paper? Consider the following:
   - finished size: 8½" x 11", 11" x 17", or 24" x 30"
   - reproduction method: photocopy, blueline print, acetate overlay, plotter
   - format: orientation, borders, headers, title block
   - information displayed: tree tag numbers, species, trunk diameter, canopy conformations, summary tables

2. **Locate base maps.** In most cases, tree survey and stand delineation maps use plans prepared by others on the design team as a starting point (e.g., topographic plans, boundary survey). Plans are available from the developer, planner, engineer, architect, and/or landscape architect. For a tree survey or inventory map, it is best to use a plan that has only existing features on it, rather than a development plan. Then, if the development plan changes, the tree map is still accurate. If the consultant is preparing a tree evaluation/ preservation plan, however, a development plan should be used as a base map so that grading and construction activity adjacent to the tree is illustrated. The consultant may request a map that emphasizes tree information by "screening" (making lines lighter) secondary information

REPRODUCTION METHODS

The most common reproduction method for plans is blueline prints. The plan is drawn on translucent paper (e.g., Mylar, vellum, polyester drafting film), then passed through a diazo machine that uses ammonia and light on chemically coated paper to produce a blueline print. The original also can be used to produce another print onto translucent paper than can then be used as an original.

When producing maps that will be reproduced by diazo, the consultant can request a "reverse-reading sepia" for the base map. In this process, the base map is printed onto the back of the translucent paper; the consultant adds tree information on the front. Special fluids are used to eradicate unnecessary information from the back of the base map without affecting what is drawn on the front.

Photocopying is the easiest method for duplicating small maps. Because translucency is not required, any information to be removed from the base map can be covered over or cut out. Originals can be produced on any type of good-quality white paper.

such as existing structures, utilities, or grading contours. Consultants with CAD (computer-aided design) capability can supply maps on disk. Whenever a base map prepared by others is used, the source of the original should be credited.

3. **Add tree information.** Once the base map is prepared, the tree information can be added. For tree surveys, the tree tag number should be included. Trees can be emphasized by drawing over the dripline with a thick pen. For tree stand delineations, vegetation types can be indicated with color, graphic film, lettering, or by drawing a pattern. If the plan will be photographically reduced when completed, the lettering must be large enough to be readable when reduced. Small-pattern graphic film fades away when reduced.

4. **Add the title block and other text.** A map must have a title block that includes the map title, name and location of the project, date of preparation, client information, source of base map, scale, north arrow, and the consultant's name and/or company logo. Notes and keys to any symbols used on the plan should be included in a box in an open area on the plan. If the size of the base map will be changed, a graphic scale should be included.

5. **Incorporate the information into a report.** Maps, details, and sections usually are incorporated into a report. Maps that are 8½" x 11" or 11" x 17" can be bound into the report. Larger maps can be folded and placed in a sleeve that has been bound into the report.

REFERENCES

Abeyta, D., ed. 1995. *Guide to Report Writing for Consulting Arborists*. Savoy, IL: International Society of Arboriculture. 142 pp.

COMPUTER-AIDED DESIGN

Most topographic and development plans today are created and manipulated in CAD (computer-aided design) systems. CAD is a type of software program in which geometrically precise drawings are created. The drawings can be created in layers, with each layer representing a specific type of information. For example, existing topographic information may be on one layer, existing services (utilities, sewer, etc.) on another layer, future grades on a third, and so forth. The graphic information is stored electronically and is printed at the desired scale with plotters.

There are several advantages to using CAD systems. First, changes can be made on the computer screen and plotted without having to redraw the entire plan. Second, desired layers of information may be selected and plotted atop each other. For example, the consultant can request a plan that shows vegetation canopy and topographic lines in full value, with the development plan screened to a lighter value. Third, the plans can be printed at any scale without the step of photographic enlargement or reduction.

Learning to manipulate CAD programs is time and equipment intensive. The consultant may prefer to provide tree information hand-drawn on a base map to the designer who will then create the "tree survey" layer.

TABLE 11.1 Types of tree preservation reports.

Type of report	Phase of development	Topics covered	Chapter reference
Tree stand delineation	Planning	Describes general character of woody vegetation	5
		Identifies opportunities and constraints for tree preservation	5
		Option: General guidelines for tree preservation during development	6
Tree inventory or survey	Planning	Describes health and structure of individual trees	5
		Assesses suitability for preservation	5
		Option: general guidelines for tree preservation during development	6
Tree report	Design	Describes health and structure of individual trees and stands	5
		Assesses suitability for preservation	5
		Evaluates impacts from development	6
		Recommends trees to be removed and preserved	6
		Provides specifications for tree preservation before, during, and following construction (including remedial maintenance)	6, 8, 9
Tree preservation plan	Design	Describes health and structure of individual trees and stands	5

TABLE 11.1 (continued)

Type of report	Phase of development	Topics covered	Chapter reference
		Recommends trees to be removed and trees to be preserved	6,7
		Provides specifications for tree preservation before, during, and following construction (including remedial maintenance)	6, 8, 9, 10
Homeowner's tree maintenance manual	Postconstruction	Describes health and structure of individual trees	5
		Describes maintenance requirements of preserved trees	10

TABLE 11.2 Range of topics covered in tree preservation reports.

Topic	Description
Text	
Introduction and Overview	Describes project and work assignment
Site Description	Describes location and character of site
Survey Methods	Describes methods and techniques used in obtaining information contained in the report
Description of Trees	Describes resource, either as individuals or a group
Suitability for Preservation	Assesses suitability for preservation of surveyed trees
Evaluation of Impacts	Describes the project Describes the types of construction impacts and their effect on trees
Recommendations for Preservation	Summarizes resource evaluation and impacts by making specific recommendations for preservation or removal
Appraisal of Value	Describes the value of trees
Tree Preservation Guidelines	Provides specifications and guidelines for tree preservation
Summary	Summarizes the results and findings
Plans	
Tree Stand Delineation	Graphic representation of stand delineation
Trees Affected by Development	Graphic representation of trees and stands potentially affected by development
Tree Survey/Location Map	Graphic representation of location of surveyed trees
Tree Evaluation/Preservation Map	Graphic representation of trees relative to the development; preservation/removal status; may include protection specifications

TABLE 11.2 (continued)

Topic	Description
Fencing Plan	Graphic representation of location of tree protective fencing
Details	Graphic representation of specific trees or areas of development
Tables	
Forest Cover Types	List of forest cover types present on the site
Tree Information	Results of tree survey; may include proposed action and/or appraised value
Species and Frequency	List of surveyed trees by species and frequency of occurrence
Species and Condition	List of surveyed trees by species and condition
Heritage, Historic Trees	List of surveyed tree that fall under specific regulations by size, age, species, etc.
Trees Recommended for Preservation	List of those surveyed trees recommended for preservation
Trees Recommended for Removal	List of those surveyed trees recommended for removal
Trees to be Located by Engineer Survey	List of surveyed trees for which horizontal and vertical elevations are to be established
Attachments	
Species Information	Information on the cultural, environmental, and maintenance requirements of trees found on the site
Details and Photographs	Additional details or representations

TREE EVALUATION
ZWICKER ESTATES

Tree No.:	265
Species:	Coast live oak
Condition rating:	Poor
Suitability for preservation:	Poor
Comments:	Tree in advanced decline (A). Many dead limbs and stubs from previous branch failures are present (B, arrows). Extensive trunk decay at site of failure of second trunk (C). Continued decline and structural failure of tree cannot be reversed.
Recommendation:	Remove tree. Replace with three 15-gallon coast live oaks.

FIGURE 11.1 Photographs can be used in reports to illustrate specific features. In this example, text was produced on a word processor, color photographs were pasted on, then color photocopies were made for report presentation. As an alternative, the images could be scanned, inserted into the text, and printed with color printer.

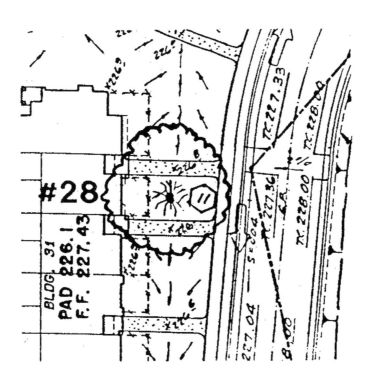

Tree #:	28
Species:	London plane (*Platanus* x *acerifolia*)
Trunk diameter:	24"
Description:	Large, striking, vigorous tree with well-structured crown.
Condition rating:	Good
Impacts:	This tree is being retained in a small, 25"-wide landscape area between two sidewalks. The building is 20' south; Black Road, 20' north.
Recommendations:	Modify sidewalk design to allow at least 15' between the trunk and the sidewalks. Place sidewalks on existing grade, using extra reinforcement to minimize subbase compaction requirements. Install root control devices at the edge of the sidewalk. Do not irrigate or plant within 5' of the edge of trunks. Prune to reduce end weight on horizontal branches.

FIGURE 11.2 Details can be used to supplement text information. In this example, a portion of the grading plan showing the subject tree was cut out and pasted onto the printed page to illustrate what construction would occur around the tree. Another way to produce this exhibit is to scan the drawing, crop the desired area, and insert it into the text. For those with CAD capability, that portion of the drawing could be excerpted and text added.

TREE RESOURCE AND DEVELOPMENT GUIDELINES
CURRID DEVELOPMENT, LTD.

Lot 7

TREE SURVEY

Tree No.	Species	Concern	Treatment
233	Coast live oak	Fill soil added at base of trunk	Remove fill
234	Coast live oak	Fill soil added at base of trunk	Remove fill
235	Coast live oak	Low canopy; at risk for failure	Prune to reduce end weight on low horizontal branch to west and remove dead wood
236	Coast live oak	Located at edge of lot, outside pad area	——
237	Valley oak	Grading adjacent to trunk; at risk for failure	Remove tree
238	Coast live oak	Leans over building pad; at risk for failure	Remove tree
239	Coast live oak	Low canopy	Prune to raise crown to provide 6' vertical clearance

DEVELOPMENT GUIDELINES

(The following are site-specific development and management recommendations that supplement the homeowner's tree preservation guidelines provided.)

1. To assess construction impacts and design structures, an engineer should accurately locate and plot on all plans the trunks of trees #233 and 234.

2. The building footprint for this lot must be staked in the field and evaluated relative to surrounding trees.

3. Trees #237 and 238 must be removed for reasons of safety and impacts.

4. Fill soil must be removed from around the trunks of trees #233 and 234 to natural grade.

5. All trees must be pruned to clean the crowns and provide adequate vertical clearance.

FIGURE 11.3 Information should be presented in a way that helps the reader understand the consultant's evaluation and recommendations and is easy to use. This format combines tree survey information with development guidelines for a project consisting of several custom lots on which the building pads had already been graded. Tree information for each lot was condensed onto one page so that as the lot was sold, the developer could easily supply the pertinent tree information for that lot. Each new owner also was provided with a homeowner's tree preservation guidelines booklet that addressed general tree protection and care issues.

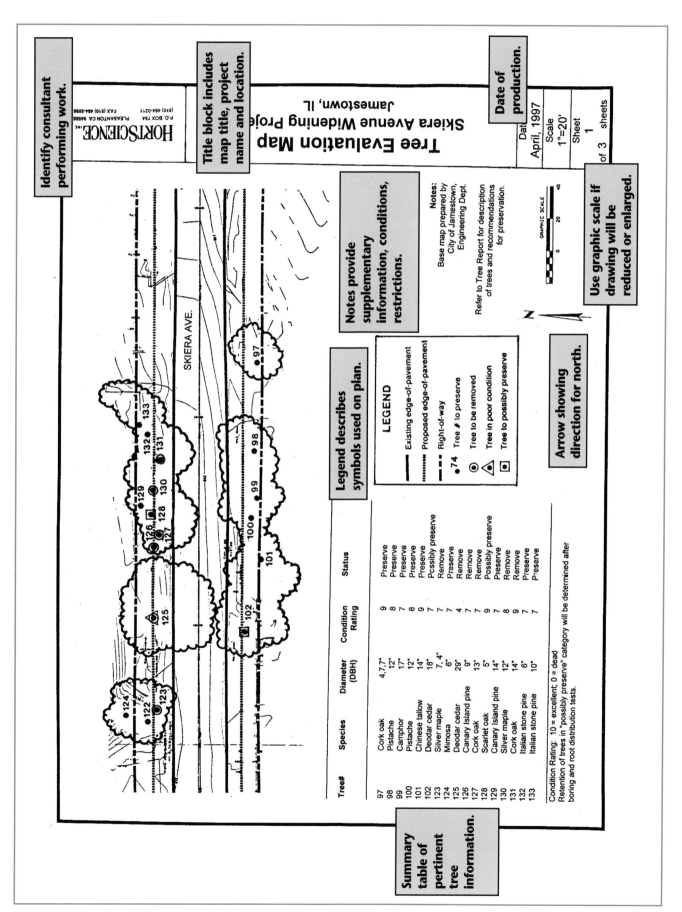

FIGURE 11.4   Components of a plan or map.

1. **Visualize the final product.** This is a stand delineation map. Two maps will be produced: a blueline print at 100 scale (24" x 30") to incorporate into the project's plan set, and a reduced 11" x 17" map, reproduced by color photocopy.

2. **Assemble appropriate base maps and materials.** A 100-scale topographic Mylar map of the site was provided by the project engineer. Blueline prints were run off that original for use in the field survey.

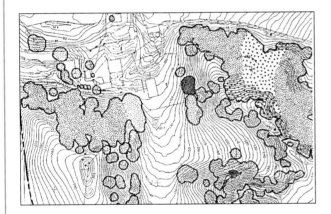

3. **Add tree information.** During the field survey, tree information was coded by species and forest association using different colored highlighting pens. That information was transferred onto the topographic map using self-sticking graphic film to denote vegetation types.

   Graphic films tend to fade out when the image is reduced. For the 11" x 17" map, therefore, the vegetation types were color coded using art pencils.

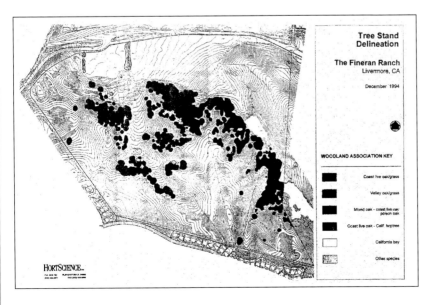

4. **Add title block, keys, and notes.** The title block for the 24" x 30" map was produced in a word processor, copied onto drafting appliqué film, and fixed to the plan.

   The title block for the 11" x 17" map was produced in a word processor, printed onto bond paper, then cut and pasted onto the colored map.

FIGURE 11.5 Preparing a tree stand delineation map.

1. **Visualize the final product.** This is a tree survey or inventory map. The final map size will be 11" x 17", and it will be photocopied and bound into the tree report.

2. **Assemble appropriate base maps and materials.** Because the purpose of this map is to record tree location, it is best to use a topographic map or boundary survey for the base. As the project is designed and the development plan redrawn, this map will remain accurate. In this case, the project engineer provided a 24" x 30" blueline print of the tentative tract map. Existing site features were shown, as well as parcel boundaries. Tree canopy lines have been screened, so they are faintly visible.

   The plan does not reproduce well and important information will need to be emphasized with a pen. The portions of the base map that are useful for the tree survey map are cut out and pasted onto a clean sheet of 11" x 17" paper. In this case, the title block and legend were removed, the site plan cut down, and the north arrow and graphic scale repositioned.

3. **Add tree information.** Tree numbers are added with a labeling machine that prints onto self-adhesive tape. The numbers are cut from the tape and positioned on the map. Numbers could be hand lettered.

   If precise trunk locations have yet to be surveyed, avoid placing a symbol representing the trunk. When trunk locations are known, a circle template can be used to draw the trunk.

   Draw in tree canopies with a heavy line.

4. **Add title block, keys, and notes.** The title block for the 11" x 17" map was produced in a word processor, printed onto bond, then cut and pasted onto the map. Notes include acknowledgment of the source of the base map, reference to the tree survey, and an explanation that the driplines and tree locations are approximate, not measured.

1. Base map

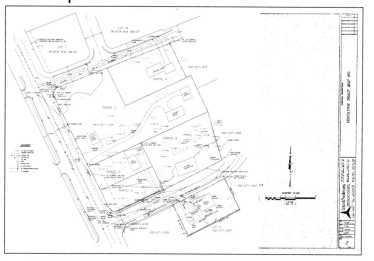

2. Add tree information

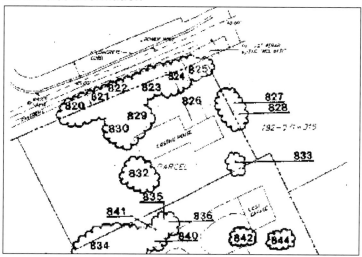

3. Add title block

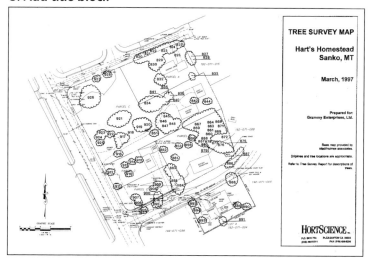

FIGURE 11.6 Preparing a tree survey or inventory map.

1. **Visualize the final product.** This is a tree protection plan for a single lot. The format is 8½" x 11", photocopied, and attached to a short report.

2. **Assemble appropriate base map and materials.** The architect supplied a 24" x 30" blueline of the site plan for use as the base map. This map was copy reduced to 11" x 17" on white bond.

3. **Add tree information.** Tree numbers were printed on a labeling machine and fixed to the plan. Canopies and fence locations were drawn with a thick pen.

4. **Add title block, key, and notes.** Title block, key, and notes were produced in a word processor, printed out, and then glued onto the map. Arrows were drawn by hand. After the map was completed, it was copy reduced to 8½" x 11" onto company stationery.

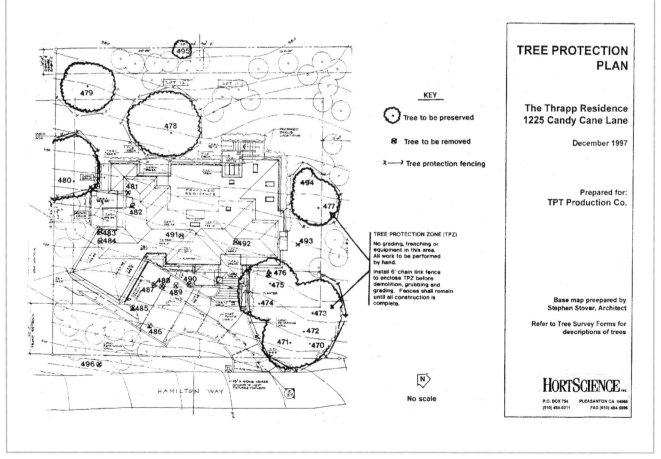

FIGURE 11.7 Preparing a tree protection map for a small lot.

There are a number of relatively simple ways to create maps on the computer, short of learning a CAD program. Map A was created using home landscape design software. Most such programs support printing in color and provide various templates for tree types. An important feature is the capability for representing noncircular tree canopies.

Another method is to scan the base map into the computer, import the graphic file into a word-processing or desktop publishing program, then add the tree information, titles, labels, and keys. In map B, a blueline print of the site plan was provided by the landscape architect. The map was copy reduced to 8½" x 11" and scanned into the computer. Tree information was added using a desktop publishing program.

Map A

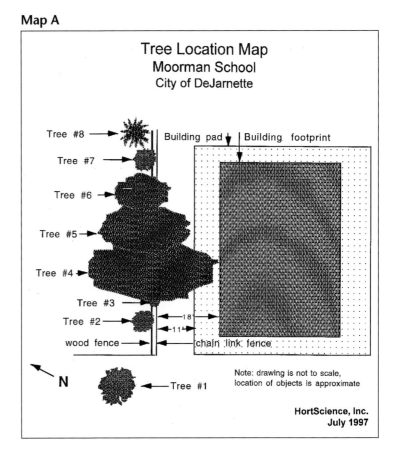

Map B

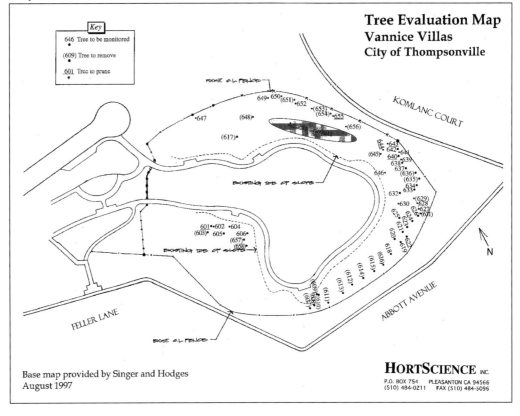

FIGURE 11.8 Preparing maps on a computer.

Case Studies

CASE STUDY #1

United Parcel Service Headquarters Campus
Atlanta, Georgia
(Case study provided by Spence Rosenfeld, Arborguard Tree Specialists, Avondale, Georgia)

The Project
"We want a work environment that blends our corporate culture with the beautiful surroundings of our location," said Kent C. "Oz" Nelson, UPS Chairman and CEO, when unveiling plans for their corporate headquarters. Their goal was to create a facility that appeared to drop from the sky into the forest.

A seven-story facility with 620,000 square feet of office space was created (Photo 1a). The building footprint covered six of the 36-acre site. Two parking decks provided space for 1,800 cars. The site was developed with less than 40 percent of the allowed density.

United Parcel Service participated in the Global ReLeaf for New Communities program, and was awarded the Global ReLeaf Award in 1994.

PHOTO 1a The UPS campus was designed to appear to have dropped from the sky into the forest (photo credit: Aerial Innovations).

PHOTO 1b The site was densely forested. Fencing marks the clearing limits.

The Vegetation
The site was densely forested with 37 percent white oak, 27 percent chestnut oak, 12 percent poplar, 12 percent hickory, 5 percent pine, and 5 percent beech (Photo 1b). Most trees were rated in fair condition. Retention of the forest, wetland, and existing ravine was a high priority.

The project was within the jurisdiction of the Fulton County Tree Preservation Ordinance. Removal of trees over 2 inches in diameter at 6 inches above grade in the protected zone (land outside the buildable area) was prohibited. A plan that identified areas of tree preservation and methods of tree protection within the protected zone was required.

The arboricultural consultants, Arborguard Tree Specialists, tagged and evaluated nearly 300 specimen trees, developed the tree protection plan, and prepared construction specifications. A critical root zone was identified and plotted on plans for each tree (Figure 1a). Arborguard was on site before and during demolition and construction to identify retention areas and ensure adherence to specifications.

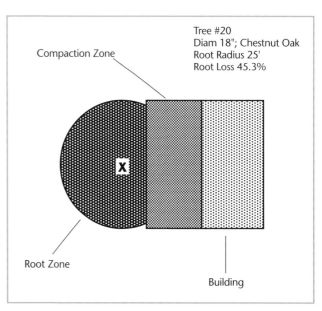

FIGURE 1a A critical root zone was identified for each tree and plotted on plans. The root radius was estimated at 1 foot per inch of trunk diameter plus 20 to 30 percent. Construction plans were plotted and the amount of root loss calculated. Root loss in excess of 50 percent was considered heavy impact; from 25 to 50 was deemed moderate; and less than 25 percent was considered light.

Special Design and Construction Techniques

The entire project, from building concept through walkway layout, was undertaken with the preservation of trees in mind. To make the buildings appear part of the native forest, the heights of buildings were designed to complement the heights of the trees. Weather balloons were set at the elevations of the roof for comparison. Photographs were taken from the tops of trees to evaluate views from windows. The facility was designed to bridge the existing ravine so water could pass beneath it. Views of the unique site feature were incorporated into the design.

Before clearing, the limits of tree removal were flagged. Tree protection fencing was installed after clearing but before grading (Photo 1c). The specifications included provisions to require fencing before clearing if clearing crews did not stay within the clearing limits. Roots were pruned prior to construction whenever soil cuts or wall installations took place within the critical root zone.

During construction, tower cranes were set up inside the building footprint to minimize land needed for construction staging (Photo 1d). This allowed trees to remain within 10 to 15 feet of building edges. Land disturbance also was minimized by placing parking on decks.

To ensure compliance with the tree preservation specifications, a penalty system was implemented. Damage was assessed using the Council of Tree and Landscape Appraisal formulas and doubled for punitive purposes. Over the course of the project, only two small fines were levied, both during initial grading.

Other special design and construction techniques were facilitated for tree preservation.

- Underground utilities were placed outside restricted tree preservation areas. Utility contractors were warned that longer-than-normal runs of cable or pipe might be required.
- Soil nailing was used to stabilize vertical cuts. This technique prevented sloped trench walls, thereby reducing encroachment in to root areas (see Chapter 8).

PHOTO 1c Tree protection fencing was installed before grading and construction.

PHOTO 1d Tower cranes were used to construct the building. This technique minimized the size of the construction area (photo credit: Aerial Innovations).

- Wood chips generated during clearing were used as mulch under retained trees.
- For new plantings, small plant material was used to minimize the amount of digging into the soil under existing trees.
- Irrigation of new plantings was accomplished with a surface-laid drip system to avoid excavation into existing tree roots.

The Team

Owner	UPS, Kent C. "Oz" Nelson, Chairman
Arboricultural Consultant	Arborguard Tree Specialists (Spence Rosenfeld, President)
Architects	Thompson, Ventulett, Stainback & Associates
General Contractor	Beers Construction Company (Martha Kitchens, Project Director)
Landscape Architects	Hughes, Good, O'Leary and Ryan (Bob Hughes and Rob Ryan)

CASE STUDY #2

Arbor Day Farm Timber Bridge and Ravine Crossing

Nebraska City, Nebraska

(Case study provided by John Royster, ASLA, The Big Muddy Workshop)

The Project

The National Arbor Day Foundation created two crossings to span South Table Creek and one of its tributaries at Arbor Day Farm. The Foundation considered protection of the native vegetation a critical component of the designs. The demonstration Timber Bridge is a 175-foot long glu-laminate beam bridge (Photo 2a). Visitors seem to walk through the treetops of the creek's native forest as they cross the bridge that spans from the crest of one side of

PHOTO 2b The ravine crossing is a set of wooden stairs and decks that cross a deep, steep-sided ravine.

PHOTO 2a The timber bridge is a 175-foot-long glu-laminate beam bridge spanning South Table Creek.

the valley to the other. The ravine crossing is a set of wooden stairs and decks that cross a deep, steep-sided ravine (Photo 2b). Seating is provided on each deck level to encourage visitors to stop and observe the lush surrounding forest.

The Vegetation

Native vegetation on the site changes from riparian species along the creek to upland oak-hickory forest on the valley's steep sides and terraces flanking the valley.

Eighty- to one-hundred-year-old bur oaks line the valley. An additional site factor that influenced design was that the loess soils become highly erosive when disturbed.

Special Design and Construction Techniques

Several potential sites were evaluated for the timber bridge location by the landscape architect, who considered vegetation, site geology, and pedestrian circulation. The arboricultural consultant met with the landscape architect and owner on site to discuss the bridge location and to evaluate the condition and vigor of adjacent trees. Slight adjustments were made to preserve a small hackberry at the bridge's north end.

Key to minimizing impacts to trees during construction of the timber bridge was planning least-intrusive construction staging and access routes:

- To eliminate haul roads for constructing five massive concrete foundations, concrete was pumped via 4-inch-diameter hoses through the forested area (Photo 2c).

PHOTO 2c Bridge foundations were constructed from concrete pumped through hoses from trunks stationed on a road at the top of the bank.

- To place the 50-foot-long bridge beams, the landscape architect worked with the contractor to pre-position the beams at each end of the bridge and then lift them into place with a heavy-lift helicopter (Photo 2d). This innovative technique not only prevented the destruction of up to half an acre of forest (which would have been required to place the beams with vehicle-mounted cranes), but actually reduced installation costs by two-thirds.

- All construction equipment on site used preapproved access routes.

- All material storage was located outside the forest on a grassed parking area.

PHOTO 2d Bridge beams were lifted into place by a helicopter.

PHOTO 2e Pier footing locations for the ravine crossing were staked before construction began and adjusted to minimize tree impacts.

To ensure that vehicle access restrictions were followed, the landscape architect was present when major pieces of construction equipment (excavator, concrete pumps, material delivery trucks) were brought on site.

The ravine crossing was designed to avoid removal of any trees. Pier footing locations were staked before construction began to determine specific impacts to trees and determine where modifications were necessary (Photo 2e). Tree root flares were analyzed to avoid root damage, affecting the size and shape of both decks and staircases.

Construction impacts were carefully controlled at the ravine crossing:

- To decrease construction impacts on the site, the structural design called for wooden components that were partially prefabricated off site and then hand carried onto the site, thereby avoiding the use of heavy equipment.

- Pier footings (12-inch diameter x 8-foot depth) were used to minimize subsurface disruption. The holes for the footings were hand dug with the exception of the piers at end of the crossing, where a skid loader with auger attachment was used to bore footing holes. Concrete was carried into the site from trucks located outside the forested area.

- Prior to construction, vehicle parking areas, concrete truck access routes, and material storage sites were defined and included in the construction contract to provide an enforceable mechanism to protect the site.

- A team of staff members of the owner, landscape architect, consulting arborist, and general contractor was formed to create a common understanding of site-protection goals and specific preservation techniques. This partnering effort resulted in suggestions that decreased construction impacts and created a higher quality project.

The Team

Owner	The National Arbor Day Foundation (John Rosenow, President)	*Arboricultural Consultant*	Urban Forest Management, Inc. (Charles Stewart, President)
Landscape Architect/ Bridge Designer	The Big Muddy Workshop (John Royster, ASLA)	*Structural Engineer*	Nielsen Baumert Engineering, Inc.
		General Contractor	Dostal/Voss Construction, Inc.

CASE STUDY #3

Heritage Tree on Residential Property
Portland, Oregon
(Case study provided by Donna Attewell and Kevin Hillery, Whole Tree Works, Inc., Portland, Oregon)

The Project
The City of Portland was planning a street improvement project that would impact a large Spanish chestnut. The owner of the property, Joshua Shulman, said, "The city will soon put this street widening project out to bid . . .

PHOTO 3a Heritage Spanish chestnut after existing vegetation was removed by hand, and before the root crown excavation and crown clearing pruning were performed.

The Tree
The approximately 100-year-old Spanish chestnut (*Castanea sativa*) was 12 feet in circumference, 80 feet tall, and had a 60-foot canopy spread. The consulting arborist

Special Design and Construction Techniques
Planned construction was to remove the existing pavement, replace the storm drain and water main line, reconstruct the street with an 18-inch-deep pavement section, and construct a sidewalk, bike path, curb, and gutter. The alignment of the curb was through the trunk of the tree.

Transportation agencies became a cooperative part of the team with the arboricultural consultants to redesign the plans to save the tree. The following changes were made:

- The street alignment was moved northward, 1 foot beyond the trunk.
- The sidewalk was placed to the south of the tree. The alignment curved away from the trunk.

and I'm afraid someone with a backhoe will mow the tree over." At that point he retained an arboricultural consultant and attorney to help work with the City of Portland Office of Transportation and the Oregon Department of Transportation to redesign the street and preserve the tree.

judged the tree to be in moderate condition for its age (Photo 3a). Decay present from old wounds was well compartmentalized.

Shulman petitioned the city to have the tree designated a heritage tree; the petition was granted. Portland's city code includes a heritage tree designation for trees that are noteworthy based on age, species, size, or historical significance. Seventy-five trees have received that designation. Not only was this tree unique in Portland for its age and species, but the Shulman home, built in the late 19th century, was historically important. The city recognized that the tree was historically significant as well. Pruning, performing a root crown excavation, or removal of heritage trees requires a permit from the city's urban forester.

The tree, originally a component of a rural landscape, had been impacted over the years as the community grew around it. Approximately 45 years ago, a road was installed about 5 feet north of the tree. Road bed preparation was minimal; no curb or gutter was installed.

The arboricultural consultants performed a root crown excavation to determine the location of the tree roots. They found only one 1½-inch diameter root extending north under the existing pavement. There were many small roots running parallel to the pavement.

Preconstruction treatments were pruning the canopy to remove dead wood and applying mulch under the tree. During construction, several techniques were employed to minimize damage to the tree:

- The tree was fenced to enclose a spindle-shaped tree protection zone approximately 100 feet long. The length of the zone was determined by the root pattern of the tree (many roots parallel to the road) and the constraints of the project.
- The sidewalk was constructed on natural grade, by hand, with no subgrade compaction or base added. The existing vegetation was removed by hand. No equipment was allowed on the south side of the tree (Photo 3b).
- Low limbs that would conflict with construction equipment were raised with ropes and tied into the tree.

• The consulting arborist was on site to supervise all excavation around the tree.

The arboricultural consultant worked in a spirit of cooperation with state and city transportation engineers, contractors, and the property owner to design and construct the project so that everyone's goals were met. A successful tree preservation project resulted (Photos 3c).

PHOTO 3b The sidewalk design was modified to place it to the south of the tree. It was constructed on natural grade, by hand, with no subgrade compaction or base added.

PHOTOS 3c Through cooperative efforts of the owner, arboricultural consultants, engineers, and contractors, the completed project retained the tree and provided necessary street improvements.

The Team

Owner	Joshua Shulman
Arboricultural Consultant	Whole Tree Works, Inc. (Donna Attewell and Kevin Hillery)
Attorney	Eric Jenson
Designer/Engineers	Oregon Department of Transportation and City of Portland Office of Transportation
General Contractor	Copenhagen Utilities and Construction, Inc.

CASE STUDY #4

Shields Library Expansion
Davis, California

The Project
The University of California, Davis, was planning to expand its primary library (Shields Library). A mature turkey oak was located in the proposed development area and was incorporated into the design as a feature of the future courtyard.

PHOTO 4a During the expansion of Shields Library, this turkey oak was to be preserved. The existing portion of the library to the north of the tree would be removed and a new building constructed on its foundation.

The Tree
The 42-inch-diameter turkey oak (*Quercus cerris*) was about 70 years old, with a canopy spread of approximately 80 feet (Photo 4a). The arboricultural consultant judged the tree to be in moderately good condition. Twig growth for the previous year averaged 8 inches. There were no external signs of wounds or decay on the trunk. The lowest limbs supported epicormic growth, while growth in the upper crown was normal.

Planned Construction
The library expansion plans were designed with preservation of the tree in mind. The goal was to surround the tree with the new building. Following is a summary of the planned changes:

- The existing building north of the tree would be demolished and a two-story building constructed in its place. The existing foundation would be left intact and used for the new building to avoid root damage to the tree.

Walls of glass would provide an uninterrupted view of the tree from the library into the courtyard. The challenge was to preserve the tree while providing a solid walking surface through the courtyard, demolishing the existing structure to the north, and constructing two new wings.

Prior to the expansion project, the library formed a U-shape to the north, east, and south of the tree. The north side of the canopy extended over the building. Thirty feet to the east was a sunken patio and an underground utility line (four feet deep). A wooden fence was a few feet to the west, beyond which were two temporary buildings on concrete slabs on grade. Approximately 8 inches of rock fill was at the base of the tree.

No one was aware of any maintenance activities that had been applied to the tree. Fortunately, the tree had been evaluated 12 to 18 months before construction was to begin. The arboricultural consultant recommended preconditioning treatments pruning, fertilizing, and several irrigations (Photo 4b).

PHOTO 4b A year before construction began, a program of irrigation, fertilization, and pruning was initiated. The low, horizontal limbs that supported primarily epicormic growth were removed (arrows).

- The temporary buildings to the west would be removed. In their place a link between the north and south wings of the library would be constructed.

- The entrance to the courtyard from the west wing would be below existing grade. The cut would begin 20 feet west of the tree and increase in depth to 4½ feet approximately 30 feet away.

- Pedestrian access across the courtyard was required. An area (5 x 8 feet) around the trunk would be retained at natural grade. Beyond that, concrete and stone paving would be installed. Approximately 6 inches of excavation would be required to install the pavement.

Special Design and Construction Techniques

To evaluate the extent of root impact that would occur from the excavation for the west wing, an exploratory trench was dug 20 feet from the tree at the top of the cut. Three 1-inch-diameter roots were encountered. The top 6 inches of soil contained few roots.

The consulting arborist recommended the following changes to the plans:

- The protected area around the base of the tree was increased to 10 feet.
- Existing grade was to be maintained within a minimum of 20 feet from the tree.
- The finish grade of the paving was raised to minimize excavation for the pavement section (Figure 4a).
- Pervious paving materials were to be used on the upper courtyard.
- Soil compaction was to be restricted to hand-tamping, and no excavation deeper than 6 inches was allowed within 20 feet of the tree.
- A tree protection zone (a minimum of 20 feet from the tree) was established and enclosed with chainlink fencing.
- An irrigation system was recommend to be installed at the edge of the pavement opening, placed just beneath the soil surface.

The landscape architect, and consulting arborist considered many pavement designs in the upper courtyard trying to find a suitable solution that would be attractive, provide a safe walking surface, and allow exchange of water and air with minimum subbase preparation. The original concept was for granite setts on gravel base within 15 feet of the tree, and poured-in-place concrete on gravel with 2-inch-wide gravel-filled aeration strips. There would be no soil compaction within the dripline. The university engineers considered such a surface unstable. The final compromise was replacing the gravel base with a class II aggregate permeable base. The gravel aeration strips in the concrete were replaced with two rows of granite setts butted with no mortar.

During the design phase, the consulting arborist became increasingly concerned about the cumulative effects of impacts to the tree as the protection zone grew smaller and smaller. Construction activity around

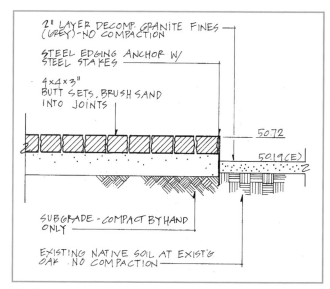

FIGURE 4a: To minimize excavation into the root zone, the finish grade of the pavement was raised and retained at the edge with steel edging. Granite setts were placed on sand over hand-compacted subgrade (see Photo 4c inset for installed pavement).

the tree was intense. However, eight years after construction, the tree has had greater growth and denser foliage than before construction. The efforts to protect the tree were well rewarded by the beauty it adds to the library (Photo 4c).

PHOTO 4c The completed project featured the oak in the courtyard. The pavement materials and design provided a stable walking surface, as well as allowed water and gas exchange in the root area (inset).

The Team

Owner	University of California, Davis, Office of Architects and Engineers
Arboricultural Consultant	HortScience, Inc. (Nelda Matheny)
Landscape Architects	Meacham O'Brien
Architects	Simon Martin-Vegue Winkelstein Moris

CASE STUDY #5

Reconstruction of Main Street
Pleasanton, California

The Project
The City of Pleasanton planned to renovate an eight-block section of Main Street through the downtown area. The project involved replacement of utilities, sidewalks, and pavement across the entire roadway section, from building front to building front (Photo 5a). The existing street trees were to be retained.

PHOTO 5a Existing street trees were retained during reconstruction of Main Street.

The Trees
Forty-nine trees were within the project area. Most of the trees were mature Modesto ash ranging in diameter from 12 to 30 inches. Other species included western catalpa, Chinese hackberry, ginkgo, tuliptree, London planetree, Bradford pear, holly oak, Purple Robe locust and black locust. All had been planted as street trees within small sidewalk cutouts surrounded by pavement. Most of the trees were in moderate to good condition.

Special Design and Construction Techniques
Tree damage during initial stages of demolition made it apparent that a consulting arborist was needed to monitor construction activity and reduce the incidence of damage. It was not possible to fence off a tree protection zone. Equipment had to work within inches of each tree to remove sidewalks, curbs, and other structures (Photo 5b). The consulting arborist was on site constantly to monitor activities and help direct demolition crews working near trees.

In most cases, when the pavement was removed around trees, large surface roots were exposed. Replacement of the pavement required removal of some of those roots. Forty of the 47 trees incurred some level of root injury and removal. In seven cases, the damage was severe: 6-to-8-inch-diameter roots were removed within 5 feet of the trunk, or the surface was changed from turf to pavement. Pavement plans were altered during construction near some trees where excavation and root removal would have damaged the buttress. In some instances, the tree grade was left higher than the surrounding pavement (Photo 5c).

Demolition and construction techniques were important to successful preservation of trees:
- The consulting arborist was present whenever activity occurred around a tree.

PHOTO 5b Equipment had to be operated within inches of each tree to remove curbs, sidewalks, and pavement.

- The consulting arborist communicated with the contractors about what needed to be accomplished, and how that could be done while protecting the tree.
- Large construction equipment was positioned in such a way that operation would stay clear of the trunk and branches.
- Large equipment was used to pull intact sections of concrete away from the tree (smaller equipment required breaking up the concrete, and pieces sometimes fell against the tree and caused damage).

PHOTO 5c When necessary, pavement was placed on top of existing grade to minimize root removal.

- Once the pavement was removed, the roots within the top 8 inches were exposed by hand, which allowed a determination of the amount of root removal required to install pavement. If impacts were determined to be too severe, possible modifications to the plan were discussed, including enlarging tree wells in pavement, eliminating aggregate base rock, rerouting utility lines as necessary, and reducing thickness of concrete section near the trunk.

- Where root removal was required, roots were cut cleanly by hand.

The following treatments were applied to trees during and after construction.

- To enhance the formation of woundwood, wounds were treated when they occurred, before monitoring began. Treatments included pruning broken roots back to sound tissue and scribing the perimeter of wounds to remove torn bark.

- Modesto ash trees with codominant trunks were cabled.

- Existing cabling systems in Modesto ash trees were inspected.

- Pruning was performed to clean the tree crowns and reduce end weight on horizontal branches (trees were crown raised before demolition began).

- One small tree with a trunk injury was removed.

- Root-impacted trees were irrigated.

- The health of all trees was monitored.

Four years after completion of the project, all trees have survived and are growing well (Photo 5d), although heavily impacted trees were defoliated more severely in the spring by anthracnose than were trees with moderate to low impacts.

PHOTO 5d Four years after completion of the project, the trees are growing well.

The Team

Owner   City of Pleasanton

Arboricultural Consultant   HortScience, Inc. (Jim Clark and Donna Attewell)

Landscape Architect   City of Pleasanton (Mike Fulford)

Project Manager   Harris and Associates (Gary Skrel)

Civil Engineers   City of Pleasanton (Douglas McMillan); Creegan and D'Angelo (Jack Steward)

General Contractor   Redgwick Construction Co.

CASE STUDY #6

Williamson Run

Carmel, Indiana
(Case study provided by Mark Boyce, C.P. Morgan, Carmel, Indiana)

The Project

When the development team for C.P. Morgan began planning Williamson Run, Chuck Morgan was hoping to preserve not only his family heritage—the site had been part of the Morgan family homestead in 1952—but also the natural features of the land that had been a part of his childhood. The project is a 120-acre site with 172 single-family homesites, encompassing both forest and agricultural land (Photo 6a). The project received the Global ReLeaf for New Communities Award in 1994.

PHOTO 6a The Williamson Run project comprises 120 acres of agricultural and forested land.

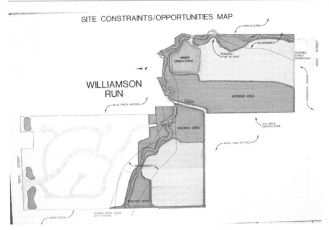

PHOTO 6b The project was designed to consider the site's natural features, described in the site opportunities and constraints map.

The Vegetation

The natural features of the site included Carmel Creek and its floodway, mature tree stands, difficult soil conditions, agricultural land, and a large lake created by a mining operation (Photo 6b). The forest was composed of 100 year-old sycamore, shagbark hickory, buckeye, sugar maple, cherry, and walnut. The approach of the design team was to preserve and highlight the positive features while transforming difficult ones into community amenities (Photo 6c).

PHOTO 6c The neighborhood is accessed by the Old Town Run Bridge, which passes over Carmel River, lined with 100-year old sycamore trees.

Special Design and Construction Techniques

The land plan for Williamson Run was the result of extensive site analysis, market research, and land planning studies by the development team over a five-year period. The plan included many protection measures for the trees:

- Lots were designed to place homes in front of the wooded areas, leaving a large rear yard (Photo 6d).

- To avoid impacting trees behind the homes, utilities were located in front yards where there were no existing trees. The locations of service drops were aligned along a utility service corridor to avoid trees.

- Grading and drainage plans were designed to maintain existing grades within tree stand areas.

- A reforestation effort was undertaken on four acres to compensate for trees lost due to unavoidable impact.

PHOTO 6d Lots were designed to reduce the front setbacks, thereby creating large rear yards to retain the natural forest.

- A homesite-specific tree conservation plan was developed for each wooded homesite.
- A nature trail was created along Carmel Creek, utilizing mulch from chipped trees and birdhouses built from scrap cedar.

The land development and home construction processes were guided by the C.P. Morgan team to ensure that the tree conservation goals were fulfilled.

- On-site preconstruction meetings were held to demonstrate tree preservation techniques to civil engineers, utility company representatives, and owners and operators of the subcontracting firms.
- The arboricultural consultant, Mark Timmons, was on hand during construction to supervise equipment use, provisions for stockpiling topsoil, methods of disposal of toxic substances, trash handling, and protective fencing.

- Signage and fencing were erected around tree preservation areas (Photo 6e).

Continuing landscape maintenance and education are important components of the program. Common areas are managed by the homeowners association. Forest stands are generally left in a natural state, with the exception of annual cutting of vines and broken limbs. Maintenance of individual homesites is the responsibility of the homeowners. C.P. Morgan provided each homeowner with guidelines for the effective maintenance of landscaping and trees. Homeowners also received a quarterly corporate newsletter that frequently includes articles on landscape and tree care.

PHOTO 6e Preconstruction meetings and tree protection fencing were important components of the tree preservation program.

The Team

Owner/Developer/ General Contractor	C.P. Morgan (Mark Boyce)
Horticultural Consultant	Mark Timmons & Associates
Civil Engineer	Schneider Engineering
Land Planning	Richard Burleson

APPENDIX

A

Equipment and Supplies for Preparing Maps and Plans

PENS

Selection is determined by type of paper you are using, quality of line required, permanence, and cost. Reserve your good pens for work on graphics only. Worn tips produce poor lines. We use:

- **Sharpie fine point permanent marker in black.** Writes on anything; useful on large maps and transparencies (too broad of a line for use on small maps).
- **Bic ultra fine in black (or similar).** Thin line is good for small maps on bond paper.
- **Berol fine point 7700 in black (or similar).** Medium line is good for maps on bond paper.
- **Staedtler lumocolor.** Fine and medium lines, permanent ink, best line quality (other brands available). Bleeds on poor quality paper.

If you are preparing your own base map on reproducible paper (e.g., Mylar, vellum), you need to use technical pens. Unless you use them frequently, they tend to clog up. We use Rotring Rapidoliner in extra fine to broad with disposable cartridges with tips (when they clog, just replace the cartridge).

COLOR

For color, what you use depends on the amount of space you need to color, type of paper, and intensity of color desired.

For small areas, use Berol Prismacolor thick-lead art pencils. Don't put a sharp point on them. The trick to coloring is to apply even, medium pressure and make all strokes in the same direction. For large areas, several brands of art markers are available, including Eberhard Faber Design 2, Chartpack, and Berol Prismacolor. Soft shades of green, gray, and tan look best. These pencils bleed to allow edges to blend, so they do not work well in small spaces. Apply in parallel, even strokes.

Color reproduction is readily available. We like presentation maps produced on glossy white paper. If the maps are part of a bound report, we have the copies made on our stationery.

PAPER

The type of paper you use depends on how you plan to reproduce the map, the finished size, and how long you expect your original to last. Light must be able to shine through the paper (e.g., vellum, Mylar) to make a blueline print. Opaque paper (e.g., bond) can be used if you will be photocopying the original.

- **Bond.** Adequate if map will be photocopied. Use high-quality paper, or ink will bleed and fibers will catch on pen nib.

- **Vellum.** Most commonly used for originals from which blueline prints will be made. Good to use for tracing. Provides good line quality. Available in sheet sizes from 8.5" x 11" to rolls, with or without fadeout grid lines, and with or without printed title block.
- **Mylar drafting film.** Highest quality for blueline reproduction and longevity, but more expensive. Available in sheets and rolls.
- **Acetate, transparency.** Clear film; use for overlays. Can be drawn on with permanent markers. Transparency film for copiers can be used for reproduction.
- **Drafting appliqué film.** Translucent, self-adhesive film that can be drawn on or put through photocopier and then applied to original.

EQUIPMENT

The basics:

good photocopier (or access to one)
scissors
x-acto knife with blades (we like No. 2 or 11)
corrective fluid for copies and ink
corrective tape (e.g., Post-it Notes) in ⅙", ⅓", and 1" widths
metal straight edge (12" to 15")
8" to 10" triangle with beveled edge
gum eraser
nonreproducible blue pencil (writing will not photocopy)
nonreproducible purple pencil (writing on original will not show on blueline print)
glue stick
clear tape
templates for circles, squares, and triangles in graduated sizes
engineer's and architect's scales

Nice to have:

electric eraser
cutting mat
paper cutter
light box or table
lettering machine (we use a Kroy DuraType 240)
large T-square
charting and graphic arts tapes (for borders, patterned lines)
graphic film (self-adhesive, translucent film with patterns)
computer and high-quality printer

Relative Tolerance of Selected Species to Development Impacts

Common name	Scientific name	Relative tolerance[1]	Comments	Source
Balsam fir	*Abies balsamea*	Good	Tolerant of root loss and saturated soils.	Hightshoe
White fir	*Abies concolor*	Moderate	Tolerant of root loss. Intolerant of saturated and high salt soils.	Day, Hightshoe
Acacia	*Acacia* spp.	Poor	Intolerant of root injury.	Matheny & Clark
Florida maple	*Acer barbatum*	Moderate	Intolerant of mechanical injury (poor compartmentalization). Response constrained by soil aeration and water availability.	Coder
Vine maple	*Acer circinatum*	Good	Best retained as clumps.	Peepre
Chalk maple	*Acer leucoderme*	Poor	Response is site dependent.	Coder
Bigleaf maple	*Acer macrophyllum*	Good	Select specimens with good crown structure.	Beck
Bigleaf maple	*Acer macrophyllum*	Poor	Tolerant of root pruning and injury but not of fill. Declines following addition of fill.	Dunster
Box elder	*Acer negundo*	Good	Tolerant of root loss and saturated soils. May tolerate some fill. Select superior individuals for preservation.	Coder, Hightshoe, Sydnor
Striped maple	*Acer pensylvanicum*	Moderate	Intolerant of mechanical injury (poor compartmentalization). Limited tolerance to microclimate change. Tolerance greatest within native range.	Coder
Norway maple	*Acer platanoides*	Moderate-good	Moderately tolerant of root pruning.	S. Clark, Fraedrich
Sycamore maple	*Acer pseudoplatanus*	Moderate		Gilbert
Red maple	*Acer rubrum*	Moderate-good	Response probably associated with geographic location. Tolerant of root pruning and saturated soils.	Coder, Fraedrich, Hightshoe
Silver maple	*Acer saccharinum*	Poor-moderate	Likely to slowly die back following root injury (Day). May tolerate some root pruning (Fraedrich) or loss (Hightshoe). Some tolerance for crown reduction pruning, fill soils and saturated soils. Response variable within species (Coder)	Coder, Day, Fraedrich, Hightshoe, Sydnor
Sugar maple	*Acer saccharum*	Poor-moderate	Tolerant of root loss. Intolerant of saturated and fill soils.	S. Clark, Hightshoe, Sydnor
Mountain maple	*Acer spicatum*	Moderate	Intolerant of mechanical injury (poor compartmentalization). Limited tolerance to microclimate change. Tolerance greatest within native range.	Coder
California buckeye	*Aesculus californica*	Good	Shows good resistance to "contractor pressures."	Matheny & Clark
Red horse-chestnut	*Aesculus x carnea*	Good	Intolerant of mechanical injury (poor compartmentalization).	Gilbert
Yellow buckeye	*Aesculus flava*	Poor	Response constrained by soil aeration and water availability.	Coder
Ohio buckeye	*Aesculus glabra*	Poor	Intermediate tolerance to root loss and saturated soils. Poor acclimation response.	Hightshoe, Sydnor
Red buckeye	*Aesculus pavia*	Moderate	Intolerant of mechanical injury (poor compartmentalization).	Coder
Tree of heaven	*Ailanthus altissima*	Good	Tolerant of root pruning. Generally good acclimation response following disturbance.	Day, Fraedrich, Sydnor

[1] Assigned either by source or by Matheny and Clark.

Common name	Scientific name	Relative tolerance[1]	Comments	Source
Alders	Alnus spp.	Good	Show considerable resistance to "contractor pressures."	Gilbert
Red alder	Alnus rubra	Poor-moderate	Retain only in groups or as individuals with strong taper and structure. Relatively short-lived. Intolerant to root injury.	Beck, Dunster, Peepre
Hazel alder	Alnus serrulata	Good	—	Coder
Serviceberry	Amelanchier spp.	Good	Intermediate tolerance to root loss. Tolerant of saturated soils. Generally good acclimation response to site change.	Hightshoe, Sydnor
Downy serviceberry	Amelanchier arborea	Moderate	Intolerant of mechanical injury (poor compartmentalization). Response constrained by soil aeration and water availability.	Coder
Devil's-walkingstick	Aralia spinosa	Moderate	Intolerant of mechanical injury (poor compartmentalization).	Coder
Madrone	Arbutus menziesii	Poor	Intolerant of site disturbance.	Matheny & Clark
Pawpaw	Asimina triloba	Good	—	Coder
Eastern baccharis	Baccharis halimifolia	Good	—	Coder
Birch	Betula spp.	Poor-moderate	Intolerant of root pruning. Mature trees particularly sensitive to development impacts.	Gilbert, Fraedrich
Yellow birch	Betula alleghaniensis	Moderate	Intolerant of mechanical injury (poor compartmentalization). Limited tolerance to microclimate change. Tolerance greatest within native range. Response varies due to soil and water availability.	Coder
Sweet birch	Betula lenta	Moderate	Intermediate tolerance to root loss. Intolerant of mechanical injury. Limited tolerance to microclimate change. Tolerance greatest within native range.	Coder, Hightshoe
River birch	Betula nigra	Moderate-good	Variable tolerance of root loss and saturated soils. Tolerant of minor amounts of fill.	S. Clark, Coder, Hightshoe, Sydnor
Paper birch	Betula papyrifera	Poor-moderate	Intolerant of construction impacts outside of native range; moderate within. Prone to sunscald. Low tolerance to root injury. Bronze birch borer much more severe under stress. Best retained in groups or as select individuals.	S. Clark, Day, Peepre, Sydnor
Gray birch	Betula populifolia	Moderate-good	Tolerant of construction impacts within native range; moderate response outside. Construction impacts/injury increases susceptibility to bronze birch borer.	S. Clark, Sydnor
Gum bumelia	Bumelia lanuginosa	Moderate	Intolerant of mechanical injury (poor compartmentalization). Response constrained by soil aeration and water availability.	Coder
Buckthorn bumelia	Bumelia lycioides	Moderate	Intolerant of mechanical injury (poor compartmentalization). Response constrained by soil aeration and water availability.	Coder
Incense cedar	Calocedrus decurrens	Moderate	Intolerant of root loss and saturated soils. Susceptible to two-lined chestnut borer, particularly under conditions of environmental stress. Limited tolerance to climatic change. Tolerance greatest within native range.	Matheny & Clark
Blue beech; hornbeam	Carpinus caroliniana	Moderate		Coder, Hightshoe, Sydnor

[1] Assigned either by source or by Matheny and Clark.

Common name	Scientific name	Relative tolerance[1]	Comments	Source
Water hickory	*Carya aquatica*	Good	—	Coder
Bitternut hickory	*Carya cordiformis*	Good	Intermediate tolerance to root loss and saturated soils. Will tolerate some fill.	Hightshoe, Sydnor
Bitternut hickory	*Carya cordiformis*	Poor	Response constrained by soil aeration and water availability.	Coder
Pignut hickory	*Carya glabra*	Moderate-good	Moderately tolerant of construction damage. Tolerant of some fill. Windfirm. Response constrained by soil and water availability.	S. Clark, Coder, Sydnor
Pecan	*Carya illinoensis*	Moderate-good	Moderately tolerant of construction damage. Tolerant of some fill.	S. Clark, Sydnor
Shagbark hickory	*Carya ovata*	Moderate-good	Moderately tolerant of construction damage. Tolerant of some fill. Windfirm.	S. Clark, Sydnor
Shagbark hickory	*Carya ovata*	Poor	Response constrained by soil aeration and water availability.	Coder
Sand hickory	*Carya pallida*	Moderate	—	Coder
Mockernut hickory	*Carya tomentosa*	Moderate-good	Moderately tolerant of construction damage. Tolerant of some fill. Windfirm.	S. Clark, Sydnor
Mockernut hickory	*Carya tomentosa*	Poor-moderate	Response constrained by soil aeration and water availability.	Coder
Florida chinkapin	*Castanea alnifolia*	Moderate	Pest problems associated with development impacts.	Coder
Allegheny chinkapin	*Castanea pumila*	Poor	Pest problems associated with development impacts.	Coder
Catalpa	*Catalpa* spp.	Moderate	Tolerant of saturated soils. Intermediate in tolerance to root loss.	Hightshoe
Southern catalpa	*Catalpa bignonioides*	Good	—	Coder
Northern catalpa	*Catalpa speciosa*	Good	Generally tolerant of disturbance including root injury. Prone to basal decay.	Day, Sydnor
Deodar cedar	*Cedrus deodara*	Good	Tolerant of root and crown pruning. Intolerant of excessive soil moisture; leads to *Armillaria* and *Phytophthora*.	Ellis
Sugarberry	*Celtis laevigata*	Good	Intolerant of mechanical injury (poor compartmentalization).	Coder
Georgia hackberry	*Celtis tenuifolia*	Moderate	Intolerant of mechanical injury (poor compartmentalization). Response constrained by soil aeration and water availability.	Coder
Hackberry	*Celtis occidentalis*	Good	Tolerant of root loss. Intermediate (Hightshoe) or low (Day) in tolerance to saturated soils.	Day, Hightshoe, Sydnor
Common buttonbush	*Cephalanthus occidentalis*	Good	Intolerant of mechanical injury (poor compartmentalization).	Coder
Katsura-tree	*Cercidiphyllum japonicum*	Poor-moderate	Sensitive to fill and root disturbance. Requires tree protection zone at the dripline. Requires postconstruction care, particularly supplemental irrigation.	Cullen
Redbud	*Cercis canadensis*	Moderate	Response constrained by soil aeration and water availability.	Coder
Alaska yellow-cedar	*Chamaecyparis nootkatensis*	Good	Relatively windfirm. Intolerant of changes in water table/soil moisture.	Peepre
False cypress	*Chamaecyparis* spp.	Good	Show considerable resistance to "contractor pressures."	Gilbert
Fringetree	*Chionanthus virginicus*	Moderate	Intolerant of mechanical injury (poor compartmentalization). Response constrained by soil aeration and water availability.	Coder

[1] Assigned either by source or by Matheny and Clark.

Common name	Scientific name	Relative tolerance[1]	Comments	Source
Yellow-wood	*Cladrastis lutea*	Poor	Response is site dependent.	Coder
Cinnamon clethra	*Clethra acuminata*	Moderate	Intolerant of mechanical injury (poor compartmentalization). Response constrained by soil aeration and water availability.	Coder
Buckwheat tree	*Cliftonia monophylla*	Moderate	Intolerant of mechanical injury (poor compartmentalization). Response constrained by soil aeration and water availability.	Coder
Pagoda dogwood	*Cornus alternifolia*	Moderate	Intolerant of mechanical injury (poor compartmentalization).	Coder
Flowering dogwood	*Cornus florida*	Poor	Intolerant of site disturbance.	Coder
Flowering dogwood	*Cornus florida*	Moderate	Intolerant of mechanical injury (poor compartmentalization). Pest problems associated with development impacts.	Sydnor
Pacific dogwood	*Cornus nuttallii*	Good	—	Coder
Swamp dogwood	*Cornus stricta*	Good	Intolerant of mechanical injury (poor compartmentalization).	Peepre
Beaked hazel	*Corylus cornuta*	Good	—	Coder
Hawthorn	*Crataegus* spp.	Moderate	Intermediate tolerance to root loss and saturated soils.	Hightshoe
Cockspur hawthorn	*Crataegus crus-galli*	Good	Sensitive to windthrow if canopy raised. Some tolerance to disturbance.	Sydnor
Washington hawthorn	*Crataegus phaenopyrum*	Good	Susceptible to windthrow. Tolerates some disturbance.	Sydnor
Dotted hawthorn	*Crataegus punctata*	Good	Susceptible to windthrow. Tolerates some disturbance.	Sydnor
Cypresses	*Cupressus* spp.	Good	Show considerable resistance to "contractor pressures."	Gilbert
Monterey cypress	*Cupressus macrocarpa*	Poor	Intolerant of site disturbance.	Matheny & Clark
Swamp cyrilla	*Cyrilla racemiflora*	Moderate	Intolerant of mechanical injury (poor compartmentalization).	Coder
Persimmon	*Diospyros virginiana*	Good	Tolerant of saturated soils. Pest problems associated with development impacts.	Sydnor
Eastern coralbean	*Erythrina herbacea*	Moderate	Intolerant of mechanical injury (poor compartmentalization).	Coder
Eucalyptus	*Eucalyptus* spp.	Moderate	Moderately tolerant of root loss. Intolerant of fill.	Matheny & Clark
Eastern wahoo	*Euonymus atropurpureus*	Moderate	Intolerant of mechanical injury (poor compartmentalization).	Coder
Beech	*Fagus* spp.	Poor	Intolerant of root pruning. Poor response to injury. Intolerant of fill soil.	Fraedrich, Sydnor
American beech	*Fagus grandifolia*	Poor	Response is site dependent.	Coder
European beech	*Fagus sylvatica*	Poor	Mature trees particularly susceptible.	Gilbert
Swamp privet	*Forestiera acuminata*	Good	—	Coder
Ash	*Fraxinus* spp.	Moderate	Moderately tolerant of root pruning.	S. Clark, Fraedrich
White ash	*Fraxinus americana*	Moderate-good	Tolerant of root loss. Intermediate in tolerance to saturated soils.	S. Clark, Coder, Hightshoe, Sydnor
Carolina ash	*Fraxinus caroliniana*	Good	Intolerant of mechanical injury (poor compartmentalization). Response constrained by soil and water availability.	Coder

[1] Assigned either by source or by Matheny and Clark.

Common name	Scientific name	Relative tolerance[1]	Comments	Source
European ash	*Fraxinus excelsior*	Moderate	——	Gilbert
Black ash	*Fraxinus nigra*	Good	Tolerant of root loss and saturated soils.	Hightshoe
Green ash	*Fraxinus pennsylvanica*	Good	Tolerant of root pruning and loss. Benefits from supplemental irrigation following injury. Tolerant of saturated soils and fill.	Coder, Day, Hightshoe, Sydnor
Blue ash	*Fraxinus quadrangulata*	Good	——	Sydnor
Shamel ash	*Fraxinus uhdei*	Good	Tolerant of root pruning. Best with irrigation following disturbance.	Ellis
Modesto ash	*Fraxinus velutina 'Modesto'*	Good	Tolerant of root pruning. Requires supplemental irrigation following root loss/injury.	Matheny & Clark
Ginkgo	*Ginkgo biloba*	Good	Tolerant of root pruning.	Fraedrich, Sydnor
Water locust	*Gleditsia aquatica*	Good	——	Coder
Honey locust	*Gleditsia triacanthos f. inermis*	Good	Tolerant of root pruning and site disturbance. Intermediate tolerance to saturated soils.	Coder, Fraedrich. Hightshoe, Sydnor
Loblolly bay	*Gordonia lasianthus*	Good	——	Coder
Kentucky coffee-tree	*Gymnocladus dioicus*	Good	Intermediate tolerance to root loss and saturated soils. Tolerant of site disturbance.	Hightshoe, Sydnor
Carolina silverbell	*Halesia carolina*	Moderate	Intolerant of mechanical injury (poor compartmentalization). Response constrained by soil aeration and water availability. Limited tolerance to microclimate change. Tolerance greatest within native range.	Coder
Two-winged silverbell	*Halesia diptera*	Moderate	Intolerant of mechanical injury (poor compartmentalization). Response constrained by soil aeration and water availability.	Coder
Little silverbell	*Halesia parviflora*	Moderate	Intolerant of mechanical injury (poor compartmentalization). Response constrained by soil aeration and water availability.	Coder
Witch-hazel	*Hamamelis virginiana*	Moderate	Intolerant of mechanical injury (poor compartmentalization). Response constrained by soil aeration and water availability.	Coder
Carolina holly	*Ilex ambigua*	Good	——	Coder
Dahoon	*Ilex cassine*	Good	——	Coder
Large gallberry	*Ilex coriacea*	Good	——	Coder
Possumhaw	*Ilex decidua*	Good	——	Coder
Mountain winterberry	*Ilex montana*	Moderate-good	Limited tolerance to microclimate change. Tolerance greatest within native range.	Coder
Myrtle dahoon	*Ilex myrtifolia*	Good	——	Coder
American holly	*Ilex opaca*	Good	Tolerates some fill.	Coder, Sydnor
Common winterberry	*Ilex verticillata*	Good	——	Coder
Yaupon holly	*Ilex vomitoria*	Good	——	Coder

[1] Assigned either by source or by Matheny and Clark.

Common name	Scientific name	Relative tolerance[1]	Comments	Source
California black walnut	Juglans hindsii	Poor	Dies slowly following even minor root injury or changes to water table. Crown reduction pruning may be fatal. Requires tree protection zone at or beyond the dripline.	Matheny & Clark
Black walnut	Juglans nigra	Poor-moderate	Intolerant of root loss. Intermediate tolerance to saturated soils. Intolerant of mechanical injury (poor compartmentalization). Response constrained by soil aeration and water availability.	Hightshoe, Sydnor
English walnut	Juglans regia	Poor	Usually grafted onto California black walnut stock.	Matheny & Clark
Rocky Mountain juniper	Juniperus scopulorum	Poor	Sensitive to root pruning and fill soil. Likely to decline following grade change and loss of roots. Very susceptible to borers when stressed.	Day
Eastern red cedar	Juniperus virginiana	Good	Tolerant of root loss. Intolerant of saturated soils. Intolerant of mechanical injury.	Coder, Hightshoe, Sydnor
Mountain laurel	Kalmia latifolia	Good	—	Coder
Tamarack	Larix laricina	Moderate	Tolerant of root loss and saturated soils.	Hightshoe
Sweetgum	Liquidambar styraciflua	Poor-good	Intermediate response to fill and root injury. Breadth of tolerance may be due to pre-existing site conditions and within species variation.	S. Clark, Coder, Matheny & Clark, Sydnor
Tuliptree	Liriodendron tulipifera	Moderate	Intolerant of root pruning. Sensitive to wounding.	Fraedrich, Sydnor
Tuliptree	Liriodendron tulipifera	Poor	Intolerant of mechanical injury (poor compartmentalization). Response constrained by soil aeration and water availability.	Coder
Cucumbertree	Magnolia acuminata	Moderate	Intolerant of mechanical injury (poor compartmentalization).	Coder
Fraser magnolia	Magnolia fraseri	Poor	Intolerant of mechanical injury (poor compartmentalization). Limited tolerance to microclimate change. Tolerance greatest within native range.	Coder
Southern magnolia	Magnolia grandiflora	Poor or good	Response dependent upon location: good within native range; poor outside it. In California, it declines following root injury and site disturbance.	Matheny & Clark, Sydnor
Southern magnolia	Magnolia grandiflora	Moderate	Intolerant of mechanical injury (poor compartmentalization).	Coder
Pyramid magnolia	Magnolia pyramidata	Poor	Intolerant of mechanical injury (poor compartmentalization). Limited tolerance to microclimate change. Tolerance greatest within native range.	Coder
Sweet bay	Magnolia virginiana	Good	Tolerant of saturated soils.	Coder, Sydnor
Apples	Malus spp.	Moderate	—	Gilbert
Southern crabapple	Malus angustifolia	Moderate	Intolerant of mechanical injury (poor compartmentalization). Limited tolerance to microclimate change. Tolerance greatest within native range. Pest problems associated with development impacts.	Coder

[1]Assigned either by source or by Matheny and Clark.

Common name	Scientific name	Relative tolerance[1]	Comments	Source
Sweet crabapple	*Malus coronaria*	Moderate-good	Intolerant of mechanical injury (poor compartmentalization). Limited tolerance to microclimate change. Tolerance greatest within native range. Pest problems associated with development impacts.	Coder, Sydnor
Apple	*Malus domestica*	Good	Tolerant of some fill.	Sydnor
Prairie crabapple	*Malus ioensis*	Good	——	Sydnor
White mulberry	*Morus alba*	Moderate	——	Matheny & Clark
White mulberry	*Morus alba*	Good	Tolerant of disturbance and fill.	Sydnor
Red mulberry	*Morus rubra*	Good	Tolerant of disturbance and fill.	Coder, Sydnor
Southern bayberry	*Myrica cerifera*	Good	——	Coder
Evergreen bayberry	*Myrica heterophylla*	Good	——	Coder
Water tupelo	*Nyssa aquatica*	Good	——	Coder
Ogeechee tupelo	*Nyssa ogeche*	Moderate	Intolerant of mechanical injury (poor compartmentalization). Response constrained by soil aeration and water availability.	Coder
Black gum	*Nyssa sylvatica*	Good	Response constrained by soil aeration and water availability.	Coder, Sydnor
Devilwood	*Osmanthus americanus*	Moderate	Intolerant of mechanical injury (poor compartmentalization).	Coder
American hophornbeam	*Ostrya virginiana*	Moderate	Intolerant of root loss and saturated soils. Two-lined chestnut borer will attack following disturbance. Response is site dependent.	Coder, Hightshoe, Sydnor
Sourwood	*Oxydendrum arboreum*	Moderate	Windfirm.	Sydnor
Sourwood	*Oxydendrum arboreum*	Poor	——	Coder
Empress-tree	*Paulownia tomentosa*	Good	Tolerant of site disturbance.	Sydnor
Redbay	*Persea borbonia*	Good		Coder
Norway spruce	*Picea abies*	Moderate	Often windthrows. Intolerant of root loss.	Sydnor.
White spruce	*Picea glauca*	Moderate	Tolerant of root loss. Intermediate in tolerance to saturated soils.	Hightshoe
Black spruce	*Picea mariana*	Good	Tolerant of root loss and saturated soils.	Hightshoe
Colorado spruce	*Picea pungens*	Moderate	Intolerant of saturated soils. Intermediate in tolerance to root loss. Often windthrows.	Day, Hightshoe, Sydnor
Pinckneya	*Pinckneya pubens*	Moderate	Intolerant of mechanical injury (poor compartmentalization).	Coder
Jack pine	*Pinus banksiana*	Good	Tolerant of root loss. Intolerant of saturated soils.	Hightshoe, Sydnor
Canary Island pine	*Pinus canariensis*	Good	Tends to have sinker roots close to trunk.	Ellis
Shortleaf pine	*Pinus echinata*	Moderate-good	Pest problems associated with development impacts. Tolerant of some fill soil.	Coder, Sydnor
Pinyon pine	*Pinus edulis*	Moderate	Tolerant of root pruning. Intolerant of saturated and poorly drained soils.	Day

[1] Assigned either by source or by Matheny and Clark.

Common name	Scientific name	Relative tolerance[1]	Comments	Source
Slash pine	*Pinus elliottii*	Good	—	Coder
Spruce pine	*Pinus glabra*	Good	—	Coder
Austrian pine	*Pinus nigra*	Good	Tolerant of some fill and root pruning/injury.	Day, Sydnor
Longleaf pine	*Pinus palustris*	Moderate-good	Limited tolerance to microclimate change. Tolerance greatest within native range.	Coder
Ponderosa pine	*Pinus ponderosa*	Good	Tolerant of fill within dripline and root pruning. Intolerant of poor drainage, overwatering, and high-soluble salts.	Day
Table mountain pine	*Pinus pungens*	Moderate-good	Limited tolerance to microclimate change. Tolerance greatest within native range.	Coder
Monterey pine	*Pinus radiata*	Moderate	Requires supplemental irrigation following disturbance.	Ellis
Red pine	*Pinus resinosa*	Good	Tolerant of root loss. Intolerant of saturated soils.	Hightshoe, Sydnor
Pitch pine	*Pinus rigida*	Good	—	Coder, Sydnor
Digger pine	*Pinus sabiniana*	Moderate	—	Matheny & Clark
Pond pine	*Pinus serotina*	Good	—	Coder
White pine	*Pinus strobus*	Moderate	Tolerant of root loss. Intolerant of saturated soils or changes in soil moisture. Response often site dependent.	Coder, Hightshoe, Sydnor
Scots pine	*Pinus sylvestris*	Good	Tolerant of root loss. Intolerant of saturated soils.	Hightshoe, Sydnor
Loblolly pine	*Pinus taeda*	Moderate-good	Moderate tolerance to root loss. Intolerant of saturated soils.	S. Clark, Coder, Sydnor
Virginia pine	*Pinus virginiana*	Poor-moderate	Injury increases susceptibility to southern pine beetle. Prone to windthrow and root decay.	Matheny & Clark, Sydnor
Virginia pine	*Pinus virginiana*	Good	—	Coder
Planer tree	*Planera aquatica*	Good	—	Coder
London plane	*Platanus x acerifolia*	Poor or good	Response appears to be location dependent. In eastern U.S., stress intolerant in northern part of range. In California, very tolerant. Benefits from supplemental irrigation.	Matheny & Clark, Sydnor
Eastern sycamore	*Platanus occidentalis*	Moderate	Intermediate tolerance to construction damage. Moderate tolerance of fill soil.	S. Clark, Sydnor
Eastern sycamore	*Platanus occidentalis*	Good	—	Coder
Western sycamore	*Platanus racemosa*	Moderate	Show considerable resistance to "contractor presssures."	Matheny & Clark
Poplars	*Populus* spp.	Good		Gilbert
Eastern cottonwood	*Populus deltoides*	Moderate-good	Intermediate to good tolerance of root loss, fill soil, and saturated soils.	S. Clark, Coder, Hightshoe, Sydnor
Western cottonwood	*Populus fremontii*	Poor	Prone to windthrow and decay.	Hightshoe, Sydnor
Bigtooth aspen	*Populus grandidentata*	Poor-moderate	Tolerant of root loss. Intolerant of saturated soils.	Matheny & Clark
Lombardy poplar	*Populus nigra* 'Italica'	Moderate-good	Tolerant of minor amounts of fill. Intolerant of changes in soil moisture. Decays rapidly. Susceptible to windthrow.	Hightshoe, Sydnor, Beck

[1] Assigned either by source or by Matheny and Clark.

Common name	Scientific name	Relative tolerance[1]	Comments	Source
Plains cottonwood	*Populus sargentii*	Moderate	Defoliation and dieback may follow excessive root loss. Intolerant of crown reduction pruning. Supplemental irrigation required following root injury. Tolerant of some grade change.	Day
Quaking aspen	*Populus tremuloides*	Moderate	Tolerant of root loss. Intolerant of saturated soils.	Day, Hightshoe
Black cottonwood	*Populus trichocarpa*	Poor	Mature trees prone to windthrow and trunk failure.	Peepre
American plum	*Prunus americana*	Moderate	Intolerant of mechanical injury (poor compartmentalization). Response constrained by soil aeration and water availability.	Coder
Chickasaw plum	*Prunus angustifolia*	Moderate	Intolerant of mechanical injury (poor compartmentalization). Response constrained by soil aeration and water availability.	Coder
Carolina laurelcherry	*Prunus caroliniana*	Good		Coder
Canada plum	*Prunus nigra*	Moderate	Tolerant of root loss. Intolerant of saturated soils.	Hightshoe
Fire cherry	*Prunus pensylvanica*	Moderate	Intolerant of mechanical injury (poor compartmentalization).	Coder
Black cherry	*Prunus serotina*	Poor	Intermediate tolerance to root loss. Intolerant of saturated soils. Select young, vigorous individuals for preservation.	Hightshoe, Sydnor
Black cherry	*Prunus serotina*	Moderate	Intolerant of mechanical injury (poor compartmentalization).	Coder
Flatwoods plum	*Prunus umbellata*	Moderate	Intolerant of mechanical injury (poor compartmentalization).	Coder
Douglas-fir	*Pseudotsuga menziesii*	Poor-good	Tolerant of fill soil if limited to one-quarter of root zone. However, may decline slowly following addition of fill. Tolerates root pruning. Intolerant of poor drainage. Susceptible to bark beetles following injury.	Beck, Dunster
Hoptree	*Ptelea trifoliata*	Moderate	Intolerant of mechanical injury (poor compartmentalization).	Coder
Callery pear	*Pyrus calleryana*	Moderate	Intolerant of root pruning.	Fraedrich
Oaks	*Quercus* spp.	Moderate		Gilbert
Coast live oak	*Quercus agrifolia*	Good	Sensitive to addition of fill soil around base of trunk. Intolerant of frequent summer irrigation. Bark is sensitive to sunburn following pruning.	Matheny & Clark
White oak	*Quercus alba*	Poor	Intolerant of root loss and saturated soils.	Hightshoe
White oak	*Quercus alba*	Moderate		S. Clark
White oak	*Quercus alba*	Good	A common survivor of construction activity. Moderate tolerance to fill soil. Response constrained by soil aeration and water availability.	Coder, Sydnor
Swamp white oak	*Quercus bicolor*	Good	Tolerant of some fill.	Day, Sydnor
Scarlet oak	*Quercus coccinea*	Poor-moderate	Intolerant of construction injury.	S. Clark, Sydnor
Scarlet oak	*Quercus coccinea*	Good		Coder
Durand oak	*Quercus durandii*	Good		Coder
Southern red oak	*Quercus falcata*	Moderate-good	Largely intolerant of construction injury.	S. Clark, Coder, Sydnor
Cherrybark oak	*Quercus falcata* var. *pagodaefolia*	Good		Coder

[1] Assigned either by source or by Matheny and Clark.

Common name	Scientific name	Relative tolerance[1]	Comments	Source
Oregon white oak	Quercus garryana	Good	—	Bell, Matheny & Clark
Shingle oak	Quercus imbricaria	Good	—	Sydnor
Bluejack oak	Quercus incana	Good	—	Coder
California black oak	Quercus kelloggii	Moderate	—	Matheny & Clark
Turkey oak	Quercus laevis	Good	—	Coder
Laurel oak	Quercus laurifolia	Moderate	Subject to nutritional problems when alkaline subbase is used. Intolerant of extreme variation in moisture. Poor compartmentalization response.	Siebenthaler
Valley oak	Quercus lobata	Moderate	Intolerant of summer irrigation and fill soil.	Matheny & Clark
Overcup oak	Quercus lyrata	Good	—	Coder
Bur oak	Quercus macrocarpa	Moderate	Relatively tolerant of root injury, although may be associated with crown dieback. Supplemental irrigation required following root injury. Intermediate tolerance to saturated soils (prairie areas, U.S.).	Day, Hightshoe
Bur oak	Quercus macrocarpa	Good	Tolerant of fill and compacted soils (eastern U.S.)	Sydnor
Blackjack oak	Quercus marilandica	Good	—	Coder
Swamp chestnut oak	Quercus michauxii	Good	—	Coder
Chinquapin oak	Quercus muehlenbergii	Good	Tolerant of site disturbance.	Coder, Sydnor
Water oak	Quercus nigra	Good	Tolerant of saturated soils.	Coder, Sydnor
Pin oak	Quercus palustris	Moderate-good	Intermediate tolerance of root loss and saturated soils.	S. Clark, Hightshoe, Sydnor
Willow oak	Quercus phellos	Moderate-good	Response constrained by soil aeration and water availability.	Coder, Sydnor
Chestnut oak	Quercus prinus	Moderate-good	Response constrained by soil aeration and water availability. Tolerant under good growing conditions.	Coder, Sydnor
Northern red oak	Quercus rubra	Moderate-good	Response constrained by soil aeration and water availability. Limited tolerance to microclimate change. Tolerance greatest within native range. Tolerant of root loss.	Coder, Hightshoe, Sydnor
Shumard oak	Quercus shumardii	Good	—	Coder, Sydnor
Post oak	Quercus stellata	Poor-good	Variation may be geographic in origin; poor in south, good in mideastern U.S. (Ohio).	S. Clark, Coder, Sydnor
Black oak	Quercus velutina	Moderate	Intolerant of root loss and saturated soils.	Hightshoe, Sydnor
Black oak	Quercus velutina	Good	—	Coder
Live oak	Quercus virginiana	Good	High tolerance for various soil types as well as trenching, compaction, and drought. Good compartmentalization response. Limited tolerance to site change. Tolerance greatest within native range.	Coder, Siebenthaler, Sydnor

[1]Assigned either by source or by Matheny and Clark.

Common name	Scientific name	Relative tolerance[1]	Comments	Source
Carolina buckthorn	*Rhamnus caroliniana*	Moderate	Intolerant of mechanical injury (poor compartmentalization).	Coder
Catawba rhododendron	*Rhododendron catawbiense*	Moderate	Response constrained by soil aeration and water availability. Intolerant of mechanical injury (poor compartmentalization).	Coder
Rosebay rhododendron	*Rhododendron maximum*	Moderate	Intolerant of mechanical injury (poor compartmentalization).	Coder
Shining sumac	*Rhus copallina*	Moderate	Intolerant of mechanical injury (poor compartmentalization).	Coder
Smooth sumac	*Rhus glabra*	Moderate	Intolerant of mechanical injury (poor compartmentalization).	Coder
Staghorn sumac	*Rhus typhina*	Good	Regenerates quickly from root sprouts following disturbance.	Sydnor
Black locust	*Robinia pseudoacacia*	Good	Tolerant of root loss and fill soil. Intolerant of saturated soils. Sensitive to borers when stressed.	Hightshoe, Sydnor
Willow	*Salix* spp.	Moderate-good	Moderately tolerant of root pruning and fill soil. Show considerable resistance to "contractor pressures."	Day, Fraedrich, Gilbert
Weeping willow	*Salix babylonica*	Moderate-good	Disturbance may lead to cankering. Tolerant of some fill. Increased likelihood of windthrow with saturated soils.	S. Clark, Sydnor
Coastal plain willow	*Salix caroliniana*	Good	—	Coder
Black willow	*Salix nigra*	Good	Tolerant of root loss and saturated soils. Tolerant of some fill.	Coder. Hightshoe, Sydnor
Silky willow	*Salix sericea*	Good	—	Coder
American elder	*Sambucus canadensis*	Poor	Response is site dependent.	Coder
Sassafras	*Sassafras albidum*	Good	Regenerates from root suckers following disturbance.	Coder, Sydnor
California peppertree	*Schinus molle*	Moderate		Ellis
Coast redwood	*Sequoia sempervirens*	Good	Supplemental irrigation required if located out of native range, as well as during construction and following injury.	Matheny & Clark
Giant redwood	*Sequoiadendron giganteum*	Moderate	Intolerant of summer irrigation and fill soil.	Matheny & Clark
Mountain ash	*Sorbus aucuparia*	Moderate	Tolerant of root loss. Intermediate in tolerance to saturated soils.	Hightshoe
American bladdernut	*Staphylea trifolia*	Good	—	Coder
Virginia stewartia	*Stewartia malacodendron*	Good	—	Coder
Mountain stewartia	*Stewartia ovata*	Good	—	Coder
American snowbell	*Styrax americana*	Moderate	Intolerant of mechanical injury (poor compartmentalization).	Coder
Bigleaf snowbell	*Styrax grandifolia*	Moderate	Response constrained by soil aeration and water availability. Intolerant of mechanical injury (poor compartmentalization).	Coder
Common sweetleaf	*Symplocos tinctoria*	Good	Response constrained by soil aeration and water availability. Intolerant of mechanical injury (poor compartmentalization).	Coder

[1]Assigned either by source or by Matheny and Clark.

Common name	Scientific name	Relative tolerance[1]	Comments	Source
Bald-cypress	*Taxodium distichum*	Good	Adapts readily to wide range of soils, wet to dry, sandy to heavy. Tolerant of alkaline soils. Trunk does not disturb pavement but knees may emerge in yards.	S. Clark, Coder, Siebenthaler
Pond cypress	*Taxodium distichum* var. *nutans*	Good	———	Coder
Northern white cedar	*Thuja occidentalis*	Good	Tolerant of root loss, some fill, and saturated soils.	Hightshoe, Sydnor
Western red cedar	*Thuja plicata*	Good	Relatively windfirm. Intolerant of changes in water table/soil moisture.	Peepre
Western red cedar	*Thuja plicata*	Poor-moderate	Response is very site dependent, probably related to soil moisture. Intolerant of fill.	Beck, Dunster
Linden	*Tilia* spp.	Moderate-good	Moderately tolerant of root pruning. Considerable resistance to "contractor pressures."	S. Clark, Gilbert, Fraedrich
Basswood	*Tilia americana*	Poor	Tolerant of root loss. Intolerant of saturated soils. Intolerant of site disturbance and fill.	Hightshoe, Sydnor
Carolina basswood	*Tilia caroliniana*	Poor	Response is site dependent.	Coder
White basswood	*Tilia heterophylla*	Poor	Response is site dependent.	Coder
Poison sumac	*Toxicodendron vernix*	Moderate	Intolerant of mechanical injury (poor compartmentalization).	Coder
Eastern hemlock	*Tsuga canadensis*	Poor	Intolerant of fill and saturated soils.	Coder, Sydnor
Western hemlock	*Tsuga heterophylla*	Poor-moderate	Prone to windthrow, decay, and dwarf mistletoe. Intolerant of grade change. Poor compartmentalization.	Beck, Dunster, Peepre
Elm	*Ulmus* spp.	Good	Tolerant of root pruning.	Fraedrich
Winged elm	*Ulmus alata*	Good	———	Coder
American elm	*Ulmus americana*	Good	Tolerant of root loss and site disturbance. Intermediate in tolerance to saturated soils.	Day, Hightshoe, Sydnor
American elm	*Ulmus americana*	Moderate	Pest problems associated with development impacts (southeastern U.S.).	Coder
Siberian elm	*Ulmus pumila*	Good	Tolerant of fill soil, root pruning, injury, a wide range of soil moisture conditions, and high-soluble salts.	Day
Slippery elm	*Ulmus rubra*	Good	Tolerant of root loss. Intermediate in tolerance to saturated soils.	Hightshoe
Slippery elm	*Ulmus rubra*	Moderate	Pest problems associated with development impacts (southeastern U.S.).	Coder
California bay	*Umbellularia californica*	Moderate	Intolerant of fill soil.	Matheny & Clark
Sparkleberry	*Vaccinium arboreum*	Moderate	Response is site dependent.	Coder
Possumhaw viburnum	*Viburnum nudum*	Good	———	Coder
Walter's viburnum	*Viburnum obovatum*	Good	———	Coder

[1] Assigned either by source or by Matheny and Clark.

Common name	Scientific name	Relative tolerance[1]	Comments	Source
Rusty black haw	*Viburnum rufidulum*	Good	—	Coder
Hercules club	*Zanthoxylum clava-herculis*	Moderate	Intolerant of mechanical injury (poor compartmentalization)	Coder

[1]Assigned either by source or by Matheny and Clark.

REFERENCES

Beck, M. 1996. Northwest Arborvitae, Woodinville, WA. Personal communication.

Bell, H. 1996. ANEW LEAF, Merlin, OH. Personal communication.

Clark, S. 1996. Steve Clark & Associates, Brentwood, TN. Personal communication.

Coder, K.D. 1996. University of Georgia, Athens. Personal communication.

Cullen, S. 1996. Consulting arborist, Greenwich, CT. Personal communication.

Day, S. 1996. Day & Associates, Littleton, CO. Personal communication.

Ellis, D. 1996. Deborah Ellis, Horticultural Consultant, Saratoga, CA. Personal communication.

Fraedrich, B. 1995. Solutions of tree and sidewalk conflicts. *City Trees.* pp. 13–15. May–June 1995.

Gilbert, O. 1996. Retaining trees on construction sites. *Arboricultural Journal.* 20:39–45.

Hightshoe, G. 1988. *Native Trees, Shrubs and Vines for Urban and Rural America.* New York: Van Nostrand Reinhold. 819 pp.

Peepre, J.S. Undated. *Saving Native Trees in the Lower Mainland.* Vancouver, BC: J.P. Peepre & Associates.

Siebenthaler, J. 1996. Clearwater, FL. Personal communication.

Sydnor, T. 1996. Ohio State University, Columbus, OH. Personal communication.

Frequently Asked Questions About Tree Preservation During Development

How do I find an arboricultural consultant to work on projects in my area?

Contact the planning department in your local community. They frequently have a list of recommended consultants.

Contact the American Society of Consulting Arborists, 15245 Shady Grove Road, Suite 130, Rockville, MD 20850, (301) 947-0483.

Contact the Association of Consulting Foresters of America, 1401 King Street, Alexandria, VA 22314, (703) 548-0990.

How do I find a qualified arborist to care for the trees on my projects?

Review "What Is a Qualified Arborist?" in Chapter 8 of this book.

For a list of Certified Arborists in your area, contact the International Society of Arboriculture, P.O. Box 3129, Champaign, IL 61826-3129, (217) 355-9411.

How do I determine the requirements for tree preservation in a community?

Contact the community's planning or parks department.

How do I obtain the standards for tree care operations and pruning?

Contact the International Society of Arboriculture, P.O. Box 3129, Champaign, IL 61826-3129,

(217) 355-9411, and request the *American National Standard for Tree Care Operations* (ANSI Z133.1), the *ANSI Pruning Standard*, and ISA's *Tree-Pruning Guidelines*.

What is a good tree preservation ordinance?

Review the section on tree ordinances in Chapter 3 of this book.

Refer to *Tree Conservation Ordinances* by Christopher Duerksen (1993. Chicago: American Planning Association and Scenic America.)

Contact the National Association of Home Builders, 1201 15th Street, NW, Washington, DC 20005-2800, (202) 822-0200.

How can I gain recognition for projects that have a strong tree preservation component?

The National Association of Home Builders has an awards program for tree preservation during development. Contact NAHB at 1201 15th Street, NW, Washington, DC 20005-2800, (202) 822-0200.

How can I find out which plants in an area may be invasive weeds?

Refer to *Invasive Plants: Weeds of the Global Garden* by Janet Marinelli and John Randall (Brooklyn, NY: Brooklyn Botanic Garden).

Contact the National Association of Exotic Pest Plant Councils, 8208 Dabney Avenue, Springfield, VA 22152.

NELDA MATHENY

Nelda Matheny is president of HortScience, Inc., an arboricultural and urban forestry consulting firm in Pleasanton, California. She founded the company in 1983 after completing an M.S. in horticulture from the University of California, Davis, and working for a landscape architect and soil and tissue testing laboratory. Matheny has written numerous scientific articles and book chapters and is coauthor (with Jim Clark) of *A Photographic Guide to the Evaluation of Hazard Trees in Urban Areas*. She is currently working with Richard Harris and Jim Clark on a revision to *Arboriculture: Integrated Management of Landscape Trees, Shrubs and Vines*.

JAMES R. CLARK

Jim Clark is vice president of HortScience, Inc., an arboricultural and urban forestry consulting firm in Pleasanton, California. Before joining HortScience, Clark spent 10 years on the faculty of the University of Washington at the Center for Urban Horticulture. He has published a number of technical articles dealing with arboriculture and urban forestry, as well as on tree growth, development, and management. He is coauthor (with Nelda Matheny) of *A Photographic Guide to the Evaluation of Hazard Trees in Urban Areas* and is currently working with Richard Harris and Nelda Matheny on a revision to *Arboriculture: Integrated Management of Landscape Trees, Shrubs and Vines*. Clark is a member of the Board of Directors of the International Society of Arboriculture and an Honorary Life Member of ISA.